Co. Min. 37.

821

COAL MINING PRACTICE

EDITED BY

I. C. F. STATHAM

M.Eng., M.I.M.E., F.R.I.C.S., F.G.S., M.Amer.I.M.E., F.A.M.E.M.E., F.R.S.A.

Certificated Colliery Manager
Emeritus Professor of Mining and formerly
Dean of Engineering in the University of Sheffield

WITH CONTRIBUTIONS BY
SEVENTEEN OTHER EXPERTS

Volume I

THE CAXTON PUBLISHING COMPANY LIMITED
LONDON · NEW YORK · MELBOURNE
TORONTO · WELLINGTON

First Published . . *April* 1958

CAXTON'S
LIST OF ENGINEERING BOOKS

©

PRINTED AND BOUND IN ENGLAND BY
HAZELL WATSON AND VINEY LTD
AYLESBURY AND SLOUGH

LIST OF CONTRIBUTORS

G. Bridgmore Brown, M.B.E., R.D., late of the Ministry of Power.

W. R. Chapman, Ph.D., M.Sc., B.Sc.Tech., M.I.Min.E., Central Research Establishment of the National Coal Board.

Wesley Hancock, Ph.D., M.Sc., M.I.Min.E., F.G.S., formerly Lecturer in Mining in the University of Birmingham.

H. S. Haslam, M.Eng., M.I.C.E., M.I.Mech.E., M.I.Min.E., F.R.G.S., F.G.S.

H. J. Humphrys, C.B.E., D.S.O., M.C., M.I.Min.E.

G. Hurst, M.Eng., F.R.I.C.S., M.I.Min.E., Lecturer in Surveys in the University of Sheffield.

R. A. Mott, D.Sc., F.R.I.C., F.Inst.F., Superintendent of the Midland Coke Research Station.

Professor D. W. Phillips, B.Sc., Ph.D., Dip.Met.Min., A.M.I.Min.E., Professor of Mining in the New South Wales University of Technology, formerly of the Safety in Mines Research Establishment.

H. Saul, B.Sc.Eng., M.I.Min.E., Area General Manager, North-Eastern Division, National Coal Board.

R. Shepherd, Ph.D., B.Sc.Eng.(Min.), F.G.S., Mining Research Establishment, National Coal Board.

Professor John Sinclair, M.Eng., Ph.D., M.I.Min.E., Barrister-at-Law, Professor of Mining in University College, Cardiff.

Robert Smith, B.Sc., A.R.T.C., Certificated Colliery Manager, formerly Lecturer in Mining Engineering at the Royal College of Science and Technology, Glasgow.

C. D. J. Statham, B.Eng., Ph.D., M.I.E.E., M.I.Min.E., A.M.I.Mech.E.

Professor I. C. F. Statham, M.Eng., M.I.M.E., F.R.I.C.S., F.G.S., M.Amer.I.M.E., F.A.M.E.M.E., F.R.S.A., Certificated Colliery Manager, Emeritus Professor of Mining and formerly Dean of Engineering in the University of Sheffield.

Professor J. T. Whetton, D.S.O., O.B.E., M.C., T.D., M.Sc., Professor of Mining in the University of Leeds.

W. H. Wilcockson, M.A., F.G.S., Lecturer in Geology in the University of Sheffield.

F. Trevor Williams, M.Sc., Dip.Met.Min., A.M.I.Min.E., Member of the National Association of Colliery Managers, Lecturer in Mining in the Post-Graduate School of Mining in the University of Sheffield.

H. B. Wood, B.Sc., A.M.I.E.E.

PREFACE

COAL is of paramount importance to the social and industrial life of the modern world. The ever-increasing applications of science and technology and the advancing standard of coal-mining techniques will afford scope for the best brains and offer great opportunities to the fully trained mining engineer and mineworker for some generations ahead.

It is natural that with the rapid development of applied science and engineering the mining industry should, during the last half-century and especially during the last decade or so, have undergone a revolution. Old methods and machines have given place to more modern practices and techniques which would have been regarded as impossible only a few years ago, and developments continue.

This progress is evident in all the multitudinous branches of the industry, from the sinking and equipment of the shafts to the final processing of the coal for use, while the growth of mining education and training, the scientific approach to the safe and efficient application of machinery to replace manual labour, and the recent changes in mining law demand close attention together with increased technical knowledge and skill on the part of all engaged in mining operations.

There is a real need for a comprehensive textbook on mining, offering in convenient form the latest information to the practising mining engineer, the mining student and the intelligent and ambitious junior official or mineworker wishing to keep abreast of the times and to qualify for advancement in the new era of mining.

Coal Mining Practice has been specially written with this need in view. Each of the eighteen contributors has been selected on account of his special qualifications, his recognised outstanding expert knowledge and his acquaintanceship with the needs of the aspirant to promotion in the mining industry. The team includes four eminent Professors of Mining, six senior members of University teaching staffs, one former Divisional Inspector of Mines and one other ex-senior member of the staff of the Ministry of Power, two occupying high positions of responsibility on the production side of the industry, two highly qualified mining and electrical engineers closely associated with the industry and two senior scientists with wide experience and specialised knowledge of coal processing.

With this unique combination of knowledge and experience the work is offered with every confidence that it reaches the highest possible standard, and no trouble has been spared to ensure its usefulness to its readers. It is

v

regretted that two of the contributors, Dr. W. Hancock and Mr. J. Smith, died at comparatively early ages, after drafting their contributions, without being able themselves finally to revise and pass their proofs for the press.

Although dealing primarily with British mining practice and equipment, the volumes will be found equally useful to overseas readers in all parts of the world and especially in those areas where British methods are practised, British mining law copied and British qualifications and certificates accepted.

Acknowledgment is given in the various chapters to a large number of individuals and firms for invaluable assistance and to many sources from which information has been obtained: the publishers and editor offer their thanks to these and many unnamed helpers, without whose assistance the preparation of the work would not have been possible.

They wish in particular to express their gratitude to the National Coal Board and to manufacturers of mining machinery and appliances for their invariable willingness to furnish information and illustrations. Thanks are also due to Mr. A. Wright, M.Eng., M.I.M.E., Mining Operations Engineer in the North-Eastern Division of the National Coal Board, for kindly undertaking to read the proof on strata control in the absence and at the request of Professor Phillips.

CONTENTS

VOLUME I

CHAPTER 1

HISTORICAL REVIEW

CHAPTER 2

MINING GEOLOGY

CHAPTER 3

PROSPECTING FOR COAL

CHAPTER 4

BORING

CHAPTER 5

SINKING

CHAPTER 6

PLANNING, LAYOUT AND DEVELOPMENT OF MINE WORKINGS

CHAPTER 7

METHODS OF WORKING COAL SEAMS

CHAPTER 8

BREAKING GROUND

PART I—TOOLS AND EXPLOSIVES

CHAPTER 9

BREAKING GROUND

PART II—THE APPLICATION OF EXPLOSIVES AND OTHER MEANS

CONTENTS

LIST OF PLATES

VOLUME ONE

COAL MINING PRACTICE

VOLUME ONE

CHAPTER 1

HISTORICAL REVIEW

COAL IN EARLY BRITAIN

THE full story of coal in Great Britain stretches back through the centuries to the Roman Occupation. There is no evidence that coal was known in Britain before Roman times, but there is little doubt that it was used to some extent by the Roman colonists. Thus coal cinders have been found in Roman remains at Wroxeter (Shropshire), on the sites of forts on the Wall of Hadrian built from the Tyne to the Solway Firth in the first century A.D., and in the heating chambers of Roman baths in a buried military station at Wall in Staffordshire. It appears that coal was used to some extent by the Romans for smiths' work, for lime burning and for heating purposes. Its use, however, was very limited, and no Roman remains have been found in old coal workings to indicate that it was obtained from underground mining operations. Even where Roman camps were established in the vicinity of the exposed coalfields in proximity to the outcrops of coal seams, little use appears to have been made of coal. With the departure of the Romans the use of coal as a fuel seems to have ceased for a long time and many centuries elapsed before the birth of the coal-mining industry as we know it to-day.

The native population and the Saxon and Danish invaders of Britain before the Norman conquest in 1066 found timber sufficient for their needs, and do not appear to have made use of coal.

The famous Domesday Book (1085), compiled for William the Conqueror as an inventory of everything of economic value in the country, makes no mention of coal although certain other minerals are mentioned. It could not, however, have been long after this date that the value of coal as a fuel became recognised, and its use extended, although the beginnings of mining operations are obscure.

Amongst the earliest records of coal mining are those contained in the Annals of the Abbey of Klosterrade which indicate that coal was being mined in the neighbourhood of Aachen on the Belgian-German frontier as early as 1113. Coal is also mentioned several times in an inventory of the See of Durham, compiled in 1183, although some authorities have expressed doubt as to whether these references were to mineral coal or charcoal which was then extensively used as a fuel.

No such doubt exists, however, regarding the records of Holyrood and Newbattle Abbeys, wherein it is recorded that digging of coal was in operation on the south shore of the Firth of Forth at Carriden and Linlithgow about 1200. Such digging would be restricted to seam outcrops and the mining operations would be of a crude and primitive character.

The signing of the Magna Charta by King John in 1215, and the Forest Charter by Henry III in 1217, which gave security of tenure of land and property, led to coal digging in certain coalfields and from that time coal has been worked and sold as an article of commerce.

In Northumberland and Fifeshire the Coal Measures extend under the sea, and, as the result of erosion and tidal action, coal was washed up on to the sea shore. This coal was (and still is in some areas) collected and sold for use as fuel in place of wood, and is said to have been known as "sea coal" to distinguish it from charcoal. The origin of the term "sea coal" has, however, been questioned, and some authorities attribute it to the fact that in those early days coal conveyed to London by sea was called "sea coal". In support of this origin of the term it is pointed out that coal is known to have been shipped to London from the Tyne and sold to lime burners in Sea Coal Lane near Ludgate Circus. Riley's *Memorials of London* records that shiploads of coal arrived in London in 1257, and that grants of money from the Exchequer were made in 1257 to 1259 for the purchase of sea coal for forging iron for use in the building of Westminster Palace.

Although used only to a limited extent and mainly by artisans such as smiths, lime burners and brewers, its use led to a public problem which has remained throughout the centuries, viz., the smoke nuisance. It is interesting to note that Nobles and Commons in Parliament protested against its use as it "corrupted the air with smoke and stink", and in 1306 the burning of sea coal in London was prohibited by Royal Proclamation. This was, however, unheeded, and although severe penalties were imposed, it proved unavailing, and the use of coal extended.

During the latter half of the 13th century coal was being mined and used in the Midlands, and it is recorded that Queen Eleanor (wife of Henry III) was compelled to leave Nottingham Castle in 1257 on account of the objectionable and unbearable smoke produced from the burning of coal.

During the first half of the 14th century coal was introduced widely as a fuel into castles, abbeys, and the larger houses, and improved chimneys were a feature of the architecture of the period.

As time went on, not only did the demand for coal for home consumption increase, but foreign markets opened, and as early as 1325 coal was being exported from Newcastle to France. In view of the subsequent expansion of coal exports and their importance, it is interesting to observe that in 1362 the export of coal was prohibited owing to fear of exhaustion of our supplies.

EARLY MINING METHODS

Authentic records of mining methods and conditions in these early days are lacking, but these must have been primitive and the workings limited by lack of tools and equipment.

Only seams lying near the surface would be worked. At first the coal was got along the outcrop by a form of quarrying, an early and crude version of the modern system of opencast working.

Where the coal became too deep for opencast working, the seam was followed underground from the outcrop for a short distance by tunnels known as day-levels, day-eyes, day-holes, or adits. Where possible these tunnels were driven on a slight rising gradient to allow of drainage as no pumps were then available. The coal was carried along the underground roadways to the surface on the backs of women, boys and girls known as "bearers".

Where the coal was more or less flat but lay at a depth too great for opencast working as in South Staffordshire, Yorkshire and other districts, extraction was effected by what were known as "bell-pits" or "beehive pits". In this primitive system of mining, first introduced by early man in pursuit of flint for use as stone implements, shallow pits were sunk to the coal seam and then were widened or belled out to remove as much coal as possible without supporting the roof, after which the pit was abandoned, and another one sunk nearby.

Evidence of rows of such bell-pits can still be traced, in the form of hollows or depressions in the surface, for miles along the outcrops of seams of coal and ironstone in most of the exposed coalfields. Near the outcrops a combination of adits and bell pits was sometimes adopted.

The coal was still carried by the bearers along the adits and up the shafts until about the middle of the 14th century, when windlasses or jack rolls, similar to those used for winding water from wells, were introduced for hoisting the coal up the shafts in baskets, this method of winding persisting in some cases until the 19th century.

The coal was got by wooden picks shod or tipped with iron, and by iron wedges.

For the sinking of shafts and driving of levels or tunnels in rock, fires were lighted in contact with the rock or stone to be broken, and these fires were extinguished and the rock cooled by water, thus causing it to split.

Little progress was made in mining methods for several centuries largely owing to lack of tools and equipment, and the miners or pit men, whose wages amounted to 3d. or 4d. per day, were more or less serfs until the reign of Queen Elizabeth who in 1574 freed English miners from serfdom: such relief from serfdom in Scotland was, however, delayed until 1799.

About the middle of the 17th century horses were employed for winding coal from mine shafts.

An early form of winding plant operated by horses was the "cog-and-rung gin". This comprised a drum, with spokes or rungs, working on a horizontal shaft and mounted directly over the mine shaft. The drum was driven by a crude horizontal cogwheel the vertical shaft of which was rotated by a long pole or lever to the outer end of which was harnessed a horse or horses, which ran in a circular track around the shaft top. A later development, introduced about the end of the 17th century, was the horse whim or gin which consisted of a horizontal drum working on a vertical shaft or spindle, placed away from the shaft. This drum was also rotated by a horse or horses trotting round a circle. The ropes which coiled on the winding drum passed over pulleys mounted on a crude headgear over the winding shaft. This permitted the use of a larger drum and increased speed of winding. The coal was usually raised in baskets or corves made of hazel twigs and having a capacity of about 5 cwt.

With deeper and somewhat more extensive, though still limited, area of working around the shafts, difficulties of ventilation and drainage arose.

Ventilation.—At first, natural ventilation alone was depended upon and explosions of firedamp, the natural gas of coal, were frequent occurrences. The explosive nature of firedamp was, however, recognised very early and is mentioned in a paper read by Roger Mostyn before the Royal Society in 1677. Mostyn tells how the miners were at first inclined to toy with firedamp, and set it alight, but that after a disaster they realised its dangers and treated it more cautiously. He also describes the early method of dealing with firedamp, and how the miners appointed "a man of resolute purpose" to go down the mine before them, who, dressed in his worst rags, saturated with water, crawled forward to where the firedamp existed and ignited it by holding in front of him a long rod carrying one or two lighted candles. He then flung himself face downward on the floor, and waited until the flame had died out. This subsequently became the recognised method of dealing with firedamp, and the person who performed this operation was called the "Fireman", the name still used in some areas for the official whose duty it is to examine mine workings for gas although this title has now been dropped from official documents and the name "Deputy" substituted.

It is recorded that it was the practice in 1798 at Lord Dudley's pits at Netherton, Staffordshire, to fire the gas three times a day at 4.0 a.m., at noon and at 7.0 p.m.

Other methods of firing gas included raising a lighted candle attached to the end of a wire into the inflammable mixture by pulling on the wire from a distance and, so it is stated, by sending a donkey with a lighted candle fixed on its back into the gas-laden workings.

Fire Lamps and Furnaces.—The necessity to augment the flow of air resulting from natural ventilation led to the introduction of the fire lamp or fire basket. This was hung in the upcast shaft, giving rise to a chimney effect which increased the amount of air flowing through the workings. The fire lamp appears to have been first used in the North of England about 1732, and was the forerunner of the ventilating furnace which served the same purpose. At first the furnace was erected on the surface and connected to the upcast shaft, but later furnaces placed below ground, with dumb drifts or airways which allowed the gas-laden air from the mine to enter the shaft at a level above the furnace, were extensively used. Some of these furnaces remained in use until quite recently, although their use was forbidden in mines newly opened after the passing of the Coal Mines Act 1911. At one mine in Whitehaven jets burning firedamp conveyed in pipes from the mine workings were substituted for the coal-burning furnace.

The obvious danger of explosion, and the discomforts arising from the use of underground furnaces led to the trial of other means for producing ventilation, one of which was the use of steam jets. In the early application of this method the boiler or steam-producing plant was placed below ground with the same attendant danger of explosion, so that later the boiler was placed on the surface, and the steam conveyed down the upcast shaft in pipes from which it escaped in jets at the pit bottom.

Mechanical Ventilation.—Meanwhile, although furnaces continued to be used largely on account of the low cost of fuel, attention was being devoted to the development of mechanical ventilators. Early types of such ventilators introduced about the beginning of the 19th century were of the displacement or piston type, being in effect large air pumps. During the second half of the same century the centrifugal fan was introduced, and as its merits were recognised, it was rapidly adopted as the standard type of machine for mine ventilation. Of recent years, however, it has found a rival in the axial-flow type of fan; but present-day developments of the centrifugal radial-flow fan offer a challenge to its rival (see Vol. 3, Chap. 6).

Mine Lighting.—The early developments of underground mining introduced a new difficulty, that of providing underground lighting, the story of which constitutes a fascinating chapter recording progress against great odds.

The realisation of the danger of explosions and firedamp led to attempts to obtain illumination by means other than the open flame which constitutes a potential cause of ignition of firedamp. Although improvements were made in ventilation, accumulations of firedamp were frequent, and many explosions resulted from the use of candles, and early forms of open flame lamps. About 1740 Carlisle Spedding introduced the steel mill or Spedding Mill which was considered to afford a safe means of lighting. This consisted of a thin wheel or disc of steel driven at a high speed by gearing against which a piece of flint was held in such a manner as to emit a shower of sparks, the brilliance of which was increased in the presence of firedamp. These mills were carried by boys, on their chests, and operated near the workers. Explosions at Wallsend Colliery in 1784 and 1785 showed, however, that even this feeble source of light was dangerous in the presence of firedamp.

About this time attempts were made to reflect light down the shafts and into the workings by mirrors, but these proved abortive, and it is recorded that subsequently use was made of the faint light emitted from phosphorescent material such as putrefying fish skins.

THE DAVY LAMP.—The first real steps in the solution of the problem of safe lighting were made by Sir Humphry Davy and George Stephenson who introduced their safety-lamps about 1815.

The principle of the wire gauze as used in Davy's lamp still constitutes the basis of the modern flame safety-lamp, although, due to the improvements made by numerous workers, the modern lamp represents considerable advance upon the Davy lamp as regards design, safety and illumination.

Amongst the many who contributed to progress in this connection, mention should be made of Stephenson, Clanny, Marsaut and Mueseler. The original safety-lamp consisted simply of an oil vessel and wick with a 28-mesh gauze cylinder arranged around the flame. Although safe in still air and in low velocity currents, the lamp became unsafe in air currents moving at any substantial velocity. Stephenson's improvement consisted in placing a glass cylinder around the flame inside the gauze in such a manner as to protect the flame from the air currents. Thus the light had to pass through both gauze and glass and the candle-power of this lamp was only about 0·16.

Clanny replaced the lower portion of the gauze by a short glass cylinder through which a greater amount of light could pass. Meanwhile Marsaut still further protected the lamp by enclosing the gauze with a metal bonnet or shield and later by the introduction of a second concentric inner gauze.

Improvements in the design of the burner, the type of fuel and in the arrangement of airfeed have given us the modern flame lamp which is perfectly safe in inflammable mixtures, and capable of giving a candle-power of 3 or more.

ELECTRIC SAFETY-LAMPS.—About the middle of the 19th century electric safety-lamps were introduced. At first these were crude in design and gave little advantage over the oil lamp, but during the present century the electric hand-lamp has been enormously improved, and the cap-lamp has been introduced. Electric safety-lamps now outnumber flame safety-lamps by about 5 to 1.

COALFACE LIGHTING BY POWER.—It is interesting to note that electric lights fed from power mains were tried out on the coalface at Pleasley Common Colliery in Derbyshire as early as 1881, and at Earnoch Colliery in Scotland in 1886. Early applications of this system of lighting were, however, attended with danger, and for this reason its use was prohibited until recently in safety-lamp mines by the Coal Mines Act 1911.

A new interest in the problem was, however, aroused in the first quarter of this century by the experience gained in its use on the Continent, and in 1927 coalface lighting by power-fed lights was introduced at Birch Coppice Colliery in Warwickshire. Subsequently, numerous trials were made in different mining fields, but little success attended these trials, in that little improvement in safety appeared to be achieved and no increase in output was obtained.

The safety aspect was given special attention and many ingenious arrangements were developed to reduce the risk of gas ignition, including the use of carbon dioxide filled lamp fittings, compressed-air protection, special cut-outs and inductive lighting.

Whilst during recent years underground lighting from power mains has been introduced on a large scale for roadway lighting, its application on the face has been on a very limited scale, but there is no doubt that recent developments open up a new field in this direction as outlined in Vol. 3, Chap. 8.

Mine Drainage.—Mention has already been made of difficulties with mine drainage which for a long time impeded progress in mine development. In 1670 chain-bucket pumps operated by horses were introduced in the North of England. These consisted of an endless chain of buckets, or of discs passing up a vertical pipe, a type of pumping arrangement which was still to be seen in use at old farms until quite recently.

There is no doubt that these difficulties with mine drainage laid the foundations of modern steam engineering, for it was to this problem that Savery and Newcomen directed attention, and for the solution of which they designed the early steam-engines bearing their names.

Savery secured a patent for raising water from mines by the action of fire in 1698. His "fire engine" in which he raised water, by suction produced by condensation, to a height of 26 feet, and then a further 60 feet or so by direct pressure of steam and water, was the prototype of the Pulsometer pump, but when applied to mine pumping it was not entirely satisfactory.

Newcomen, however, was more fortunate in his attempt to solve the problem, and the Newcomen atmospheric engine, of which the first was installed near Walsall in South Staffordshire about 1715, and a second at Griff Colliery in Warwickshire, represents the real beginning of the successful use of steam power which led to enormous developments. The use of this engine for mine pumping spread to other coalfields, and made possible the working of deeper seams than hitherto. At this time mine shafts were small, seldom more than 7 to 8 ft. in diameter, and the area worked around the shaft was limited. Subsequent developments in pump design, especially the centrifugal pump and the application of electrical drives have solved the problems arising from the presence of water in mines.

The Use of Gunpowder in Mines.—Another notable innovation of this period was the introduction of explosives in the form of gunpowder for shaft sinking, said to have been first used in Germany about 1627 and in Great Britain in 1719 for sinking in Somerset and for blasting in coal about 1813.

Early Winding Methods.—Shafts were still of limited depths, and in 1760 a medal was struck to commemorate reaching the Main Coal seam at Walker Colliery on the Tyne at a depth of 200 fathoms.

At this time coal was still largely wound by horse whims or gins of the type previously mentioned, and winding at this colliery was by such a machine, having a drum actuated through gearing. Eight horses were employed to work the whim and on these being driven at a rapid trot, a basket of coal weighing 6 cwt. was wound from a depth of 200 yards in 2 minutes, representing a possible output of about 9 tons per hour from one such winding plant.

Coal was also raised by the use of waterwheels which were not uncommon during the latter part of the 18th century. Where a natural head of water was not available water was sometimes pumped by Newcomen's engines to the requisite elevation, and used for operating the water wheel, representing the indirect use of steam for coal winding operations.

The Steam Winding Engine.—The next natural step was the use of steam for winding and in 1763 coal was wound at Hartley Colliery by a "fire engine", but difficulty was experienced in imparting rotation to the drum.

About 1780 Watt invented the crank and a winder incorporating its use was installed at Walker Colliery in 1784.

From that time onwards steam-engines were increasingly applied at collieries for winding; the old horse whims and waterwheels were gradually replaced, and by about 1800 steam winding engines were common.

These engines were generally of the vertical single-cylinder type and various methods of balancing the load were introduced. One such method, "the chain balance", consisted in lowering into a staple pit a heavy chain coiled on a special drum on the winding-drum shaft when the coal load was being raised, the chain being raised again when the empty cage was lowered.

The first steam winders were of small power; up to the year 1840 they had not exceeded about 50 h.p., but about that time a winding engine of 150 h.p. was installed at Monkwearmouth, and from then onwards larger and larger powers were employed.

From the middle of the 18th to the middle of the 19th century the tempo of inventions increased and many new ideas and methods were introduced into the mines.

Wooden corves or tubs were introduced by John Curr of Sheffield in 1787. At first these ran on wheels on wooden rails; Curr also introduced guides for guiding them up and down the shafts. It was claimed that by the use of guides, tubs could be wound at a speed of 14 ft. per second, which appears to be slow compared with modern winding speeds which reach 80 ft. or more per second in some deep shafts.

The use of cages was also introduced about this time.

Wire ropes were first made for winding about 1825 and their many advantages caused their use to spread rapidly.

Growth in Output of Coal.—By the year 1800 the total output of coal in Great Britain was only about 10,000,000 tons per annum and the mines were small: the maximum output per day of 12 hours being about 300 tons in 1835. By 1850 the total output was some 60,000,000 tons per annum and maximum outputs of 800 tons per day of 12 hours were reached.

DEVELOPMENT OF PRESENT-DAY METHODS OF WORKING

Underground developments were also made about the end of the 18th century up to which time Pillar methods of working were universal, but about 1794 the Longwall method was introduced in Cumberland, having been previously employed to a small extent in the Shropshire Coalfield.

Ventilation was also improved and the original system of coursing the air round the whole mine in a single current was replaced by the method of splitting introduced by John Buddle in 1810, and still employed.

The Effect of the Industrial Revolution.—Meanwhile industrial developments outside the mining industry were giving rise to rapidly increasing demands for coal. Amongst these may be mentioned the increasing use of coke for iron smelting first introduced by Darby in 1735, the use of coal-gas for lighting which began about 1800, and, of major importance, the development of railways starting with the invention of the locomotive by Stephenson in 1815, followed by his *Rocket* of 1829, the forerunner of the modern locomotive. This last-named development stimulated trade and industrial progress in many directions, and side by side with this progress the mining industry developed very rapidly.

The Lancashire boiler came into use about 1850 and developments in steam engineering led to general industrial progress which reflected itself in increased demand for coal. About this time boilers were often placed below ground and compressed air was introduced underground for power purposes.

From 1850, when the output of coal was about 60,000,000 tons per annum, enormous strides were made in the mining industry. Output expanded and mining technique developed with increasing rapidity until the maximum output for the country of 287,430,000 tons was obtained in 1913 when the number of persons employed in the industry was 1,107,000.

Many large new mines were sunk, some with outputs of upwards of 1,000,000 tons per annum. Thereafter production declined, due to various circumstances, war, shortage of manpower, and industrial strife, reaching the lowest figure (except 1926—the year of the General Strike) of 183,000,000 tons in 1945. Since then output of deep-mined coal has increased to 210,232,000 tons in 1955 with 704,000 persons employed, excluding 11,366,000 tons of opencast coal employing 9,544 persons.

Electricity Introduced into Mines.—The mining industry played an important part in the development of engineering generally. As we have seen, it was mining power problems which largely gave birth to the steam engine, and if electricity was not similarly born in the mines of Great Britain it was largely cradled and reared therein. Mining engineers, ever on the look-out for means for increasing efficiency, were not long in recognising the advantages of a form of power which could be conveniently and economically transmitted long distances underground; for about the year 1882 the first electric motor was installed underground only some fifteen years after the introduction of electric motors. By 1891 electric motors were used for winding and it is worthy of note that the first turbo-alternator to be employed was installed at Ackton Hall Colliery, Yorkshire in 1901. So rapid was the growth of the use of electricity at collieries that by 1910 we find a colliery operated entirely by electricity—the first all-electric pit, the Britannia Colliery in South Wales. An idea of the rate at which the use of electricity in mines has grown is shown by the fact that in 1913 the aggregate horse-power of electric motors used in British coal mines was 628,000 (371,000 below ground and 257,000 on the surface), whereas in 1930 the aggregate horse-power was 1,816,500 (954,800 below ground and 861,700 on the surface) and by 1955 the aggregate had grown to 3,875,300 (2,222,300 below ground and 1,653,000 on the surface). These figures indicate clearly the enormous extent by which the use of electrical power at collieries grew in the 42 years from 1913 to 1955.

Developments in Haulage.—The more extensive size of mines led to the replacement of manual labour by the use of horses and the increasing use of mechanical power for haulage. Gradually rope haulages worked by the steam-engine, and later by the compressed-air engine, and electric motor, replaced both manual and horse haulage, and these in turn have been superseded to some extent in recent years by the use of conveyors and locomotives as mentioned later. In 1913 there were 73,034 horses at work in mines but by 1955 the number had fallen to 12,516.

Mechanical Coal Cutting.—The replacement of manual labour in mines by mechanical and electrical power is perhaps best illustrated by the application of coal-cutting machines. Prior to about 1866 all coal was got entirely by hand, but this year witnessed an innovation by the introduction of the first really successful mechanical coal cutter. Hitherto the miner had under-cut or holed the coal by the use of hand picks, but now a new tool began to present itself for use. The early coal cutters, including the manually oper-ated "iron man" of 1768, were crude in design and unreliable in operation with frequent breakdowns, and the lack of means for applying mechanical power retarded evolution and progress. By sheer perseverance, however, types of mechanically-operated machines capable of performing this arduous operation were later introduced and developed. The evolution of the modern coal cutter affords an interesting story of gradual improvement in design and materials, thanks to the assistance afforded to the miner by the mechanical and electrical engineer and the metallurgist.

It was largely during the period 1860 to 1880 that pioneers, with many failures and discouragements and but few successes, hammered into practical shape the first machines which established the economic advantages of mechanical coal cutting.

Three general types were developed, the disc machine, the bar machine and the chain machine. The first really successful coal cutter, the disc machine, represents the successful attempt to employ the principle of the traversing circular saw and this attained great popularity between 1900, when 160 disc machines were in use, and 1923 when some 1,250 of these machines were being used.

The bar machine, which embodies the principle of a traversing rotating toothed bar, attained limited success and some 920 of these were in use by 1924 as compared with 18 in 1900.

The chain machine, which in principle resembles a traversing band-saw with replaceable cutting teeth, appeared at first to be unsuccessful, but from the beginning of the present century (there were only four chain machines in use in 1900) it has developed until it is now the most popular type, of which over 7,000 were in use in 1949 out of a total of some 11,000 machines. The versatility of the chain machine is shown by the wide variety of uses for which it is employed to-day in the different methods of coal working.

The successful development of mechanical coal cutting is also indicated by the fact that during the period 1913 to 1955 the percentage of coal cut by machinery in British mines rose from less than $8\frac{1}{2}$ per cent. to 86 per cent.

The Introduction of Conveyors.—A similar story of early failures and ultimate success is revealed in the history of the application of underground conveying of coal. Up to the beginning of the present century the coal was filled into tubs at the working face. If the thickness of the seam permitted, the tubs were taken along the face and filled at the site of coal-getting; but in thin seams it was thrown back along the working face and filled into tubs at the gate end.

An obvious advance was the introduction of conveyors to transport the coal along the face and deliver it into tubs at the gate end. This represented the first step in the application of conveyors underground, made in 1902 by the invention of the Blackett Chain Conveyor which was first installed at Altoft's Colliery in 1905.

About the same time the belt conveyor was first successfully applied by Sutcliffe in 1905 and, in 1913, the jigging conveyor, originally developed on the Continent, was introduced into British mines.

Here again we find that at first progress was slow, waiting on suitability of design, and by 1928 only 12 per cent. of the coal mined was conveyed. Rapid progress has, however, been made in recent years and in 1955 no less than 91·4 per cent. of the coal produced in Great Britain was mechanically conveyed on some 24,600 conveyors of various types.

The Locomotive Goes Below Ground.—Mention has already been made of the progress in underground transport and of the introduction of the locomotive for haulage purposes. The utility and high efficiency of locomotives under suitable conditions has long been recognised on the Continent and in the United States of America. Four types of locomotives have been used extensively on the Continent, viz., the electric battery locomotive, the trolley locomotive, the compressed-air locomotive and the diesel locomotive, but in Britain limited use has been made only of the battery locomotive and the diesel locomotive, chiefly on account of the dangers associated with the trolley locomotive and the low efficiency of the compressed-air type. Battery locomotives were introduced into British mines (Cowpen Mill) about 1924, and diesel locomotives at Kingshill Colliery about 1935. The application of underground locomotives was, however, retarded by the need for the introduction of flame-proof designs. The first flame-proof diesel locomotive was delivered to British pits in July 1939 and the number has increased slowly, there being 191 in use in 1948. But some idea of the future possibilities of increase in the use of these locomotives is shown by the fact that the National Coal Board ordered 250 of these in 1948. They are now used for the transport of men and coal.

The battery locomotive has never attained much popularity in British mines; in 1948 the National Coal Board owned 44 such locomotives. In 1955 there were 548 diesel locomotives and 146 battery locomotives in use.

Considerable interest has been shown in recent years in the application of trolley locomotives in Britain, the use of which was prohibited by the

Coal Mines Act 1911. The recognition of the advantages of this type of
locomotive and the possibility of eliminating to a large extent its dangers,
has led to the removal of this embargo, and pilot installations have been
planned, the first of which came into operation at Sandhole Colliery in
Lancashire in 1953. In 1955 there were four electric-trolley locos in use.

Power Loading.—Further evidence of the technical progress in underground operations is afforded by developments in mechanical loading of
both coal and stone. For many years abortive attempts were made to
design machines suited to this work.

By the early twenties of the present century power-loading machines
were being introduced rapidly in American mines where pillar and stall
methods of mining are almost universal. The designing of machines suitable
for use in longwall work, however, presented special difficulties and the
first attempts at power loading in this country were made with American
machines designed primarily for pillar and stall mining. One of the earliest
of such attempts was made at Easthouses pit of the Lothian Coal Company
about 1927, when a Sullivan tank-type loader was used with a certain amount
of success.

Attempts were also made in the early thirties of the present century to
use other American machines, i.e., Joy loaders, in British longwall workings.
Although unsatisfactory for this method of working, these machines proved
satisfactory for bord and pillar methods, and for the driving of development
headings for longwall; and, especially during the Second World War, a
number of them were applied in Great Britain.

Longwall methods, however, call for machines specially designed for the
class of work in which a continuous buttock is filled from a face, and British
machinery manufacturers devoted themselves assiduously to the problem
of producing such machines. The original Meco-Moore loader, introduced
about 1934, which cut the coal as it travelled along the face in one direction
and loaded it on to a belt as it travelled in the opposite direction, represented
a landmark in the development of mechanical mining. Later this machine
was modified to cut and load the coal in a single operation and such machines
came into operation about the beginning of the Second World War.

Meanwhile a number of other machines, like the Shelton loader, the
Huwood loader, the Logan "Slab-cutter" and the Samson "Stripper", were
developed and applied to a limited extent with varying success. New types
of machines have proved successful in pit trials; amongst which mention
should be made of the Gloster "Getter", the Huwood "Slicer", the Anderton
"Shearer" and various forms of coal plough, all of which have as objective
the introduction of continuous mining, and there is no doubt that eventually
machines suitable to the varied conditions of mining will be evolved.

Although progress has been slow—in 1955 only 11·1 per cent. of the output of coal was power-loaded by some 547 machines—power loading is now
established as a practical proposition both for coal and stone, and will increase
in the future. In 1955 there were 627 stone loaders in use.

Power Stowing.—To complete the picture of technical progress as

(*Hair's Mining Sketches*, 1844)

A DURHAM COAL MINE OF THE EARLY NINETEENTH CENTURY. THE CHURCH PIT,
WALLSEND

(*Hair's Mining Sketches*, 1844)

THE AIR SHAFT AT WALLSEND COLLIERY

CL. I—12]

"LE PÉNITENT"

A "fireman" clearing out gas by igniting it as practised in the early days of coal mining. (From *La Vie Souterraine*, by Louis Simonin, 1857.)

indicated by developments in underground mechanisation, mention is made of the comparatively recent introduction of pneumatic stowing in Scotland, Yorkshire and South Wales. This represents another step in the direction of replacing the hand shovel by the machine as the material for the building of packs is transported in pipes and deposited in position by compressed air. The use of self-advancing mechanised supports should also be noted.

Coal Preparation.—With regard to progress in the preparation of coal for the market, coal screens for sizing of coal appear to have been first used at Willington about 1770.

Coal sizing formed the subject of a section of an Act of Parliament in 1816 (George III c. 127), and since that time screening of coal has developed by the introduction of numerous types of screens. Coal washing was in use on the Continent in 1840 and began to be practised in Great Britain shortly afterwards, although the high quality of British coals did not at that time call for its extensive application. A jig coal washer was patented in 1856 and the Elliot Washer was introduced in 1892. Not until the 20th century did intensive cleaning of coal become necessary, but progress has been rapid, and many types of both wet- and dry-cleaning plants have been developed and used. In 1928 only 25 per cent. of the output was cleaned, whereas in 1954 the percentage cleaned at 667 plants (461 washeries, 114 dry-cleaning plants and 92 froth flotation plants) was 55·4 and 25 per cent. was hand cleaned.

Much of the foregoing has been devoted to what may be regarded as purely technical progress in the mining industry. Side by side with these developments there has been a growing awareness of the importance of safety, health and welfare.

The chronological relations of the three branches, technical progress, safety and health progress and human progress make a fascinating study.

PROGRESS IN SAFETY AND HEALTH MATTERS

The First Mines Act.—On the question of safety little progress is to be recorded until Davy invented the safety-lamp about 1815 as already mentioned. During the first half of the 19th century conditions in the mines were far from satisfactory and explosions of firedamp were frequent occurrences. Reports on the appalling conditions in mines, the long hours of labour, the employment of women and children, roused the public conscience and led to the passing in 1842 of the first Coal Mines Act incorporating provisions for the improvement of conditions in the mines, which marks the beginning of mining safety legislation in this country.

This Act prohibited the employment below ground of women and girls and of boys under ten years of age and specified that the minimum age of persons working winding engines must be 15 years. It also made provision for the appointment of Inspectors of Mines to examine and report on mines, but the powers granted to these Inspectors were so limited as to be useless and were never really implemented. Nevertheless this Act established the principle of Government inspection, and the right of the State to legislate for the safe conduct of the industry. By successive Mines Regulations Acts passed in 1850, 1855, 1860, 1862, 1865, 1872, 1887 and 1911, and various other Acts dealing with special problems in the industry, the principle was extended and there has grown up an extensive code of mining law which is designed to ensure the safety and welfare of persons employed in the mining industry.

The Act of 1850 demanded the keeping of mine plans and that notice of all fatal accidents should be given to the Home Office, and by 1852 the number of Inspectors appointed was increased to six.

Under the Act of 1855, a standard of safety was ordained by the introduction of seven "General Rules to be observed at all Mines", while each colliery was required to formulate and observe its own "Special Rules" made with the approval of the Secretary of State.

The general rules related to ventilation, fencing and supporting shafts, means of signalling in shafts, provision of indicators and brakes on winding engines worked by steam or water power, and steam gauges, water gauges and safety valves on steam boilers.

In the Act of 1860 the miners were given the statutory right to appoint a check-weigher and the age limit for employment of boys was raised to 12, except in the case of those who could read and write, and that of winding engine boys to 18 years. The general and special rules were extended and the powers of Inspectors increased.

Two years later, in the Act of 1862, the provision of two shafts or outlets at every mine was made obligatory. By these Acts the law was brought to a state in which it was not seriously behind the mining science of the day.

During the 1860s the miners' organisation, the forerunner of the Miners' Federation, pressed increasingly for further legislation. Many Bills were put before Parliament and in 1872 the Coal Mines Regulation Act of that year was passed which codified and stabilised mining law for the next 15 years.

This Act required that henceforth every mine must be managed by a person holding a certificate of competency obtained in a State examination. The workmen were empowered to conduct, through their own representatives, periodical inspections of mine workings. It also recognised for the first time the principle of restricted hours of labour by instituting a maximum of a ten-hour day for boys, who were also required to attend school for 20 hours each fortnight. This latter provision anticipated to some extent the Elementary Education Act of 1872 which made school attendance compulsory for all children. The general rules were brought up to date and workmen were given the right to criticise special rules before they were enforced. This Act incorporated in some measure the general principles of future safety legislation and later Acts largely extended these principles in the matter of detail.

Thus the comprehensive Act of 1887 reveals not so much an extension of legislative policy as of the effect of development in mining science. The use of safety devices and methods of proved value was enforced, and eight new general rules were introduced. State certification was extended to include second-class certificates of competency to be held by undermanagers, the age of winding engine-men was raised to 22 years and of all boys employed below ground to 12 years, while the check-weighing provisions were revised and extended.

In the year 1900 the age limit for boys working underground was raised to 13 and later to 14 by the Coal Mines Act of 1911, referred to later.

The Coal Mines Regulations (Limitation of Hours of Work Below Ground) Act of 1908, usually referred to as the "Eight Hours Act", limited the length of shift worked below ground to 8 hours. This was subsequently amended by other Acts. Thus in 1919 the working shift was reduced to 7 hours, in 1926 it was extended to 8 hours (for 5 years), in 1931 it was reduced to $7\frac{1}{2}$ hours for 1 year, and by an Act of 1932 the $7\frac{1}{2}$ hour shift was to remain in force until an Act was passed in accordance with the recommendations of the international convention of hours of work.

The 1911 Act.—The Coal Mines Act of 1911, which, until the passing of the Mines and Quarries Act 1954, constituted the principal Act in force relating to coal mines, repealed the Coal Mines Act of 1887 (with the exception of certain sections relating chiefly to check-weighing problems), and consolidated and amended the law relating to coal mines and certain other mines.

This Act, the wide scope of which is indicated by its division into eight parts dealing respectively with (1) Management, (2) Safety, (3) Health, (4) Accidents, (5) Regulations, (6) Employment, (7) Inspection and (8) Legal Proceedings, extended considerably the principle of State regulation of the mining industry and enters into minute detail on many matters.

The General Rules of the earlier Acts were replaced by an elaborate code of General Regulations and the Secretary of State (later the Minister of Mines or the Minister of Fuel and Power) was, by the Act, given power to amend or add to these safety requirements without further legislation. This provision rendered unnecessary the passing of a further Mines Act for 43 years, when the Mines and Quarries Act 1954, covering as its name implies all classes of mining and quarrying, was passed as mentioned later.

The 1911 Act extended the principle of State certification to include surveyors, firemen, examiners or deputies and shot-firers, the qualifications of whom are governed by elaborate regulations.

Between the two world wars a considerable body of legislation was directed to improving the safety and efficiency of mining and the welfare and standard of living of the mine workers.

AFTER THE FIRST WORLD WAR

During the First World War the coal mines were taken over and controlled by the Government through a Minister of Mines. As the result of intense dissatisfaction in the industry the Coal Industry Commission of 1919, under the chairmanship of Lord Justice Sankey (the Sankey Commission) was appointed to enquire into the conditions in the industry and to make recommendations for its reorganisation. This Commission made many and far-reaching proposals which led to the passing of the Mining Industry Act 1920.

This Act gave recognition to the vastly increased importance of the administration of the Mines Acts by the establishment of a Department of the Board of Trade, known as the Mines Department, under a Parliamentary Secretary of the Board of Trade. It gave wide powers to the Board of Trade to give directions on many matters including the regulation of coal export, of pithead prices of coal, wages and the distribution of profits. It provided for the appointment of Advisory Committees, with representation from many interests both within and without the industry, to advise the Board of Trade on matters under the Act.

It also made provision for the establishment of Pit Committees, District Committees, Area Boards and a National Board whose constitution and functions were specified.

These bodies were composed of an equal number of representatives of the owners and mineworkers.

It was, however, stipulated that if after the expiration of one year, by reason of failure on the part of the persons entitled to appoint representatives, the scheme was rendered abortive, it should cease to have affect. In point of fact it was not accepted by the parties concerned and thus became null and void, but it is worthy of note on account of its far-reaching character.

The Mining Industry Act of 1920 also provided for the establishment of a fund for the improvement of the social conditions of colliery workers. This fund, known as the Miners Welfare Fund, was derived from a sum of money equivalent to one penny per ton of output to be set aside for the purpose specified. Of this amount one-fifth was to be spent on education and research and four-fifths on general social improvements of the conditions in mining areas. This provision was to apply for five years and it is to be noted that in 1926 it was extended for a further five years and again in 1931 for five years, but from 1932 to 1938 the levy on tonnage was reduced to $\frac{1}{2}$d. per ton, the full amount of 1d. per ton being restored in 1939 for a further 13 years.

The year 1923 saw the passing of the Mines (Working Facilities and Support) Act, which as its name implies deals with the granting of facilities for the working of minerals and with problems of support, both under specified conditions.

In spite of the passing of the Mining Industry Act 1920, the mining industry declined and a general stoppage in 1925, with the threat of a general strike, was averted by a Government subsidy and the appointment of the Royal Commission on the Coal Industry 1925, under the chairmanship of Sir Herbert Samuel (the Samuel Commission). The report of this Commission contained many novel and far-reaching suggestions. Amongst these were State acquisition of royalties and the encouragement of amalgamations within the industry.

The Mining Industry Act of 1926 gave effect to many of the Commission's proposals but excepted the nationalisation of royalties. It incorporated recommendations of the Samuel Commission regarding facilities for re-organisation of the coal-mining industry by amalgamations and absorptions of undertakings. It supplemented the Miners' Welfare Funds of the 1920 Act by a levy of 5 per cent. on all coal royalties and directed that the proceeds from this levy should be devoted to the provision of pithead baths. It also limited recruitment into the industry and legalised the establishment of profit-sharing schemes notwithstanding any provision in the articles of association of any company.

(After the nationalisation of mines, the Miners' Welfare Joint Council was set up in 1947 for planning and directing all welfare activities.)

The Great Stoppage of 1926.—In spite of these and other provisions the Act came too late to avert a general stoppage in the industry which started in May 1926 and lasted until towards the end of November, being at first supported by a General Strike.

By 1930 conditions in the industry had not greatly improved and a further attempt to meet the requirements was made in the Coal Mines Act 1930. This Act provided for a central scheme and for district schemes regulating the production, supply and sale of coal, which schemes were to be approved by or made by the Board of Trade.

It also provided for reorganisation of the coal-mining industry and the constitution of a Coal Mines Reorganisation Commission composed of five members all of whom were unconnected with the industry: for amendment of hours of labour and the constitution of a Coal Mines National Industrial Board to consider agreements as to wages and labour conditions with a view to avoiding disputes or the settlement of disputes.

NATIONALISATION OF ROYALTIES

In 1938 a further step for promoting the interest, efficiency and better organisation of the industry was taken by the nationalisation of coal royalties.

The Coal Act of 1938 laid down that after 1st January 1939 no coal leases should be renewed; all royalties were unified by 1st July 1942 and all interests in coal were purchased by the State for the sum of £66,450,000.

DURING AND AFTER THE SECOND WORLD WAR

The outbreak of the Second World War was followed by the introduction of special war-time legislation and regulations.

Under the Coal Mining Undertakings Control Order of 13th July 1942 the Minister of Mines took control of all coal undertakings in Great Britain and laid down that directions should be given to such undertakings on his behalf by the Controller General of the Ministry or by Regional Controllers of the Ministry. On 6th April 1943 the Essential Work Order was applied to the coal-mining industry.

Thus in 1942 the control of the industry passed from the private owners to the State and from then onwards numerous Regulations appertaining to various aspects of the industry were introduced.

In March 1945 the Minister of Fuel and Power presented to Parliament the Report of the Technical Advisory Committee on Coal Mining (the Reid Report) prepared by seven members of the Committee, all Mining Engineers, under the chairmanship of Mr. C. C. Reid (now Sir Charles Reid).

This Report, which is worthy of careful study, analysed in detail the system of mining, the methods of working and the normal practices in operation, pointed out shortcomings and made recommendations on many matters.

Mining a Nationalised Industry.—The Coal Industry Nationalisation Act was passed in 1946 and on 1st January 1947 the coal mines of Great Britain passed from private enterprise to State ownership.

The valuation of the mines was placed in the hands of the Central Valuation Board who awarded a global sum of £164,600,000 to the owners to cover the cost of the coal-mining interests. This global sum was subsequently divided between the 21 District Mining Associations in Stage II of the valuation proceedings.

In Stage III of the proceedings the District sums were distributed amongst the various owners by District Valuation Boards appointed by the Minister of Fuel and Power for the purpose.

The Act vests powers for working the mines in the National Coal Board which is charged with the duties of:—

(*a*) working and getting the coal in Great Britain to the exclusion (save as in the Act provided) of any other person.

(*b*) securing the efficient development of the coal-mining industry; and

(*c*) making supplies of coal available, of such qualities and sizes, and in such quantities and at such prices, as may seem to them best calculated to further the public interest in all respects, including the avoidance of any undue or unreasonable preference or advantage.

The functions of the National Coal Board include the carrying on of all such activities as may appear to the Board to be requisite, advantageous or convenient for them to carry on for, or in connection with, the discharge of their duties.

The Board is also responsible under the Act for the safety, health and welfare of persons in its employment.

The Mines and Quarries Act 1954.—The Mines and Quarries Act 1954, "an Act to make fresh provision with respect to the management and control of Mines and Quarries and for securing the health and welfare of persons employed thereat", which came into force on 1st January 1956, repealed the Coal Mines Act 1911 and various other enactments. Its fifteen parts, comprising 195 sections, consolidated the law relating to both mining and quarrying and contains provision for the issue of new or amended regulations, to extend and replace those made under the Act of 1911 (see Vol. 4, Chap. 8).

INCREASING SAFETY THROUGH THE YEARS

Coal mining has always been regarded as amongst the most dangerous of all industrial occupations, with a high death rate and a high accident rate.

This was inevitable in view of dangers associated with the winning of coal, the limited knowledge of the precise nature of the risks involved and of the means for mitigating the dangers of the mine. For many years, however, mine owners, the legislature and others have worked steadily toward an increasing standard of safety in the mines and with fruitful results.

Side by side with technical progress there has been a steady growth of knowledge and understanding of the causes of accidents accompanied by strenuous and commendable efforts for their elimination which has reduced the risks and increased the safety of mining operations as shown by official statistics.

Careful study of the underlying causes of accidents and the introduction of preventive measures, as these became available, both voluntarily and under compulsion of legislation, have reduced the number of accidents from all causes especially during recent years.

A full account of the steps by which this improvement has been achieved is beyond the scope of this work but is to be found in the official reports of the Mines Department and the Ministry of Fuel and Power, in the reports of the Safety in Mines Research Board and other research organisations and in the publications of technical bodies associated with the mining industry.

Striking testimony to the progress made is afforded by the fact that the average death roll in British coal mines is at present less than half what it was in the last quarter of the last century.

Thus in the last quarter of the 19th century the average number of persons killed per annum was about 1,060. During the 25 years 1931 to 1955 the death roll fell to 683 and, still more encouraging, during the ten years 1946 to 1955 inclusive the figure was 468, whilst the number of deaths in 1956 of 329 is the lowest on record.

In considering the statistics relating to accidents it is important to recognise that the number of persons killed or injured does not give a true assessment of the problem owing to variations in the number of persons employed, and better bases of comparison are the death rates per 1,000 persons employed, per 1,000,000 tons of coal produced, or per 100,000 manshifts worked.

From whichever standpoint the position is viewed there is the same indication of progressive increase in safety in our mines.

Thus the average death rate per 1,000 employed in the decade 1873 to 1882 was 2·24, whereas in the period 1946 to 1955 inclusive it fell to 0·64; in the year 1954 it was still more satisfactory at 0·50, but rose to 0·58 in 1955.

Again during 1873 to 1882 the deaths per million tons raised were 8·18 compared with 2·57 for the ten years 1944 to 1953 inclusive, whilst the death rate per 100,000 manshifts worked shows a decline from 0·43 during 1923–32, when records were first published, to 0·256 for the period 1946 to 55, being 0·20 for the year 1954 and 0·24 for 1955.

The many factors which have contributed to this recent improvement are discussed in Vol. 4, Chap. 4, but it is worth while to review here the gradual improvement over a long period of years.

Colliery Explosions.—Thus accidents due to explosions of firedamp and coal-dust have been reduced by improved ventilation, the increased use of safety devices including safety-lamps, flame-proof and intrinsically safe electrical apparatus, improved explosives, precautions against coal-dust and closer inspection coupled with the spread of knowledge of the dangers to be overcome.

Taking, however, the number of persons killed by explosions, it is found that in the decade 1873 to 1882 the average number of deaths per annum from this cause was 263 whilst for the decade 1946–55 the average number was 32·9. This average was swollen by the high number of deaths from explosions in 1947 which reached 168 and 99 in 1951, serving to remind us of this ever-present danger. On the other hand, the figures of 1 for 1952, 4 for 1954 and 7 for 1955 indicate the extent to which the menace of mine explosions is being overcome.

If the problem is viewed from the standpoint of death rate per 1,000 persons employed, we find the same encouraging reduction in the danger of explosions. Thus the death rate from this cause in the decade 1873 to 1882 was 0·65 whilst for the years 1945–54 inclusive it was less than 0·05. Similar improvements are observed if the death rate is expressed in relation to tonnage raised or manshifts worked.

A study of the frequency and severity of explosions shows that during the third quarter of the 19th century explosions were all too frequent occurrences. In this period of 25 years no less than 81 explosions occurred, each causing the loss of 10 or more lives; of these 19 caused 50 or more deaths and 6 caused 100 or more.

During the last quarter of the same century the number of explosions causing 10 or more deaths fell to 54, but the magnitude of the explosions increased and 21 caused 50 or more deaths whilst 11 caused 100 or more deaths.

Happily during the first quarter of the 20th century the number of explosions again fell, the total number causing 10 or more deaths being 21. At the same time the average magnitude of disasters was reduced and only 9 caused the death of 10 or more persons. In this period, however, two of the explosions were major disasters causing the loss of 344 and 439 lives respectively.

During the 22 years 1926 to 1947 inclusive the number of explosions causing 10 or more deaths showed an increase on the preceding quarter century, the number being 31, but the severity was materially less as shown by the fact that only 6 caused 10 or more deaths and only 2 caused 100 or more deaths. In the ensuing seven years, 1948 to 1954 inclusive, only one explosion (in 1951) resulted in more than 10 deaths.

The noteworthy decrease in the average magnitude of mine explosions during the present century is due largely to the recognition of the explosive

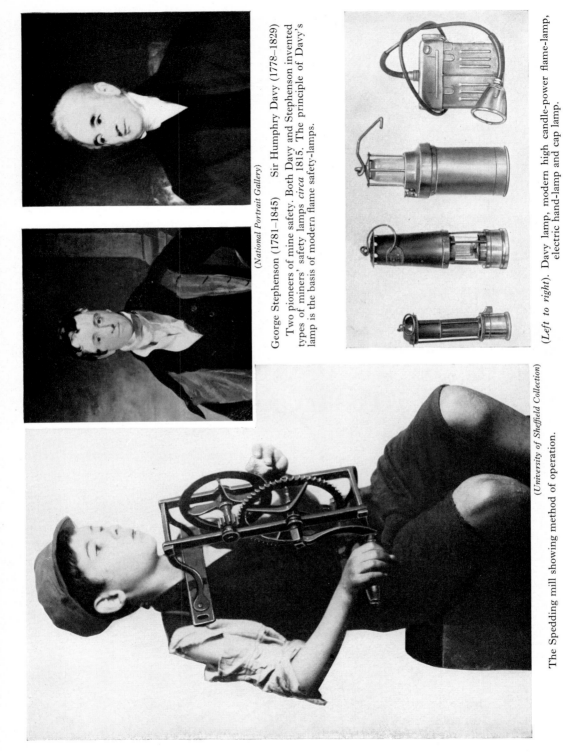

(National Portrait Gallery)

George Stephenson (1781–1845)   Sir Humphry Davy (1778–1829)

Two pioneers of mine safety. Both Davy and Stephenson invented types of miners' safety lamps *circa* 1815. The principle of Davy's lamp is the basis of modern flame safety-lamps.

(Left to right). Davy lamp, modern high candle-power flame-lamp, electric hand-lamp and cap lamp.

(University of Sheffield Collection)

The Spedding mill showing method of operation.

SOME STAGES IN THE DEVELOPMENT OF MINE LIGHTING

Putters or trolley boys. (Illustration from *La Vie Souterraine*, 1857.)

(*Coal Magazine*)

The whim gin or horse gin used for winding coal.

EARLY METHODS OF HAULING AND WINDING COAL

character of coal-dust, which played an important role in many explosions in the past, and the adoption of preventive measures.

The advent of coal cutting and mechanical haulage resulted in the production of fine coal-dust in increasing quantity, but for many years the danger of this dust was unrecognised by the mining industry in general. The danger was first apprehended about the middle of the 19th century but for many years it was disputed whether it did or did not contribute to mine explosions. As early as 1875 Galloway reached the conclusion that coal-dust was the principal agent in colliery explosions. Several Royal Commissions inquired into the subject (1881, 1891, 1907) but their conclusions were indefinite and for a long time opinion was divided. Some held that coal-dust and air alone could cause an explosion, others that the presence of firedamp was necessary.

An explosion at Altofts Colliery in Yorkshire in 1886, in which 22 lives were lost, focused attention upon the coal-dust danger and led Mr. William Garforth (later Sir William Garforth) to carry out experiments in large surface galleries. These experiments proved conclusively the explosive character of coal-dust-air mixtures in the absence of firedamp, and these and later experiments carried out for the Coal Owners' Association, first at Altofts in 1908 and then at Eskmeals from 1911 to 1924, together with experiments in the U.S.A., France, Belgium, Germany and Austria, brought home to the mining world the dangers of coal-dust as an explosive agent.

They also established that the admixture of stone-dust with the coal-dust to a sufficient degree, as suggested by Garforth, afforded protection against the danger of coal-dust explosions.

In 1920 General Regulations enforcing precautions against coal-dust were issued, and since that time stone-dusting of mine roadways has become general practice. The present relative immunity from major disasters is due in no small measure to these precautions and to the excellent work of the Safety in Mines Research Board which has, since its inception in 1921, made valuable contributions to increased safety in this and other directions.

The widespread adoption of means for dust suppression, especially by water infusion at the coalface and other methods at conveyor transfer and loading points and on mine roadways generally, has done much to reduce the risk of coal-dust explosions as well as the deleterious effects of dust on the health of the miner.

Important contributions to the elimination of the explosion hazard have been made by improvements in mining explosives represented by the introduction of permitted explosives in 1897, of sheathed explosives in 1934 and equisafe explosives in 1949. Improved techniques in blasting practice following investigation of the factors affecting safety in the use of explosives, and the better training of shot-firers have also had a significant effect upon the incidence of explosions (Chap. 8).

Accidents from Falls.—Although the big explosion with appalling loss of life at one fell swoop stirs the public imagination and rouses the nation's sympathy, it will be noted that explosions do not constitute the major cause of loss of life in and about our coal mines. The greatest source of underground accidents is falls of ground. This has been so ever since records were kept and remains so, but here again notable progress has been achieved especially during recent years.

During the last three decades of the 19th century about 450 persons lost their lives per annum due to falls of ground, and during the first three decades of the present century the average number of persons killed per annum by falls rose to 572. It is, however, gratifying to observe the considerable improvement in recent years and to note that during the ten years 1945 to 1954 inclusive, the average number of deaths per annum from this cause has fallen to 220, which is less than 40 per cent. of what it was in the earlier part of the century. During recent years in particular the improvement has been most marked.

Here again the position is more accurately represented by the death rates than by the actual number of persons killed, and a study of the death rates from falls expressed in the various ways previously mentioned reveals an increasing standard of safety.

This has been brought about by careful study of the underlying causes of accidents from falls and remedial measures by many bodies and by individual workers, notably by committees operating for some years in the various coalfields under the aegis of the Safety in Mines Research Board, and by an intensive campaign by the Ministry of Fuel and Power through the Mines Inspectorate as well as by researches carried out in the Universities and like institutions.

These have led to a more complete knowledge of the principles of strata control and to improved methods of support arising largely from the wider adoption of steel props and steel arches. More recently the introduction of the hydraulic prop, of the hydraulic chock and the automatic chock promise still greater safety against falls.

Much might be written of the reduction through the years of accidents from haulage, in shafts and from miscellaneous causes underground and on the surface, in all of which there are found the same reductions due to study of the problems of accident prevention and the introduction of preventive measures.

The statistics quoted are those for fatal accidents only, but it will be realised that serious non-fatal and minor injuries in the mines attain formidable proportions at all times. Nevertheless serious non-fatal accidents show the same progressive decline as do fatal accidents, but over a period of years the number of minor injuries reported showed an increase. This does not, however, indicate a real increase in such accidents owing to the encouragement given to workers to report minor injuries so that they can be promptly treated.

CHAPTER 2

MINING GEOLOGY

Introduction.—The word "Geology" signifies the science of the Earth and covers everything from the atmosphere down to the centre of the globe. The coal miner is concerned only with the thin surface layer of sedimentary rocks, and the following pages are chiefly devoted to consideration of this layer, but it is necessary to give a brief survey of some other aspects of the subject which bear directly or indirectly upon the work of the mining engineer.

Composition of the Earth's Crust.—An estimate of the composition of the earth's crust made by F. W. Clarke[1] is as shown in Table I.

TABLE I

COMPOSITION OF THE CRUST OF THE EARTH

SiO_2	..	..	59·08	K_2O	3·11
Al_2O_3	..	..	15·23	H_2O	1·30
Fe_2O_3	..	..	3·10	TiO_2	1·03
FeO	..	..	3·72	CO_2	0·35
MgO	..	..	3·45	P_2O_5	0·285
CaO	..	..	5·10	S	0·049
Na_2O	..	..	3·71	Rest	0·486

The "rest" includes principally the oxides of zirconium, barium, strontium, manganese, nickel, chromium, vanadium and lithium, together with some chlorine and fluorine; and modern spectographic methods have shown the very wide-spread distribution of the rarer elements referred to as the "trace elements".

MINERALS AND ROCKS

The above-listed common oxides enter into chemical combinations that may be collected into groups of closely related compounds, often showing the phenomena of "solid solution". These groups of related compounds are the "minerals" in the scientific sense, such as the felspars, amphiboles, micas, etc. They form the components which go to build up the rocks that may be described as aggregates of mineral particles either loose and unconsolidated as sand and mud, or hard and compact like sandstone and slate.

For purposes of description rocks may be divided into three groups according to their mode of origin as follows:—

(1) Igneous rocks, consolidated from fusion, as granite and basalt.
(2) Sedimentary rocks, deposits of materials derived from the break-down of igneous or other rocks, e.g., sand, sandstone, mud, limestone.
(3) Metamorphic rocks, derived from any of the foregoing by the action of heat or pressure or both together, giving types such as slate, schist or marble.

THE PROPERTIES OF MINERALS

To arrive at the composition of a rock, it is necessary to be able to identify its component minerals. The common "rock-forming" minerals are few in number and it is usually possible to give a description of a rock using only about a dozen or less mineral names, though if more precision is required, greater detail is necessary. The identification of a mineral may be carried out by reference to its chemical and physical characters. It is not proposed to enter into a discussion of chemical analysis, but it is necessary to consider some of the more important physical properties. These are as follows:—crystal form, state of aggregation, cleavage, fracture, hardness, specific gravity, taste and smell, surface energy, electrical and magnetic properties, and the properties dependent on light such as colour, lustre, refraction, double refraction, pleochroism and extinction.

Crystal Form.—All matter is made up of aggregates of atoms or ions linked together in various ways; when these atoms or ions are bound together in a regular pattern or lattice they are said to assume the crystalline state. Crystalline material need not have a definite external form, but under favourable circumstances will solidify as a crystal, or a solid bounded by planes or faces having definite geometrical relationships controlled by the internal planes of atoms or ions. This results in the angles between the faces being constant for any one substance and thus of diagnostic value. The relative positions of the faces of a crystal are defined by reference to crystallographic axes which intersect in a common origin. There may be three or four such axes. Crystals are classified according to symmetry and grouped into six systems shown in Table II and Fig. 1 on the following pages.

Crystals rarely, if ever, show true geometrical symmetry. They are usually distorted by the expansion of some faces at the expense of others; nevertheless the angles between the faces remain constant and it is this angular relation that determines the symmetry. They do not always exhibit the full symmetry of their system and may develop forms with one-half or one-quarter of the normal number of faces. Such forms are the pyritohedron of iron pyrites in the cubic system, a 12-face form with half the number of faces of the tetrahexahedron, and the rhombohedron of 6 faces in the hexagonal system with half the number of faces of the hexagonal bi-pyramid. Another modification of symmetry is twinning, where a crystal is composed of more than one individual symmetrically disposed about a plane known as the twinning plane. All the angles contained by the faces of a normal simple

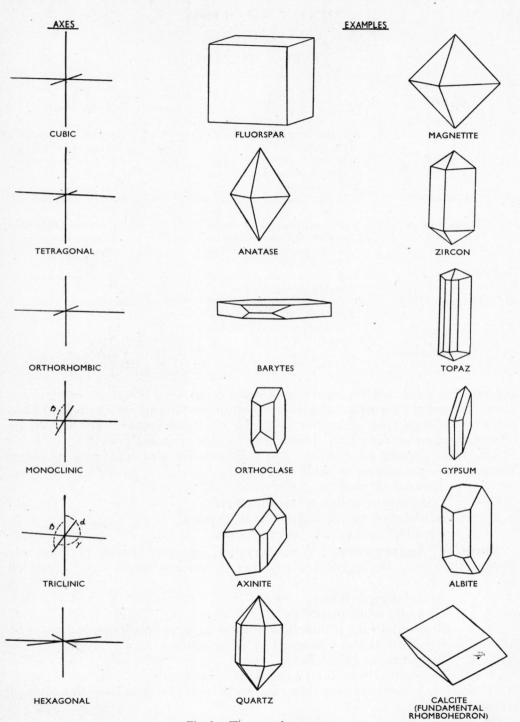

AXES

EXAMPLES

CUBIC — FLUORSPAR — MAGNETITE

TETRAGONAL — ANATASE — ZIRCON

ORTHORHOMBIC — BARYTES — TOPAZ

MONOCLINIC — ORTHOCLASE — GYPSUM

TRICLINIC — AXINITE — ALBITE

HEXAGONAL — QUARTZ — CALCITE (FUNDAMENTAL RHOMBOHEDRON)

Fig. 1.—The crystal systems.

25

TABLE II

CRYSTAL SYSTEMS

	System	Axes	Planes of symmetry	Typical minerals
(1)	Cubic	3 equal, at right angles to one another	9	Fluorspar, Rock salt, Garnet, Pyrite.
(2)	Tetragonal	3 at right angles, 2 equal and horizontal, vertical axis unequal	5	Zircon, Cassiterite, Rutile.
(3)	Orthorhombic	3 at right angles. All unequal	3	Barytes, Olivine.
(4)	Monoclinic	3 all unequal, 2 at right angles and one inclined in the same plane as the vertical axis	1	Gypsum, Orthoclase felspar, Hornblende Augite, Mica.
(5)	Triclinic	3 all unequal, all at oblique angles to one another	0	Plagioclase felspar, Axinite.
(6)	Hexagonal	4, 3 equal and horizontal inclined at 60° to one another, vertical axis unequal	7	Beryl.
(6a)	Trigonal division	,,	3	Calcite.

crystal are solid angles, never re-entrant angles. Though by no means always present, re-entrant angles are commonly found on twins and thus serve to indicate their character (Fig. 2). Re-entrant angles are also to be observed when crystals have grown side by side (parallel growth).

The faces present on a crystal and their relative size constitute its habit. Some common varieties of habit are:—

Tabular or platy as in barytes,
Prismatic or columnar as in quartz,
Acicular or needle-shaped as in gypsum,
Capillary or hair-like as in asbestos.

State of Aggregation.—When crystals are very small or minutely fibrous they may be aggregated together in various ways, some of which are:—

Nodular as in flint,
Globular as in marcasite,
Botrioidal (like a bunch of grapes) as in psilomelane,
Reniform (kidney shaped) as in hematite,
Stalactitic as in calcite,
Dendritic (branched) as in native copper.

A mineral not showing any external form may be granular, massive or compact.

Cleavage.—Many minerals have a tendency to split along one or more directions parallel to an actual or possible crystal face. This splitting gives plane surfaces known as cleavage planes. Their directions are determined by the constitution of the atomic lattice and they are of different degrees of perfection. Mica, for example, has one perfect cleavage, felspar has two good cleavages and one much less perfect.

Fracture.—This is the name applied to the surface when a mineral is broken independently of the cleavage. The property is best seen in minerals with a poor cleavage. The type of fracture is characteristic of some minerals; varieties are: conchoidal (like a shell) as in quartz, uneven as in tourmaline, hackly as in copper and other metals.

Hardness.—This is a valuable diagnostic character and is directly related to the distances between the ions in the crystal lattice. In practice hardness is

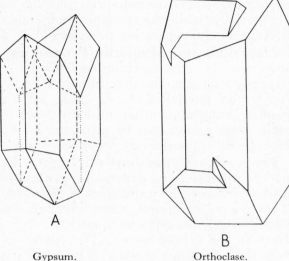

A
Gypsum.

B
Orthoclase.

Fig. 2.—Twin crystals.

measured by reference to a standard set of minerals known as Mohs' Scale of Hardness. This is as follows:—

1. Talc	5. Apatite	8. Topaz
2. Gypsum	6. Felspar	9. Corundum
3. Calcite	7. Quartz	10. Diamond
4. Fluorspar		

These minerals do not give any regular progression of hardness, which is determined by scratching standard specimens with the mineral in question. Diamond is not ten but very many times harder than talc.

Specific Gravity.—If pure material can be obtained its specific gravity is readily determined by weighing in air and in water and noting the loss of weight in water, or, if a pure sample cannot be obtained, by finding the specific gravity of the liquid in which it will just float.

Taste and Smell.—Rock salt, alum and some other substances can be recognised by their taste, and clay emits a characteristic odour when breathed upon.

Surface Energy.—This property is of little value for the identification of minerals, but is of the greatest importance in many processes concerned with the use or purification of mineral materials. Among solids the elements such as the metals possess the highest surface energy, the sulphides of the heavy metals come next, followed by the compounds of the light metals and non-metals. The phenomenon of wetting is brought about by the high surface energy of a solid overcoming the relative weak surface tension of a liquid so that a solid with a high surface energy is more easily wetted than one lower in the scale. When a mixture of finely divided minerals is agitated in water containing a little oil, the oil wets those with high surface energy, leaving the others uncoated, air bubbles form in the oil film and float the oily particles, while the remaining minerals sink. This is the basis of flotation used in mineral separation processes (Vol. 4, Chap. 7).

Electrical and Magnetic Properties.—Advantage is taken of electrical properties in dust-catching machinery. Magnetic properties are more generally useful in the determination and separation of minerals; magnetite Fe_3O_4 and pyrrhotite Fe_nS_{n+1} are attracted by an ordinary permanent magnet, but many other minerals such as ilmenite, biotite, hornblende, augite and garnet can be attracted by an electromagnet and, by varying the current, quite delicate separations can be carried out.

Properties Dependent on Light.—COLOUR.—The colour of a mineral may be intrinsic, i.e., dependent on the presence of some essential element, or may be caused by impurities. An example of the former is the green colour of the copper carbonate, malachite, and of the latter the purple amethystine colour of certain types of quartz. Colour in minerals may also be due to strain in the crystal lattice. The colour of a massive mineral often differs from that of its fine powder. The latter is shown by its streak on a plate of unglazed porcelain. The colour of a mineral in the mass is often variable but its streak is always the same.

LUSTRE.—The lustre of a mineral varies in part with its constitution and in part with its state of aggregation. Examples of lustres are adamantine as in diamond; metallic as in pyrites; sub-metallic as in pitchblende; vitreous as in quartz; greasy as in nepheline; pearly as in calcite; silky as in fibrous gypsum. The lustre may be changed by surface oxidation producing a tarnish like that of the partly oxidised copper pyrites, "peacock copper".

REFRACTION.—When light passes the boundary between two substances of different optical density it changes its velocity and may be bent and even undergo total internal reflection. In a thin slice of a rock seen under the microscope a mineral of refractive index different from that of the mounting medium, e.g., canada balsam, will give the appearance of standing up in relief, an effect which varies in intensity with the difference in the refractive index.

DOUBLE REFRACTION.—Transparent materials may be either isotropic or anisotropic. In the former light is transmitted in all directions with the same velocity, while in the latter it is broken up into two rays which are polarised, i.e., the waves of each ray vibrate in one plane and at right angles to the plane of the waves of the other ray. Of these rays, one, the ordinary ray, travels at the same velocity in all directions while the velocity of the other, the extraordinary ray, varies in different directions giving different refractive indices. Glass, liquids and crystals of the cubic system are isotropic while all crystalline substances belonging to systems other than the cubic are anisotropic. A petrological microscope is fitted with a polariser below the stage and an analyser above it. The polariser and analyser pass light vibrating in one direction only and are set at right angles so that when they are both in position (crossed nicols) no light passes. When a plate of an anisotropic crystal is placed between them interference colours are seen that vary with the relative value of the two refractive indices. When this difference is small the colour is grey but when larger the colours are brighter.

EXTINCTION.—In four positions in each rotation of the microscope stage the vibration directions in a mineral plate lying on the stage are parallel to those of the polariser and analyser and the light is passed by the plate without change. The plate then appears dark and these positions are called the positions of extinction. These positions may be parallel to the crystal axes (straight extinction), or oblique to them (oblique extinction); and thus this property may be used for the identification of a mineral.

PLEOCHROISM.—The colour of a mineral by transmitted light is caused by the absorption of some of the wavelengths of the white light. This absorption varies with the direction of vibration of the light in the crystal, so that when a plate of a coloured anisotropic crystal is rotated in a beam of plane polarised light it is found to change colour, sometimes only in intensity, but sometimes in shade as well. This is well shown by biotite, hornblende and tourmaline (See Fig. 3e).

DESCRIPTIONS OF SOME COMMON MINERALS

In describing the minerals it is convenient to divide them into the rock-forming minerals and the ores. Attention is here confined to the more important and most common species, and for greater detail the reader is referred to standard textbooks on mineralogy.

The Rock-forming Minerals.—These may be divided into the essential minerals that make up the bulk of the rocks, the accessory minerals, present only in small quantities, and the secondary minerals derived from the breakdown of the others. With the exception of quartz and the carbonates the essential minerals are all silicates. They have long been classified according to their properties into groups and within recent years this grouping has been confirmed by the study of their atomic structure by the methods of X-ray analysis. It is unnecessary in a book on coal mining to enter into a full discussion of these structures, and attention is here confined to what may be seen with the eye or with the aid of a microscope. In the following descriptions the abbreviations H. and S.G. are used for hardness and specific gravity respectively.

The Essential Minerals.—QUARTZ.—Composition SiO_2, crystallises in the trigonal division of the hexagonal system, usual habit prismatic with pyramidal terminations (see Fig. 1). Colourless when pure, but many varieties are coloured due to traces of impurities, e.g., amethyst purple, smoky quartz brown, rose quartz pink, milky quartz white. Lustre vitreous, fracture conchoidal, H.7 (cannot be scratched by a knife), S.G.2·66. Quartz is an essential mineral of the acid igneous rocks, such as granite and quartz porphyry, and is abundant in mineral veins where it forms prismatic crystals in cavities.

(a) Orthoclase.

(b) Microcline.

(c) Plagioclase.

(d) Muscovite.

(e) Biotite.

(f) Augite and olivine.

Fig. 3.—Minerals under the microscope.

30

These occasionally reach enormous size. It is also an important constituent of the metamorphic rocks and of the clastic sediments, particularly sands and sandstones.

THE FELSPARS.—These are the most abundant of all the silicate minerals and make up the greater bulk of the igneous rocks. They crystallise in both the monoclinic and triclinic systems but have many properties in common. Chemically they are all silicates of aluminium with potash, soda and lime, and may be regarded as mixed crystals of three compounds. The following are examples:—

Mineral	Composition	Crystallographic system
Orthoclase	$KAlSi_3O_8$	Monoclinic.
Microcline	$KAlSi_3O_8$	Triclinic.
Albite	$NaAlSi_3O_8$	Triclinic.
Anorthite	$CaAl_2Si_2O_8$	Triclinic.

Mixed crystals of albite and anorthite are found in all proportions and go by the name of the plagioclases. Orthoclase can make limited solid solutions with the plagioclases; those are more complete at high temperatures than at low temperatures, and on cooling show phenomena of unmixing, producing an intimate intergrowth of orthoclase and plagioclase called perthite.

ORTHOCLASE ($KAlSi_3O_8$).—Monoclinic, crystal forms often simple (see Fig. 1) with two cleavages at right-angles to each other. Usually develops simple twins, particularly the carlsbad twin, which is recognised by the cleavages of the two halves being inclined in opposite directions; colour white or pink, lustre vitreous, H.6, S.G.2·56. Orthoclase is a prominent mineral in granites and syenites and in some of their equivalent lavas and dyke rocks; it also occurs in gneisses and felspathic sandstones. In thin section it is characterised by low relief, grey polarisation colours and the simple twin (see Fig. 3a).

MICROCLINE ($KAlSi_3O_8$).—Crystal system triclinic. Very similar in appearance to orthoclase except that the two cleavages are not quite at right-angles, see Fig. 1. In thin section it shows multiple twinning with tapering lamellae crossing at angles near 90 degrees and giving the "cross-hatched" effect (Fig. 3b). Its distribution is similar to that of orthoclase.

THE PLAGIOCLASES.—Crystal system triclinic. These are a series of mixtures (solid solutions) of albite and anorthite. The cleavages are similar to those of orthoclase, but intersect at angles a few degrees less than 90 degrees. They may form simple twins, but these are always combined with a lamellar twin (the albite twin) that appears as fine parallel striations on the plane of the best cleavage. Colour usually white or grey, lustre vitreous, H.6 to 6·5, S.G.2·60 albite, 2·76 anorthite. In thin sections under the microscope plagioclase is to be distinguished from other felspars by the presence of lamellar twins (Fig. 3c). Plagioclase felspars occur in most igneous rocks especially the darker varieties rich in lime, also in metamorphic rocks and felspathic sandstones.

THE MICAS.—Crystal system monoclinic.—The characteristic property of this group is that of splitting into thin flakes along one perfect cleavage, determined by the sheet type of atomic lattice. They usually form flat hexagonal crystals (pseudo-hexagonal). The common rock-forming micas are muscovite and biotite.

MUSCOVITE $(KAl_2(Si_3Al)O_{10}(OH)_2)$.—Colourless, lustre pearly, H.2 to 2·5, S.G. about 2·9. Under the microscope it is clear and colourless, with one good cleavage, a low relief and bright polarisation colours, extinction is parallel to the cleavage (Fig. 3d).

BIOTITE $(K(FeMg)_3(Si_3Al)O_{10}(OH)_2)$.—Colour black or brown, lustre pearly, H.2·5 to 3, S.G.2·7 to 3·1. Under the microscope brown or green, pleochroic, low relief, high polarisation colours, extinction parallel to the cleavages (Fig. 3e).

The micas are common in igneous and metamorphic rocks. Muscovite is an abundant component of many sandstones and of clays and shales and is a good electrical insulator, but biotite is not, as it contains ferrous iron.

THE PYROXENES.—These are a group of minerals having the general formula $R''SiO_3$, where R is Mg, Fe'' or Ca, usually with some Al in addition. They crystallise both in the monoclinic and orthorhombic systems, but all possess in common two good cleavages parallel to the prism faces and intersecting at 87 degrees, determined by the arrangement of the atomic chains in the crystal lattice. The commonest variety is the monoclinic augite, having eight-sided prismatic crystals, usually with two terminal faces at each end; the colour is black, the lustre vitreous, H.5, S.G.3·2 to 3·6. Under the microscope it is colourless with high relief and bright polarisation colours, in sections at right-angles to the vertical axis it shows the two cleavages intersecting at 87 degrees, while in sections parallel to the vertical axis only one set of cleavages is seen (Fig. 3f). In these sections the extinction angle may be as wide as 45 degrees. Augite is a usual constituent of the basic and ultra-basic igneous rocks. It is often altered to chlorite.

THE AMPHIBOLES.—These, like the pyroxenes, are a group of minerals, mostly silicates of Ca, Mg, Fe'' and some Al, but containing also some hydroxyl, i.e., (OH). All the ordinary amphiboles are monoclinic with two cleavages parallel to the prism faces and intersecting at 124 degrees. The commonest rock-forming type is hornblende which occurs as six-sided crystals, usually longer in proportion to their width than augite, colour black, lustre vitreous, H.5 to 6, S.G.3 to 3·4. Under the microscope it is usually green or brown, pleochroic, with moderate relief, polarisation colours bright, but masked by the colour of the mineral. Sections at right-angles to the vertical axis show the two cleavages at 124 degrees, but sections parallel to the vertical axis show only one set of cleavages; the extinction angle does not exceed 25 degrees. Hornblende is often altered to chlorite. It occurs in the intermediate igneous rocks and in metamorphic rocks like hornblende schist.

The Olivines.—These are the most "basic" of the silicate minerals. They are a series of mixtures of Mg_2SiO_4 and Fe_2SiO_4. They crystallise in the orthorhombic system, they have a very poor cleavage and do not form twins, colour pale green or yellow, lustre vitreous, fracture conchoidal, H.6·5, S.G.3·2 to 3·6. Under the microscope they show a granular form, high relief, bright polarisation colours and crystals traversed by irregular cracks often marked by lines of magnetite granules along which the mineral is undergoing alteration to serpentine (Fig. 3f). Olivines are found in the basic and ultra-basic igneous rocks and in metamorphic limestones.

The Carbonates.—Three varieties are considered here, calcite ($CaCO_3$), dolomite ($CaMg(CO_3)_2$) and ankerite ($Ca (MgFe) (CO_3)_2$). All three make trigonal crystals and are characterised by cleavages in three directions parallel to a crystal form known as the fundamental rhombohedron (see Fig. 1).

Calcite.—Common crystal habits, the scalenohedron, dog-tooth spar, or the flat rhombohedron, nail-head spar, often in combination with the hexagonal prism, usually colourless, lustre pearly, H.3, S.G.2·71, dissolves in cold dilute acid with effervescence. Under the microscope it shows moderate relief with polarisation colours so high that they have lost their brightness and show mixed pinks and greens.

Dolomite.—Usually crystallises as the simple fundamental rhombodedron often with curved faces and broken edges, usually buff-coloured, does not dissolve readily in cold dilute acid. Calcite and dolomite make up the greater bulk of the limestones but are also found as veinstones and as secondary minerals in the igneous rocks.

Ankerite.—This is very common as "cleat spar" in coal. It is very like dolomite but is stained brown by iron oxide when exposed to the weather.

Secondary Minerals.—These are numerous, but only four of the most important need be discussed here, viz., kaolinite, sericite, chlorite and serpentine.

Kaolinite ($Al_4Si_4O_{10}(OH)_8$).—The principal constituent of china clay and one of the clay minerals. It is usually a fine white powder, soapy to the touch, S.G.2·6. Under the microscope it appears as small six-sided scales with low relief and very faint grey polarisation colours. It is one of the products of the breakdown of felspar by the action of water and CO_2, and occurs in great quantities in the kaolinised granites of Cornwall.

Sericite.—The identity of this species is rather uncertain, but the name is used for highly doubly-refracting flakes apparently allied to muscovite, found with kaolinite in decomposed felspar.

Chlorite.—The chlorites are a large group of hydrous silicates of Mg, Fe and Al, they are green in colour and usually have a flaky habit with perfect basal cleavage like micas. They originate from the decomposition and hydration of those ferro-magnesian minerals that contain notable quantities of aluminium.

Serpentine ($Mg_6Si_4O_{10}(OH)_8$).—Serpentine is produced by the hydration of olivine or of the orthorhombic pyroxenes. It usually occurs as a mass of scales or fibres replacing the original mineral, but also takes a fibrous form filling veins and fissures. This variety is known as chrysotile and is worked for commercial asbestos. Pure serpentine is colourless but it is usually found stained to a variety of colours, H.3, S.G.2·6. In thin section it appears as a mass of scales or fibres with low relief and faint grey polarisation colours.

Ore Minerals, etc. MAGNETITE (Fe_3O_4).—Crystal system cubic, occurs as octahedra (see Fig. 1) or massive in form, colour black, opaque, lustre metallic, streak black, H.5·5 to 6·5, S.G.5·17, readily attracted by an ordinary permanent magnet. It occurs widely distributed in small amounts in both igneous and sedimentary rocks. When segregated into large masses it forms an important ore of iron.

HEMATITE (Fe_2O_3).—Crystal system trigonal, occurs as flat tabular crystals, black or steely grey with a high metallic lustre (specular iron ore) or in reniform fibrous masses (kidney ore) or massive. Colour normally red, streak red, H.5·5 to 6·5, S.G. about 5·2. It occurs as a secondary mineral in igneous rocks, as a cement in sandstones and as large masses in sedimentary and metamorphic rocks. It is the most important ore of iron.

LIMONITE ($2Fe_2O_3 3H_2O$).—Usually occurs as radiating masses or massive. Colour black, brown or yellow, streak brown, H.5, S.G.3·8. When further hydrated it forms a yellow powder (yellow ochre). It is the ordinary oxidation product of iron compounds in temperate climates and as such constitutes an ore of iron.

ILMENITE ($FeTiO_3$).—A black iron ore similar to magnetite but only moderately magnetic. Occurs mostly in basic igneous rocks.

IRON PYRITES (Pyrite) (FeS_2).—Crystal system cubic, occurs as cubes, pyritohedra or massive, colour brassy yellow, lustre metallic, streak greenish black, H.6 to 6·5, S.G. about 5·0. Occurs in small quantities in igneous rocks and often as a secondary mineral in sedimentary rocks, especially shales, limestones and coals. It is exceedingly common in mineral veins of all kinds and often carries gold.

GALENA (PbS).—Crystal system cubic, crystals usually the cube or the cube and octahedron, also massive, cleavage perfect parallel to the cube faces, colour lead grey, lustre metallic, H.2·5, S.G.7·5. Occurs in veins associated with blende, calcite, fluorspar, barytes, etc.

BLENDE (ZnS).—Crystal system cubic, crystals tetrahedral, also massive, colour red, brown or black, lustre resinous, H.3·5 to 4, S.G. about 4. Occurs in veins with galena, etc.

FLUORSPAR (CaF_2).—Crystal system cubic, crystals cubes (see Fig. 1) with perfect cleavage parallel to the octahedron, colourless, purple, green or yellow, lustre vitreous, often transparent, H.4, S.G.3·2. Occurs in veins as above, especially where they traverse limestone. A purple and white banded variety (Blue John) is found at Castleton in Derbyshire.

BARYTES ($BaSO_4$).—Crystal system orthorhombic, crystals either prismatic or tabular, often as radiating groups or massive, cleavage perfect parallel to the basal plane and prism faces, colour white, yellow, red or blue, lustre vitreous, H.3 to 3·5, S.G.4·5. Commonly found in mineral veins associated with the ores of lead and zinc.

GYPSUM ($CaSO_4 2H_2O$).—Crystal system monoclinic, crystals usually tabular and diamond shaped (see Fig. 1) or arrowhead twins (see Fig. 2), also occurs in fibrous form (satin spar) or massive (alabaster), cleavage perfect parallel to the side face, colourless, lustre pearly, H.1·5 to 2, S.G.2·3. Found in sedimentary rocks, having been formed by the drying up of salt lakes or in calcareous clays and shales where pyrites has decomposed to give sulphuric acid.

THE IGNEOUS ROCKS

The igneous rocks are those which appear to have crystallised from a cooling silicate melt containing much volatile matter and known as magma. Magma has its origin in the crust of the earth and may rise through fissures to the surface as lava (extrusive rocks) or it may be trapped and cooled among the outer rocks of the crust (intrusive rocks). Extrusive rocks emerge from volcanoes either as lavas or as fragmentary rocks, volcanic ashes. Some of the different types of volcanoes are, (1) *Fissure eruptions* where lavas, generally of basic composition, well up quietly through long fissures and cover wide expanses of country, (2) *Shield volcanoes*, gently sloping cones of basic lavas round central vents, as in the volcanoes of the Sandwich Islands,

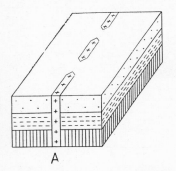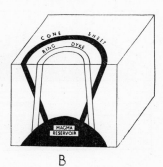

Fig. 4.—A, dyke; B, cone sheet and ring dyke.

(3) Composite cones with some explosive activity, made up partly of lavas and partly of ashes like Mounts Etna and Vesuvius. Intrusive igneous rocks may occur as *discordant* and *concordant intrusions* and as *subjacent masses*. The simplest discordant intrusions are dykes, narrow tabular masses of rock cutting across the strata usually at a high angle to the bedding. They may be straight or curved as in cone sheets and ring dykes (see Fig. 4). The commonest concordant intrusions are the sills, Fig. 5a; these are sheets of igneous rock inserted along bedding planes. A similar kind of intrusion, of less lateral extent and greater thickness, is the laccolith, Fig. 5c, where the strata are bent upwards by the pressure of the magma; and another is the lopolith, where the underlying beds have sagged down, Fig. 5d.

The subjacent intrusions are known as batholiths, Fig. 5b. These masses widen downwards and have no visible base. They are nearly always composed of granite and may be hundreds of miles in extent.

The Composition and Classification of Igneous Rocks.—The classification is carried out on a two-fold basis, (1) the chemical and mineralogical composition and (2) the mode of occurrence or the size of the crystals.

Rocks are classified according to the percentage of silica and again by the relative proportions of lime to the alkalis, potash and soda. Excess silica is shown by the presence of quartz and the alkali content may be gauged by

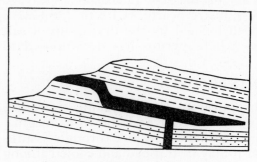

(a) A sill fed by a dyke. The sill is transgressive across the beds.

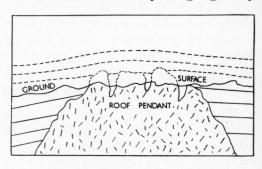

(b) Section through a batholith, showing how it has penetrated the strata leaving pendants hanging from the roof.

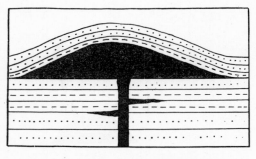

(c) Ideal section through a laccolith.

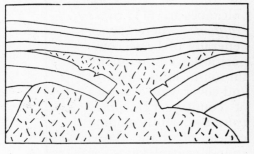

(d) Theoretical section through a lopolith.

Fig. 5.—Types of intrusions.

the proportions of alkali felspar to the lime-rich plagioclases. The deep-seated, slowly cooled rocks have large crystals and are known as *Plutonic*, the rocks of the minor intrusions are finer grained, the *Hypabyssal* rocks,

TABLE III

CLASSIFICATION OF IGNEOUS ROCKS

		Acid > 65% SiO$_2$ Quartz abundant Ferromagnesian minerals Micas	*Intermediate* 65–55% SiO$_2$ Quartz in small amount Ferromagnesian minerals Hornblende and Augite	*Basic* 55–45% SiO$_2$ No Quartz Ferromagnesian minerals Augite and Olivine	*Ultra-basic* < 45% SiO$_2$ Little or no Felspar Ferromagnesian minerals Olivine, Augite Hornblende, Biotite
Alkaline Series (Excess Alkali Felspar)	Plutonic Hypabyssal Volcanic	Alkali Granite Microgranite Rhyolite, Obsidian	Alkali Syenite Micro-syenite Trachyte	Syeno-gabbro Micro-syeno-gabbro Tephrite	Plutonic types— Picrite Peridotite Dunite
Monzonite Series (Alkali and Calcic Felspars in equal proportions)	Plutonic Hypabyssal Volcanic	Adamellite Micro-adamellite Rhyolite, Obsidian	Monzonite Micro-monzonite Trachy-andesite	Essexite Micro-essexite Trachy-basalt	Hypabyssal and Volcanic types— Limburgite Monchiquite
Calcic Series (Calcic Felspars in excess)	Plutonic Hypabyssal Volcanic	Granodiorite Micro-granodiorite Dacite	Diorite Micro-diorite Andesite	Gabbro Dolerite Basalt	

while the *Volcanic rocks* are finer grained still and may even be glassy. Originally the rocks were divided under these three heads according to their mode of occurrence, but this led to difficulties and the classification is now based on the average grain size of the rocks, though the same names are used. Plutonic rocks are those with an average grain size of more than 0·5 mm., Hypabyssal rocks are those with grain size from 0·5 to 0·05 mm. and Volcanic rocks those with grain size less than 0·05 mm.

Table III shows a classification on these lines.

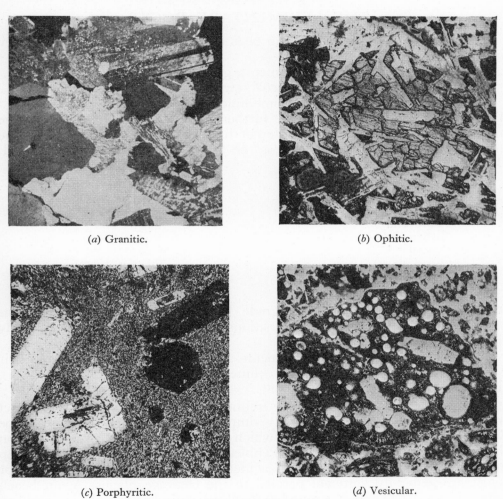

(*a*) Granitic.

(*b*) Ophitic.

(*c*) Porphyritic.

(*d*) Vesicular.

Fig. 6.—Textures of igneous rocks.

Textures of the Igneous Rocks.—The plutonic rocks are composed of relatively large crystals, usually equally developed and forming an equi-granular mosaic, known as a *Granitic texture* (Fig. 6*a*). The hypabyssal and volcanic rocks are liable to have large crystals set in a finer grained groundmass. This is described as *Porphyritic texture* (Fig. 6c) and the large crystals are called *Phenocrysts*. The phenocrysts are not taken into account in measuring the average grain size for classification. Another texture common in dolerites is *Ophitic* (Fig. 6b). Lavas are often wholly or partly glassy and are said to have a *Vitreous texture*; they are often full of holes caused by the expansion of the magmatic gases; this gives *Vesicular texture* (Fig. 6d), and when the holes are filled with minerals deposited from solution *Amygdaloidal texture*.

THE SEDIMENTARY ROCKS

These are the rocks laid down in beds on the surface of the earth. They are classified according to origin:—

(1) Mechanical or clastic sediments: gravel, sand, sandstone, shale, etc.
(2) Organic: limestone, peat, coal, etc.
(3) Chemical: salt deposits, some limestones and ironstones.

The mechanical sediments may be further subdivided according to the size of their constituent particles. Different limits have been proposed for the grades, but a convenient division is the following, by Professor P. G. H. Boswell:

Boulders	above 10 cm.
Gravel	10 cm. to 2 mm.
Very coarse sand	2 to 1 mm.
Coarse sand	1 to 0·5 mm.
Medium sand	0·5 to 0·25 mm.
Fine sand	0·25 to 0·1 mm.
Coarse silt	0·1 to 0·05 mm.
Silt	0·05 to 0·005 mm.
Clay	below 0·005 mm.

A rock is not generally all of one grade, but is usually made up of portions of different grades, giving combinations like silty sandstones and sandy shales.

The organic and chemical sediments are subdivided according to their composition, e.g., calcareous (e.g., limestone), carbonaceous (e.g., coal), siliceous (flint), saline (e.g., rock salt).

Pebbly Deposits.—Pebbles are frequently fragments of rock as distinct from sand grains which are usually simple minerals. Their size and shape depend in part on the rock from which they were derived, and in part on the treatment they have received. Pebbles of homogeneous granite are often nearly spherical, while pebbles of a metamorphic rock such as a slate or schist are generally flattened parallel to the cleavage planes. Again beach pebbles are, as a rule, better rounded than river pebbles, and glacial boulders are typically subangular. When cemented to make hard rocks, pebbly deposits are known as conglomerates, and if the fragments are angular they are called sedimentary breccias to distinguish them from fault breccias.

Arenaceous Deposits, Sands and Sandstones.—Most sand grains consist of quartz with lesser amounts of felspar and muscovite. A far travelled sand or one that has been washed to and fro on a beach for a long time will contain little but quartz and perhaps muscovite. A sand that has been transported by wind in a dry climate or one that has been carried very quickly from its point of origin may be rich in felspar. Wind-borne sands do not, as a rule, contain any mica, since this soft mineral is broken up by the hard blows sustained during wind transport. In addition to the above minerals most sands contain a small amount of "heavy minerals" such as magnetite, garnet, zircon, tourmaline, sphene, kyanite, staurolite and hornblende. These all have a specific gravity higher than 3·0 and can be separated from the light fraction (quartz, felspar and mica) by floating on a heavy liquid. A convenient liquid for this purpose is bromoform with a specific gravity of 2·9.

The Shape of Sand Grains.—The shape of a sand grain depends on two factors, viz:—its origin and its treatment after leaving its parent rock. The quartz of acid igneous rocks like granites and quartz porphyries is generally rather irregular, but not far from spherical, and, after the projecting points have been rubbed off, may approximate to a sphere. The quartz of metamorphic rocks, on the other hand, is often lenticular and can, at best, only give rise to subangular sand grains. In general, the farther a grain travels the more rounded it becomes. The sands from Highland rivers are more angular than those from nearby sea beaches. Wind-borne sands sometimes are almost entirely spherical, as in the so-called millet seed sands; round grains are more easily rolled along the desert floor than others and become segregated together.

Mechanical Analysis.—In order to assess the value of a mechanical sediment for practical use, it is often necessary to know the proportions of the different grades; for example, a good glass sand should be as nearly as possible all of one grade. The analysis can be carried out for the coarser grades by sieving through a standard set of sieves, but for the finer grades, recourse must be had to methods dependent on the rate of settling of the grains in a liquid. A particle sinking in a fluid soon attains a constant velocity, the final velocity, depending on its diameter and specific gravity and the viscosity and density of the fluid (Vol. 4, Chap. 7). The final velocity can be calculated for spherical particles, and the results for a sand are only accurate in so far as the grains approximate to spheres. The final velocities for quartz in water at 15° C. are:—

Diam.	0·035	0·05	0·10	0·15	0·20	0·25	0·30	mm.
Vel.	1	2	7	13	19	25·5	32	mm./sec.

The analysis may be carried out in various ways. In one, the pipette method, the sediment is stirred up in a deep vessel full of water and a sample is taken in a pipette from a certain depth after a definite time. The sample is evaporated to dryness and the sediment weighed, and from this the proportion of sediment over a certain grade can be calculated. The experiment can then be repeated as often as desired to determine the relative proportions of the finer grades. Or the sample can be separated in an elutriator which consists essentially of a parallel-sided vessel, A, Fig. 7, up which can be directed a current of water with a constant velocity. The sample is placed in A through which an upward current is directed, the fines are washed out through the jet B and caught in a container. In this way each grade may be washed clean, collected and weighed. The results are plotted on a cumulative curve against the logarithm of the grain size as shown on Fig. 8 which illustrates grain size analyses of various sands.

Sandstones.—When a sand is buried under further accumulations of sediment, any soft minerals or partially decomposed materials are crushed between the more resistant grains, causing partial consolidation which is completed by the deposition of cement. The commonest cementing materials are silica, iron oxides and carbonates, often associated with clay. The silica may take the form of quartz, either in crystalline continuity with the quartz grains or as aggregates of small quartz crystals. Such a rock will be almost entirely composed of quartz and is called a quartzite. Frequently the silica takes the form of chalcedony either by itself or permeating clay material between the sand grains, as often takes place in the sandstones of the Millstone Grit and the Coal Measures (Fig. 9a) where corrosion of the quartz grains sometimes goes on at the same time. Iron oxide as cement usually forms a skin round the sand grains and makes an adhesive collar where the grains are in contact, leaving many empty pores. Carbonates, on the other hand, generally fill all the interspaces and

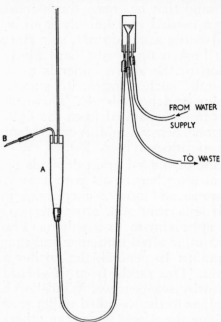

Fig. 7.—Sketch of an elutriator.

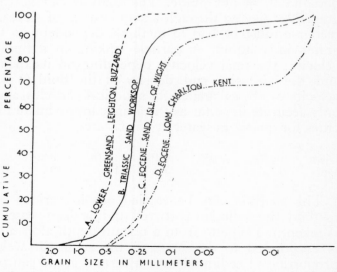

Fig. 8.—Cumulative curves representing sands. A, B and C are glass-making sands, D is a moulding sand. (*After measurement by Prof. P. G. H. Boswell.*)

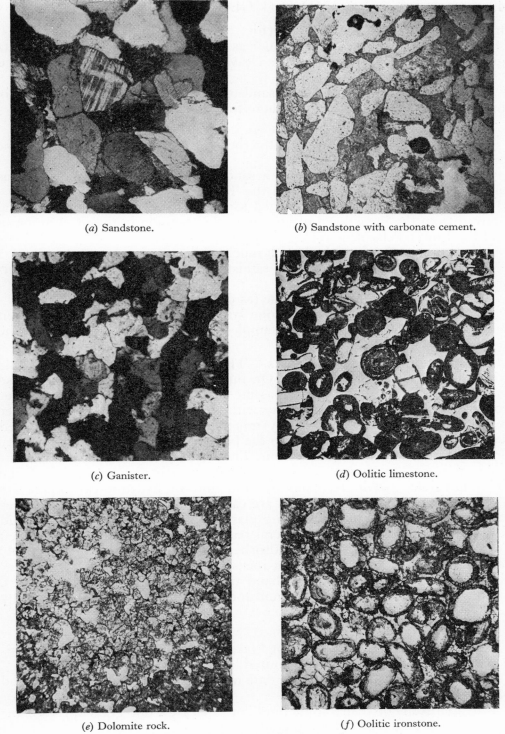

(a) Sandstone.

(b) Sandstone with carbonate cement.

(c) Ganister.

(d) Oolitic limestone.

(e) Dolomite rock.

(f) Oolitic ironstone.

Fig. 9.—Sections of sedimentary rocks.

make a very compact sandstone (Fig. 9b). When the cement is calcite it sometimes grows into crystals as much as an inch across enclosing the quartz grains which appear as dots on the cleavage surfaces, a phenomenon called "lustre mottling".

Some of the different types of sandstone have already been referred to, but a more complete list is given here for convenience:—

Siliceous sandstone and quartzite (as described previously).

Ganister, a fine-grained quartzitic rock forming the seat-earth of some coal seams (Fig. 9c).

Felspathic sandstone or arkose, a sandstone with much fresh felspar as in the coarser Millstone Grits and the Torridonian Sandstone.

Greywacke, a dark well-compacted sandstone, containing much material derived from the breakdown of igneous rocks common in the pre-Cambrian and the Lower Palaeozoic rocks.

Micaceous sandstone, a rock with much muscovite.

Flaggy sandstone, a thin-bedded sandstone with muscovite flakes concentrated on the bedding planes.

Calcareous or dolomitic sandstone (as described previously).

Glauconitic sandstone, a sandstone with numerous grains of the green mineral glauconite. Uncemented examples of this are the Greensands of the south of England.

Argillaceous (Clayey) Rocks.—These are first deposited as muds with about 70 per cent. of water. On burial they are compressed and lose a large proportion of the water, passing first to clay and later, by further compression, to mudstone or shale with a water content of about 8 per cent. In the compression the flaky minerals of which they are composed are rotated into positions parallel to the bedding, giving to the rock a fissility or tendency to split in this direction. These rocks frequently contain a fair proportion of quartz and felspar, but are principally composed of the "clay minerals" (kaolinite, halloysite and illite or hydro-mica). These are all minerals with layer lattices and are capable of taking up large quantities of water, so swelling and becoming plastic. On the compaction of a mud to a shale or mudstone some mineral rearrangement takes place, but, even after this, water may still be re-adsorbed so that the rock weathers fairly rapidly to a clay. The argillaceous rocks of the Coal Measures show considerable variations. On the one hand they pass into the flaggy siltstones, and on the other into shales and mudstones, so fine grained as to be hardly resolved by an ordinary microscope.

Some varieties are as follows:—

Flaggy siltstone, "stone-bind" or "fakes", banded rock with a high proportion of quartz in the lighter coloured layers.

Banded mudstone, a fine-grained dark mudstone with thin lighter-coloured bands richer in quartz.

Blue mudstone or shale, "blue bind" or "blaes", a fine-grained rock composed almost entirely of clay minerals.

Grey mudstone, "grey bind," a mudstone with a fair proportion of quartz scattered through it.

Black micaceous shale, a dark fine-grained shale with numerous tiny flakes of mica visible on the bedding planes.

Bituminous shale, a black fine-grained shale containing an appreciable amount of bituminous matter.

Oil-shale, a bituminous shale worth distilling for oil.

Fire-clay, the fine-grained seat-earth of a coal seam, traversed by the roots of plants with no trace of bedding; the seat-earths are sometimes highly refractory.

The strength of Coal-Measure sediments in general varies inversely with the grain size: the sandstones and flaggy siltstones provide strong roofs, the binds are weaker, and some of the very fine-grained shales are exceedingly soft and difficult to support.

Organic Deposits or Organically Formed Rocks.—LIMESTONES.—These rocks are composed essentially of carbonates, either calcite (or aragonite), or dolomite as in the magnesian limestones. They frequently contain fossil remains of organisms, but many are relatively poor in fossils.

Some types of limestone are as follows:—

CHALK.—An earthy limestone containing some shells of microscopic foraminifera and larger fossils, but mostly composed of calcite prisms from lamellibranch shells, coccospheres and minute calcite crystals. It contains much silica in the form of flint nodules. It is found in the Cretaceous system (see p. 74) in the east and south of England.

COMPACT CRYSTALLINE LIMESTONE.—This is the kind of limestone met with in the Carboniferous and older systems. It may contain fossil shells, but the matrix of calcareous mud is always recrystallised to give a strong crystalline base.

OOLITIC LIMESTONE (Fig. 9d) is really a chemical deposit. It is made up of small oval or spherical bodies, usually less than a millimetre in diameter with a concentric structure. The ooliths or grains have been precipitated chemically from rather highly saline waters in shallow tropical seas, where the water was in a constant state of agitation. Oolitic limestones are of all ages, but are specially abundant in the Jurassic system of England (see p. 73).

DOLOMITIC OR MAGNESIAN LIMESTONE.—A rock in which the calcite has been changed either wholly or in part to dolomite. The dolomite forms small rhomb-shaped crystals giving the rock a granular appearance (Fig. 9e), moreover the change from calcite to dolomite is accompanied by a contraction of about 12 per cent. so that dolomitic limestones are usually porous.

COAL.—This is, of course, an organic rock, as explained in a later section.

Chemical Deposits or Chemically Formed Rocks.—Dolomite, rock-salt, anhydrite and gypsum are precipitated from salt water in lakes undergoing desiccation. In parts of Britain they make extensive beds, e.g., the rock-salt beds of the Cheshire Trias and the anhydrite in the Permian of Billingham.

Ironstones.—In the Coal Measures ferrous carbonate has been precipitated in the muds, either as bands or as layers of nodules of siderite (Clay ironstones), or as bands of siderite associated with carbonaceous material in the roofs of coal seams (the Black Band ironstones). The former are abundant in all coalfields, and the latter have, in the past, been of great importance in the coalfields of Scotland and North Staffordshire but are now mostly worked out. Of a different character are the ironstones of the Jurassic system; these are oolitic, being composed of ooliths of an iron-bearing chlorite called chamosite or the carbonate siderite, or both (Fig. 9f). The iron compounds are usually associated with calcite or clay and the ores are not of high grade, but on account of their availability for large-scale quarrying they are the chief home source of ore for British furnaces, though their iron content rarely exceeds 32 per cent. and much of it is as low as 20 per cent.

EXTERNAL PROCESSES AND THEIR EFFECTS ON THE ROCKS

Denudation.—The processes included in the term denudation are weathering or the disintegration of rocks; and transport or the removal of the debris. If to these is added deposition, it completes the cycle of destructive and formative processes whereby a rock is destroyed, its debris transported and deposited elsewhere to take part in the formation of a new rock.

Weathering.—Heat and Cold.—If a rock is subjected quickly to considerable changes of temperature, strains are set up between the crystals and even inside the minerals themselves. This results in the development of cracks and, if the changes are sufficiently great, in the spalling off of flakes of the rock. This type of weathering is, of course, most important in deserts but is in operation everywhere. The cracks thus produced allow the penetration of water to further the weathering.

Rain and Dew.—The effects of water are two-fold, physical and chemical. The chief mechanical effect of water is wetting and drying. Some minerals in clay have the property of taking up water and swelling and contracting again on drying. One result of this is the formation of the familiar polygonal cracks in drying mud. This swelling and contracting, when repeated many times, causes the disintegration of the minerals, as may be seen in the "falling" of clods in a garden even in the absence of frost.

The Chemical Effects of Water.—Water, especially when containing CO_2 in solution, is a potent chemical agent; its effects are most clearly seen in limestones, where the rock, soluble in carbonated water, undergoes solution with the widening of joints to make "grikes" (Fig. 10) and the formation of underground caverns. Water also exercises important effects in the hydration of minerals like hornblende and augite with the production of chlorite and, with oxygen in solution, in oxidising sulphide minerals with the subsequent enrichment in depth of mineral veins.

Frost.—The action of frost is similar to that of wetting and drying, but more intense. Water expands on freezing, and if a rock containing numerous cracks or pores filled with water is frozen and thawed many times, the surface rapidly becomes disintegrated. This process is most potent in mountain regions in temperate climates, where the rocks in summer pass through the freezing point at least twice a day. In addition to the break-up of minerals and the disintegration of rock surfaces, frost is capable of larger-scale work and of widening joints and cracks.

WEATHERING BY ORGANIC AGENCIES.— Plants, by retaining moisture, assist the action of water, they also exercise mechanical disruption by the growth pressure of their roots. Animals also carry on a considerable amount of destructive work, especially the burrowing animals like rabbits and earthworms.

Transport.—THE WORK OF GRAVITY.— On steep slopes or cliffs rock fragments, loosened by weathering, fall and slide to the bottom where they form an accumulation known as

Fig. 10.—Grikes, joints in limestone widened by solution.

"scree" or "talus". When rocks are reduced to soft incoherent material by weathering they become unstable on sloping ground and landslips occur. These are most common where a hard pervious rock such as a Coal Measure sandstone overlies a soft impervious shale or clay and especially so when the rocks dip towards the low ground, as in Fig. 11a. Water passing through the sandstone wets and softens the shale beneath, the sandstone displaces the resulting soft clay by its own weight and slips towards the valley, becoming inclined towards the hill as it moves.

THE WORK OF RIVERS.—Rivers erode their beds mainly by abrading them with the aid of stones rolled along the bottom or bounced up and down in the water. The rock fragments broken from the bed are added to the load carried by the water. A given volume of water flowing at a definite velocity can only carry a certain load and when this is exceeded deposition takes the place of erosion. Transporting power varies as the volume and as the sixth power of the velocity, hence nearly all river work is done in flood periods. Where a river crosses outcrops of hard rocks, the cutting down is retarded and the river flows in rapids. If the hard rock rests on a softer

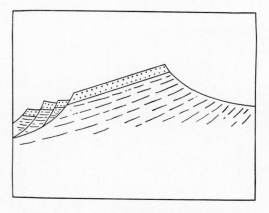

(a) Landslip occurring where a previous bed overlies an impervious shale with dip towards the low ground.

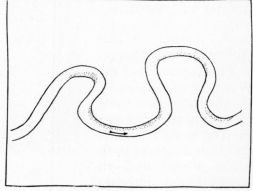

(b) A waterfall where a river flows over a hard jointed sandstone resting on soft shale.

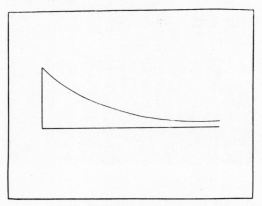

(c) The logarithmic curve of water erosion.

(d) Meandering river, deposition takes place at the convex bends.

Fig. 11.—Erosion features.

one, e.g., a bed of sandstone on shale, the river will erode the soft rock more rapidly and a waterfall will result. The continuous erosion of the soft rock undermines the hard one which breaks off along its joints, falls down and is carried away; thus the fall recedes up-stream leaving below it a steep-walled gorge (Fig. 11b). As time goes on the river smooths out all such irregularities and the profile of the stream course approximates more and more closely to a logarithmic curve (Fig. 11c), the curve of water erosion. When a river has established this curve it is said to have reached base level. At this stage erosion is still active near the source, while the slowly-moving river of the lower reaches has more load than it can carry, and there deposition is in progress. In this tract, the river, being unable to cut down any more, begins to work sideways, eroding on the concave banks and depositing on the convex banks (Fig. 11d). In this way the course becomes more curved and the river is said to "meander". As it shifts about the sands and gravels are constantly moved from side to side and form the flood plain or alluvial flat. It is in the alluvial flats that "placer deposits" of gold, diamonds, tinstone, etc., are found. If at some later time the region is further raised above sea level, the velocity of the river will be increased. It will then begin to cut downwards again, either making deep gorges along the lines of the old meanders or establishing a new alluvial flat, leaving remnants of the old one at higher levels on the valley sides as river terraces. This process is known as rejuvenation.

River Deposits.—The ordinary river alluvium of the flood plain is mostly composed of sand and gravel. The general smoothness of the surface gives a false idea of the regularity of the deposits, which, as a result of the meandering of the river and their constant erosion and redeposition, are very irregular with rapidly alternating bands of sediment. When a river runs out into a sheet of water such as a lake or a tideless sea like the Mediterranean its velocity is immediately checked on entering the deeper water and its load is deposited as a *delta*. Here is displayed to perfection the phenomenon of *current bedding*. Sedimentary rocks are all laid down in beds which may be thick or thin and are divided by lines of discontinuity, called "bedding planes", that mark temporary cessations of deposition. Normally, these bedding planes should be nearly horizontal, but when the water deepens abruptly the velocity of the stream is checked suddenly and the coarse sediment is deposited in a bed sloping downwards in the direction in which the current is flowing, at or near to the angle of rest, while the finer grained material is carried farther and laid down as horizontal beds in front of the sloping ones. The former are known as the *foreset beds*,

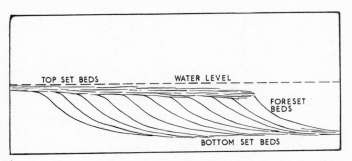

Fig. 12.—Section of a delta.

the latter as the *bottom set beds*, and the whole is referred to as *current bedding*. The foreset beds gradually grow out over the bottom set beds filling the hollow and, finally, as the velocity of the stream diminishes, they may be covered with a further set of horizontal strata, the *top set beds* (Fig. 12). Often, however, the top set beds are eroded. If the ground subsides room is left for a second series of current beds and in this way a compound delta may be built up. When the rocks are consolidated and tilted, the whole delta is inclined and the true dip of the rocks is shown by that of the bottom set beds or by that of the erosion surface above the foreset beds. The dip of the foreset beds is not the true dip of the rocks and is sometimes called *false bedding* (Fig. 13). With variations in current velocity and depth of water the sandy deltas often alternate with beds of mud that eventually give rise to shales. These were the conditions under which the Millstone Grit and the Coal Measures were laid down.

Fig. 13.—False or current bedding in Coal Measures sandstone.

The Work of Ice.—In high latitudes and high mountains where the annual snowfall exceeds the amount melted, accumulations of hardened snow, known as névé or firn, are found in the heads of the valleys. By compression, accompanied by melting and re-freezing, the hardened snow gradually passes into ice which begins to move slowly down the valleys as glaciers. This moving ice erodes its bed, modifying the topography of the valleys and transports debris that is eventually left behind as glacial deposits. The load is obtained in two ways; first rocks fall on to the glacier and are carried along as elongated heaps called *moraines*; and second the glacier plucks rocks from its bed and carries them along frozen in the lower layers of ice. These embedded blocks act as a file and scratch the rocks over which the glacier moves, giving the striated *glaciated pavements*, or, where there are prominent rocks, giving the smoothed, rounded rocks called *roches moutonnées*. In the scratching much fine rock "flour" is produced. Some of this is retained in the ice as *ground moraine*, but some is washed out by the sub-glacial streams and imparts the milky appearance to streams flowing from a glacier. As the glacier moves downwards, friction is developed between the ice and its bed, resulting in the formation of cracks, the *crevasses*. Down these is washed morainic material to assist in the erosion of the bed. A glacier, like a river, is only capable of carrying a load suited to its volume and velocity, and if either are reduced, some of its load is deposited, and the ice moves on over it. The remainder is carried forward till the ice melts, where it is deposited in heaps as *terminal moraines*. Glacial deposits have a variable composition; much is boulder clay, a stiff clay containing boulders and rock fragments of all sizes, but they also include a considerable amount of sand and gravel deposited by streams of melt water and similar to river deposits. If the excess of snowfall over melting is great, the glaciers may reach the lowlands where they coalesce as a *piedmont glacier*. During periods of intense cold, the "glacial periods", these may grow into *ice-sheets* of continental dimensions and spread *glacial drifts* over wide areas so as to conceal the "solid rocks", as happened in the British Isles during the Glacial Period.

Wind.—Wind does not play a great part in weathering, but in dry countries and in coastal regions it is an important agent of transport. Sand is drifted along and piled up as belts of dunes, while dust is often blown out of a desert to accumulate elsewhere. Such a dust deposit is the loess of Europe and Asia which is the glacier-carried dust of the Glacial Period blown away by the winds circulating round the glacial anticyclone. Where much dry sand exists as a result of marine erosion, it may be blown ashore as belts of dunes.

The Work of the Sea.—The sea is the most easily appreciated of the agents of destruction of land. Its erosive power is derived from the force of the waves and the energy of marine currents, helped by tools in the form of boulders, pebbles and sand grains. When a wave dashes

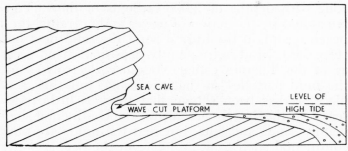

(a) Wave-cut and wave-built platforms.

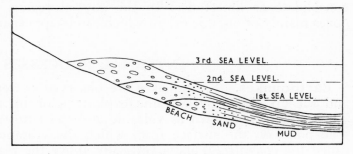

(b) Marine deposition.

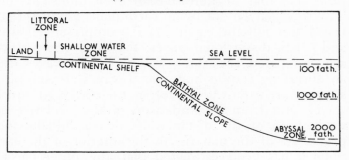

(c) Depth zones of the ocean.
Fig. 14.—The works of the sea.

against a cliff it hurls boulders and pebbles against the rocks. As the wave recedes, the beach material is dragged back by the undertow, thus eroding the flat in front of the cliffs. In this way the cliff is pushed back and a wave-cut platform is developed at its foot (Fig. 14a). Outside the littoral zone, off-shore currents also erode the sea bottom by rolling pebbles along it. In the end the land is reduced to a plain of marine denudation, and if subsidence follows a new marine formation will be deposited on this platform.

Marine Deposits.—The seas can be divided into zones according to depth; the littoral zone between the tide marks, the shallow-water zone or continental shelf where the bottom slopes gently downwards to a depth of about 100 fathoms, the continental slope or bathyal zone and the abyssal zone with depths of 2,000 fathoms or more (Fig. 14c). Marine sediments are sorted by the action of waves and currents; the pebbles are found on the beaches, and, in the littoral zone, the sand next outside and finally the mud (Fig. 14b). Mud is frequently deposited at no great distance from the land, as in the Thames estuary, because electrolytes in the sea-water flocculate the mud particles so that they sink, but this is not its permanent resting place. It has been shown that there is little mud on the floor of shallow seas like the North Sea, or on the continental shelf, where the deposits are mainly sands and silts, but that the muds are pushed over the edge of the continental shelf to accumulate in the deeper water. In places where there is little clastic sediment, there are formed calcareous muds that eventually consolidate as limestones. In the abyssal region the only sediments are oozes mainly of organic origin which rarely appear in the sedimentary rocks.

INTERNAL PROCESSES

Earthquakes.—Earthquakes are observed as tremors felt on the surface and set up either by volcanic explosions or by movement along faults. The former are known as volcanic and the latter as tectonic earthquakes. The point on the surface from which the vibrations appear to radiate is called the *epicentre*. This is vertically above the real point of origin or the *focus* that may be hundreds or even thousands of feet below the surface. The waves given out by an earthquake are of three kinds: of these, two sets travel through the earth: (1) P, compressional waves like those of sound, and (2) S, distortional waves; the third group travel along the surface and are designated L or long waves. The P waves travel fastest and arrive at an observing station first, the S waves are second and the L waves, being slowest, arrive last. The deeper the waves go into the earth the faster they travel, and from a comparison of their relative speeds, estimates can be made both of the distance of the earthquake focus and of the physical properties of the material of the interior of the earth. From these observations it has been estimated that the outer parts of the earth under the continents is made up as follows:

Sedimentary rocks	0 to 10 km.
Upper or granitic layer	10 to 15 km.
Intermediate or basaltic layer	20 to 30 km.
Lower layer .. from the base of the intermediate layer to a depth of about 2,900 km.	

The core below 2,900 km. is probably liquid. The top three layers constitute the crust. The upper two layers, called together the *Sial*, float as it were on the lower, heavier layer, the *Sima*. The Sial is thicker under the continents and thinner under the oceans.

Earth Movements.—Conformity and Unconformity.—When beds of sedimentary rock are laid down in continuous sequence they are said to be *conformable*. If these rocks are uptilted and reduced to a plain of marine denudation, a second series of rocks laid down on this plain is said to be *unconformable* to the first and the surface dividing them is called *a plane of unconformity*. In some instances where the land has sunk unevenly beneath the sea the later beds may reach farther than the earlier. They are then said to overlap them and the whole is described as an *unconformity with overlap* (Fig. 15).

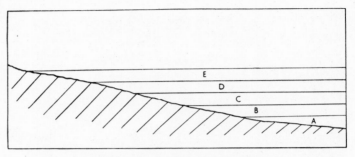

Fig. 15.—Unconformity with overlap.
The newer series A to E rest on the eroded edge of the older series. The higher beds of the newer series transgress further on to the old land than the lower beds.

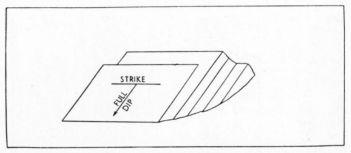

Fig. 16.—Dip and strike.

Dip and Strike.—When a bed of rock is tilted evenly the direction of the horizontal line is referred to as the "*strike*" and the maximum inclination at right-angles to it as the "*full dip*" or "*true dip*" (Fig. 16). If only a small exposure is available, it may be impossible to determine the direction of the full dip and the observed inclination is recorded as the apparent dip.

Jointing.—When rocks are tilted by earth movement they are subjected to stresses with the production of planes of weakness that may later, and, especially near the outcrop, give rise to cracks called *joints* (Fig. 17a). Joints are usually perpendicular to the bedding and are often found in two directions, one more or less parallel to the strike and the other to the dip; they may, however, have many different directions. Joints are of varying importance; some, the *master joints*, persist through considerable thicknesses of strata, while others traverse only a few beds. One very striking and important case of jointing is the "*cleat*" in coal. This is a series of close joints which are generally persistent over wide areas and, as explained elsewhere, often influence the working of the coal since they determine the direction of the "bord" faces; the joints at right angles to the cleat, which determine the "end" faces, are much less perfect. The cleats have often been opened and coated with ankerite (cleat spar) or pyrites. Natural jointing is not as a rule so clearly marked in rocks in deep mines, but a series of fractures of a similar character are induced by the mining which have been described by Prof. D. W. Phillips[3] as "induced cleavage". The development of induced cleavage is of great importance in mining.

(a) Bedding and jointing in carboniferous limestone.

Joints also appear in the igneous rocks (Fig. 17b). Some like those mentioned above are of tectonic origin, while others, especially in lavas, are due to contraction on cooling.

Folds.—As a result of movements in the earth's crust strata are thrown into folds and broken by faults. The simplest folds are the symmetrical *anticline* and the *syncline*. The folds may be cylindrical in shape or the axis may be bent to give a *dome* or *basin* (see Figs. 18a, b

(b) Jointing in granite.
Fig. 17.—Jointing.

and c). When the axes have a regular inclination in one direction the folds are said to *pitch* and the slope of the axis is the *angle of pitch*. The outcrop of the rocks is then sinuous as in Fig. 18d. With unequal lateral pressure the folds become asymmetrical when the axial planes are no longer vertical, as shown in Fig. 18e. And when this becomes more intense the asymmetrical folb becomes an *overfold* and eventually a *recumbent fold*. In these folds the middle limbs are turned over so that the apparent succession of the rocks is reversed;

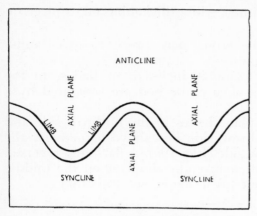

(a) Section of symmetrical folds.

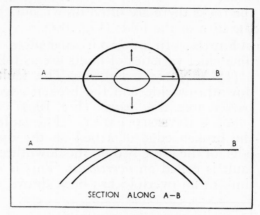

(b) Plan and section of a dome.

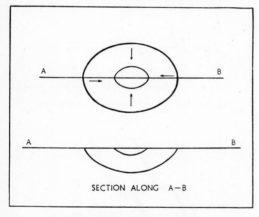

(c) Plan and section of a basin.

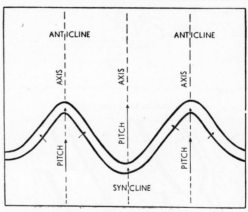

(d) Plan of outcrop of pitching folds.

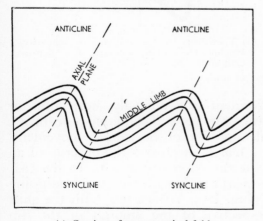

(e) Section of asymmetrical folds.

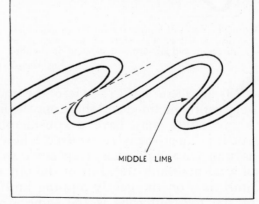

(f) Section of an overfold passing into an overthrust by the thinning of the middle limb.

Fig. 18.—Types of folds.

the rocks there are often drawn out thinner while thickening takes place on the turn of the folds (Fig. 18*f*).

Faults.—In other circumstances the strata may break to give faults. The chief varieties of faults are as follows:—

(1) A Normal Fault.—The fault plane is inclined, or hades, to the downthrow side and the broken edges of any one bed are separated by a barren area, the *"want"* (Fig. 19*a*).

(2) A Reversed Fault.—The fault plane hades to the upthrow side and the broken edge of a bed on the upthrow side lies above or *overlaps* the edge of the same bed on the downthrow side (Fig. 19*b*). A flat-lying reversed fault is called an *overthrust*. This is often brought about when the middle limb of an overfold has been drawn out till it snaps (see Fig. 18*f*).

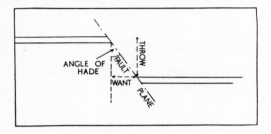

(*a*) Section of a normal fault.　　　　　(*b*) Section of a reversed or overlap fault.

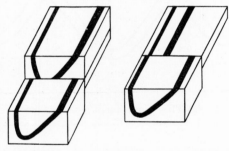

(*c*) The effect of a normal fault on an asymmetrical syncline. The shift of the outcrop in direction and amount is dependent on the dip.

(*d*) The effect of a tear fault on an asymmetrical syncline. The shift of the outcrop is not dependent on the dip.

Fig. 19.—Types of faults.

(3) A Tear Fault.—Here the movement is principally horizontal or very gently inclined and there may be little or no vertical component or throw. Many faults may have a considerable amount of horizontal movement, but it is most easily recognized where a tear fault crosses the outcrop of an asymmetrical fold at a steep angle to the direction of the axis. In the case of a normal fault the shift of the outcrop will be less on the steeply dipping limb than on the gently dipping limb (Fig. 19*c*). With a tear fault the shift of the two outcrops is the same irrespective of the amount of the dip (Fig. 19*d*). When faults are parallel to the dip they are called *"dip faults"* and when parallel to the strike *"strike faults"*. Faults rarely occur singly;

when two faults throw down towards each other so that a block of strata is let down between higher measures on each side, the pair are known together as a *"trough fault"*; a group of two or more faults throwing down in the same direction are known as *"step faults"*.

Mountain Building.—A mountain chain is a strip of the earth's crust where the rocks have been subjected to intense lateral pressures, folded, fractured and raised to a considerable height. In the geologically youthful chains like the Alps, the mountains are still high, but many of the older mountains have been worn down by denudation to low levels. The first stage in the formation of a mountain chain is the preparation of the rocks in a trough called a geosyncline, in which are accumulated great thicknesses of sediments (Fig. 20).

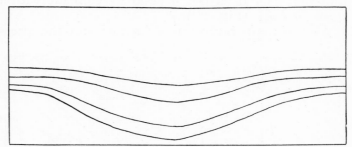

Fig. 20.—Diagram of a geosyncline.

Either one or both of the sides of the geosyncline then move in, crumpling the soft sediments and causing them to be thrust on to the "forelands" on either side (Fig. 21).

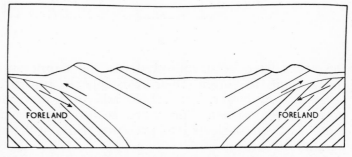

Fig. 21.—The uprise of mountains on the site of a former geosyncline.

METAMORPHISM

Metamorphism, or change of form, is a word used to describe the changes in rocks resulting in the development of new minerals and structures which are stable under changed conditions of equilibrium. It can be treated under three heads, viz., thermal or contact, dynamo-thermal or regional, and pneumatolytic metamorphism. In the first are included the changes that take place in rocks when brought into contact with intrusive igneous masses, in the second those produced by high temperature and pressure and the third the alterations brought about by the action of hot gases or solutions in the neighbourhood of igneous intrusions.

The Effects of Contact Metamorphism. —These are most easily studied in the argillaceous rocks. As we approach a granite intrusive into slates the latter first begin to show spots which gradually begin to change into imperfect crystals of cordierite, a silicate of magnesium, iron and aluminium, together with andalusite, a silicate of aluminium; at the same time the groundmass of the slate becomes recrystallised with the development of much new biotite. Finally, close to the igneous rock the slate becomes a compact fine-grained rock or hornfels. Under similar circumstances sandstones change into quartzites and limestones into marble.

Dynamo-thermal or Regional Metamorphism.—In the building of mountains, where earth movement affects strata under intense pressure, folds are developed till the rocks are no longer competent to transmit the pressure. This causes some of the minerals in the rocks to be rotated bodily, while others are re-formed as flakes with their greatest dimensions a tright-angles to the maximum pressure. This gives a fissility to the rock in a direction that does not necessarily coincide with the bedding, and this is *slaty cleavage* (Fig. 22).

As the temperature rises further and the pressure is maintained, new

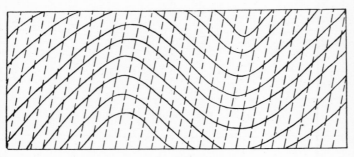

Fig. 22.—Slaty cleavage crossing folds.

minerals are formed including chlorites and micas. With their appearance the size of the flakes increases and the slate becomes a *phyllite*, and finally, a *mica schist*. In the schists new minerals, such as garnet, kyanite and staurolite, are found, depending on the temperature and pressure to which the rocks have been subjected. As the temperature increases further, the rocks begin to soften, their resistance to pressure is diminished and the crystals grow larger. The schists take on a more massive character and are now named *gneisses*. This word is also used to describe an igneous rock that has been subjected to pressure while still plastic and has acquired a parallel structure.

Pneumatolysis.—Granite magmas, on crystallisation, yield great quantities of water, CO_2, boron and fluorine which attack the already consolidated granite and the country rocks, leaching them and adding to them with the development of new minerals; this process is known as pneumatolysis. As a result of leaching, the granites are converted into china clay rocks, composed of quartz, sericite and kaolinite.

If boron is present, tourmaline is formed and granite is converted into tourmaline quartz rock. In the presence of fluorine, there is developed greisen, a rock composed of quartz, muscovite and topaz. Metalliferous compounds associated with the residual solutions give rise to many ore deposits.

GEOLOGICAL MAPS

A geological map represents the rocks as they appear on the surface. They are of two kinds, "drift maps" and "solid maps". On the former all the superficial deposits are shown and on the latter the superficial deposits are omitted with the exception of the valley alluvium, and the boundaries of the "solid" formations are completed by inference. On the maps of the Geological Survey the stratified rocks are represented by colours with letters for the systems. Igneous rocks are shown by colours and letters indicating their composition, e.g., B for basalt, and in the case of volcanic rocks the system letter is added, thus Bd_1 for Lower Carboniferous basalts.

The outcrops of faults are marked by white or coloured lines and underground positions by different colours. The direction of the downthrow is indicated by a short line at right-angles to the fault on the downthrow side with the amount of the throw in figures. The dip of the strata in direction and amount is given by an arrow with the number of degrees alongside it. An example of a geological map is given in Fig. 23.

The Mapping of Coal Measures.—In country where the rocks are hard and resistant and outcrops are numerous, a map may be built up from direct observations of strikes and dips. Softer rocks like Coal

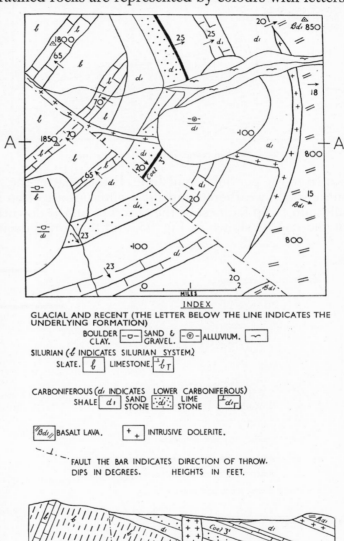

INDEX

GLACIAL AND RECENT (THE LETTER BELOW THE LINE INDICATES THE UNDERLYING FORMATION)

BOULDER CLAY. SAND & GRAVEL. ALLUVIUM.

SILURIAN (l INDICATES SILURIAN SYSTEM)

SLATE. l LIMESTONE.

CARBONIFEROUS (d_1 INDICATES LOWER CARBONIFEROUS)

SHALE d_1 SAND STONE LIME STONE

BASALT LAVA. INTRUSIVE DOLERITE.

FAULT THE BAR INDICATES DIRECTION OF THROW.

DIPS IN DEGREES. HEIGHTS IN FEET.

SECTION ALONG LINE A–A.

Fig. 23.—An example of a geological map.

Measures require different treatment. Coals seldom crop out and only occasionally appear in stream beds or show their presence by dark lines across ploughed fields caused by disintegration by surface weathering. Shales also are only occasionally exposed, but the more resistant sandstones stand up as escarpments. From Fig. 24 it will be seen that an escarpment presents a steep slope, the *"scarp" slope*, on one side and a more gentle slope, the *"dip slope"*, on the other. On the scarp slope the upper part is steeper and the lower

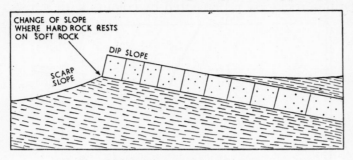

part gentler, the change of slope marking the base of the sandstone. The boundary of the sand-stone at the bottom of the dip slope has usually to be fixed by observing the change from sandy to clay soil. The junction of sandstone and shale may sometimes be marked by springs given

Fig. 24.—Diagrammatic section of an escarpment.

out from the pervious sandstone. Faults shatter the rocks, so rendering them more easily weathered and their outcrops are often in valleys and covered by alluvium. Dip faults shift the outcrops on the downthrow side in the direction of the rise, as shown in Fig. 25, and they often declare their position by the

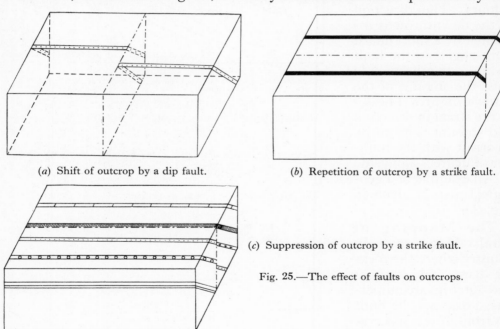

(*a*) Shift of outcrop by a dip fault.

(*b*) Repetition of outcrop by a strike fault.

(*c*) Suppression of outcrop by a strike fault.

Fig. 25.—The effect of faults on outcrops.

sudden cessation of a sandstone ridge or a shift in its position. The recognition of strike faults is not so easy as, according to the direction of the throw, they either repeat or hide an outcrop (Fig. 25), and their presence may often only be inferred when mapping has been in progress for some time. The outcrops of faults also are sometimes marked by springs.

The Interpretation of Geological Maps.—The order of succession of the rocks is usually indicated on the key to the colours and often a "vertical section" of the strata with measured thicknesses is given, but if not, these may be determined from the map with or without the drawing of horizontal sections. Dip arrows often give a clue to the structure. If these are absent the problem is one of solid geometry. If the map has no contours the general structure can be made out from the forms of the outcrops. Where an outcrop crosses a valley it will have the form of a V with the point at the bottom of the

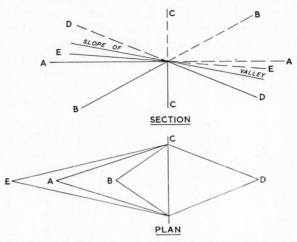

SECTION

PLAN

Fig. 26.—Section and plan of outcrop of beds striking at right angles to the course of a stream.

A, horizontal bed; B, bed dipping upstream; C, bed vertical; D, bed dipping downstream more steeply than the slope of the valley; E, bed dipping downstream less steeply than the slope of the valley.

valley, and the V's will point up or down stream according to the relation of the dip to the gradient, as indicated in Fig. 26. Where the map is contoured graphical methods are available. Fig. 27 shows how horizontal lines or strike lines may be drawn by joining points on the outcrop at the same height and from these the direction and amount of full dip may be found. The thickness of the beds may then be deduced by drawing a horizontal section, or, in beds with a gentle dip, an approximate value may be found by a simple graphical method given in Fig. 27. Here a line (x–y) parallel to the strike is drawn across the outcrop of the bed and the difference in height between the top and the bottom, giving the approximate thickness, may be read directly.

The Throw of Faults.—A dip fault shifts the outcrop of a bed in the direction of the rise on the downthrow side, and the throw may be determined by measurement of this shift with a know-

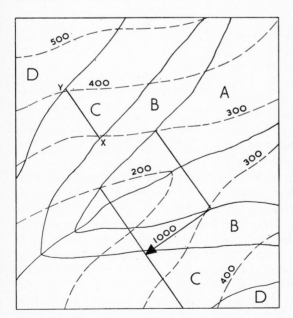

Fig. 27.—Map showing the method of determining dip and thickness of strata.

ledge of the dip (Fig. 25). It may also be determined by projecting the horizontal lines across the fault as shown in Fig. 28. Here x–y is the horizontal line in a coal seam on one side of the fault, at 500 ft.; if produced across the

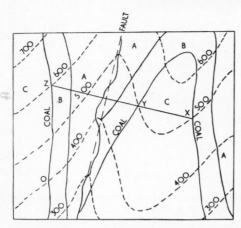

Fig. 28.—Determination of the throw of a dip fault.

fault it meets the coal seam at z, at 600 ft., indicating a throw of 100 ft. The throw of a strike fault may sometimes be determined by similar methods but often requires the drawing of a section.

The Drawing of Sections.—To interpret structures a section should be drawn as nearly as possible in the direction of the full dip. Where the geometry of the beds is completely known, as in Fig. 27, the section can be plotted directly; but if dip arrows only are available the profile of the ground must first be drawn and the boundaries between the beds shown as short lines with their proper dip. The lines will then have to be drawn as parallel lines or in curves to fit the dips. In drawing sections it is advisable, as far as possible, to use the same scale for horizontal and vertical measurements and, where this is not possible, to exaggerate the vertical as little as possible. If great exaggeration of the vertical scale is used, and changes of dip occur, anomalous variations in thickness appear as in Fig. 29.

The Work of the Geological Survey in Britain.—The Geological Survey was established in 1835 and since then almost the whole country has been surveyed on the 1-in. scale, and much of it, especially the coalfields and other important mineral areas, revised on the 6-in. scale. Maps are published on the scales of 25 miles to an inch, 10 miles to an inch, 4 miles to an inch, 1 mile to an inch

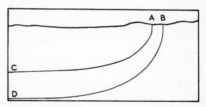

Fig. 29.—Section to show anomalous variations in thickness where the vertical scale is exaggerated. Vertical scale three times the horizontal. A B=true thickness, C D=exaggerated thickness.

and, for the coalfields, 6 inches to a mile. Much of the revision work is done on the 6-in. scale and copies of these maps may be inspected at the Survey office in London. Explanatory memoirs giving detailed geological data are published for most sheets of the 1-in. map and for certain special areas, such as coalfields, and the London district. During the last war and since the war there have been published a number of pamphlets dealing with water supply and mineral resources and with the Midland Coalfields. Following the last world war there was an unfortunate shortage of Geological Survey publications, both maps and memoirs, owing to destruction of stocks by enemy action.

STRATIGRAPHICAL GEOLOGY

General.—Stratigraphical geology which deals with the relative position of strata is, in effect, the unravelling of the history of the earth. This procedure is governed by two principles :—(1) the Law of Superposition and (2) Correlation by Fossils. The first states that a bed of rock is newer than that on which it rests and the second that the same or similar fossils are always found in the same order in the rocks of any one system. Some fossils

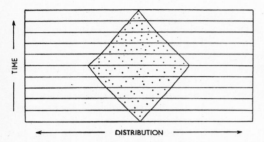

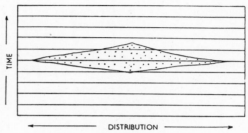

(a) Diagram to illustrate the distribution in time and space of an organism with a long time range and a restricted lateral range, of little use for purposes of correlation.

(b) Diagram to illustrate the distribution in time and space of an organism with a short time range and a wide lateral distribution. The most valuable type for stratigraphical purposes.

Fig. 30.—Use of fossils for correlation purposes.

have a long range in time and others a short range and it is the latter that are of value in stratigraphy (Fig. 30).

The Geological Column.—The unit used in the correlation of strata is the *zone*. This is ideally a group of rocks laid down during the life period of one organism and named after that organism, e.g., the zone of *Monograptus sedgwickii* is that zone in which the fossil *Monograptus sedgwickii* is found. This ideal condition is rarely attained, though approximations to it are numerous. Where no one zone fossil is available the zone may be defined by a number of fossils which constitute a fauna, or by the state of development attained by a group of organisms, as has been done by Dr. Trueman for the fossil non-marine lamellibranchs of the Coal Measures. A number of successive zones taken together constitute a "Series" and several conformable series are grouped together as a "System" which should normally be divided from the systems above and below by a major unconformity. The larger unit is the "Era" and this usually contains several systems with the exception of the Quaternary Era which includes only the Pleistocene or Glacial period, as shown in Table IV.

Nowhere in the world is there a complete sequence of the sedimentary rocks since periods of uplift and erosion, during which certain rocks have been removed, have alternated with periods of deposition. The geological systems in general use were first defined in north-western Europe and do not hold exactly all over the world, but major unconformities indicate mountain-building movements, often of world-wide extent, so that general correlations may be carried out from one continent to another. The Geological Succession as developed in the British Isles is as given in Table IV.

TABLE IV

GEOLOGICAL SUCCESSION IN GREAT BRITAIN

Era	System	Age in millions of years	Rock types
Quarternary	Pleistocene	1	Superficial glacial deposits.
Tertiary or Cainozoic	Pliocene	12–15	Sands and gravels, mainly in eastern England.
	Miocene	26–32	No representatives.
	Oligocene	38–47	Sands, clays and lignites in the south of England.
	Eocene	58–68	The London clay, sands and gravels in the South, volcanic rocks in the North-west.
Secondary or Mesozoic	Cretaceous	127–140	The Chalk, etc., of south and east England.
	Jurassic	152–167	The oolitic limestones, ironstones and clays of eastern England, the Midlands and the South.
	Triassic	182–196	Red sandstones and marls with salt and gypsum.
Primary or Palaeozoic — Upper	Permian	203–220	Breccias and red sandstones of the Midlands, Magnesian Limestone of the North-east.
	Carboniferous	255–275	The Carboniferous Limestone, Millstone Grit and Coal Measures.
	Devonian	313–318	The Old Red Sandstone of Scotland and south Wales, slates of Devon and Cornwall.
Primary or Palaeozoic — Lower	Silurian	350	Slates in Wales, the Lake District and southern Scotland, shales and limestones in the Midlands.
	Ordovician	430	Slates and volcanic rocks of Wales, the Lake District and south Scotland.
	Cambrian	510	Quartzites and shales in the Midlands, grits and slates in Wales, quartzites and limestones in north-west Scotland.
Pre-Cambrian or Archean	Upper	*	The Torridonian sandstone of north-west Scotland, slates and grits of the Longmynd, volcanic rocks of Wales and the Midlands.
	Lower	*	Schists and gneisses in the Highlands of Scotland, Anglesea and north-west Ireland.

* The age of the Pre-Cambrian systems is great but not known.
The figures apply to the age of the base of each system.

The major post-Cambrian mountain-building periods in north-western Europe were: the Caledonian which occurred at the end of the Silurian, the Hercynian at the end of the Carboniferous, and the Alpine during Tertiary times, principally in the Miocene period. The absolute age of the rocks in years is not easy to determine, but a method depending on the rate of decay of uranium to lead has given reasonably consistent results. According to determinations based on this method the age of the oldest known rocks is about 3,350 million years. The latest figures as estimated by Professor A. Holmes[4] are given in the list of systems in Table IV. The figures apply to the base of the system in each case.

Distribution of the Geological Systems in Great Britain.—The distribution of the pre-Cambrian and Lower Palaeozoic rocks in the British Isles is shown in Fig. 31.

THE PRE-CAMBRIAN. —These rocks crop out in the Western Isles and the Highlands of Scotland, Anglesea, the western parts of north and south Wales, at the Lizard and along lines of uplift, presumably important faults, in the Malvern Hills, Charnwood Forest and elsewhere in the Midlands. They are hard rocks and make

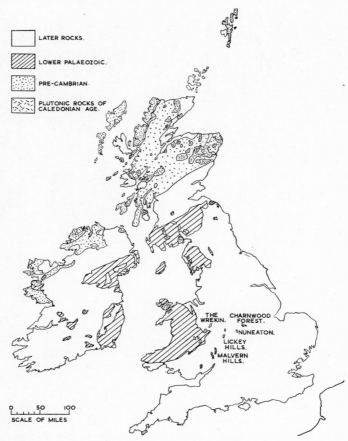

LATER ROCKS.

LOWER PALAEOZOIC.

PRE-CAMBRIAN.

PLUTONIC ROCKS OF CALEDONIAN AGE.

THE WREKIN.
CHARNWOOD FOREST.
NUNEATON.
LICKEY HILLS.
MALVERN HILLS.

0   50   100
SCALE OF MILES

Fig. 31.—Sketch map showing distribution of the pre-Cambrian and Lower Palaeozoic rocks.

much of the mountain ground of these islands. Where they crop out among the softer rocks of the Midlands they make striking hills like the Malvern Hills and the Wrekin. Economically, in Britain, they are of little value and provide only the most barren of land, but elsewhere in the world they are the repository of important metalliferous deposits, especially gold, iron, nickel, copper and manganese.

THE LOWER PALAEOZOIC.—The outcrops of these rocks are found in Wales, the Lake District, the southern uplands of Scotland, the north-west of Scotland and in small isolated areas or inliers in the Midlands. They are also known in many places under the later rocks in south-eastern England. With the exception of the Cambrian rocks of north-west Scotland, the lower Palaeozoic rocks were laid down in a marine trough with its northern shore in Scotland and its southern shore sometimes in the Midlands and sometimes

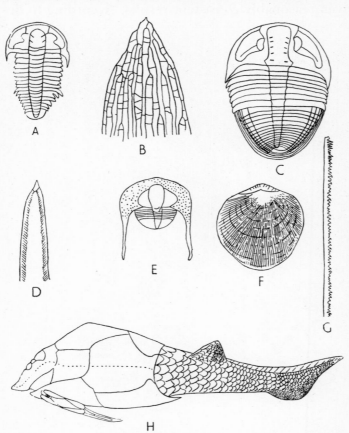

south of the English Channel. Deposition went on with short interruptions throughout the period and these systems, in Britain, afford a good example of a geosyncline. The Ordovician strata of Wales and the Lake District contain a large proportion of volcanic rocks that make most of the high hills of these regions, but otherwise the predominant rocks are greywacke grits and slates making hilly ground of little agricultural value, but important as catchment areas for impounding reservoirs. At the close of the Silurian there occurred one of the great periods of mountain building, the Caledonian, during which a mountain chain was raised extending from Northern Ireland across the Scottish Highlands and the North Sea into Scandinavia. It was probably during this period

Fig. 32.—Pre-carboniferous fossils.

A, *Olenus* (Trilobite) Cambrian; B, *Dictyonema* (Graptolite) Cambrian; C, *Ogygia* (Trilobite) Ordovician; D, *Didymograptus* (Graptolite) Ordovician; E, *Trinucleus* (Trilobite) Ordovician; F, *Atrypa* (Brachiopod) Silurian; G, *Monograptus* (Graptolite) Silurian; H, *Pterichthys* (Fish) Devonian. (*Based on drawings by the Geological Survey. Reproduced from* British Regional Geology, *by permission of H.M. Stationery Office.*)

that the rocks of the Highlands were converted into schists and gneisses. The foothills of this chain lay to the south over southern Scotland, northern England and the northern parts of Wales. Here the metamorphism though less intense was still strong, and slaty cleavage was developed especially in north Wales where, on either side of Snowdonia, slates have been worked on a large scale for many years. To this period also belong the granite masses of the Highlands, Southern Uplands, Shap in Westmorland and Mount Sorrel in Leicestershire.

The name Palaeozoic signifies old life, and the fossils have little in common with present-day life-forms, but they include most groups of invertebrate organisms of which the more abundant are brachiopods, trilobites, graptolites and tabulate corals. Examples of such fossils are illustrated in Fig. 32 A to G.

THE UPPER PALAEOZOIC ROCKS.—Fig. 33 shows the distribution of the upper Devonian and Carboniferous rocks in the British Isles.

THE DEVONIAN SYSTEM.—This comprises rocks of two distinct types, the Old Red Sandstone and the Marine Devonian. The latter is found only in Devon and Cornwall, while the former is found northwards of the Bristol Channel. In the North the Old Red Sandstone occurs in the Cheviot Hills, the Midland Valley, around the Moray Firth and in the Orkneys and Shetlands. As indicated by the name much of it is red sandstone and conglomerates with pebbles of Highland schists, associated

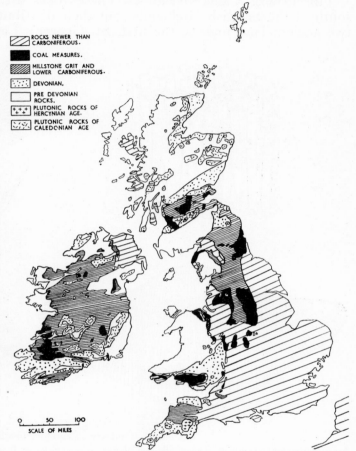

Fig. 33.—Sketch map showing distribution of Devonian and Carboniferous rocks.

with volcanic material and accumulated in lakes or shallow gulfs between the Caledonian ranges. From the Cheviot Hills to the Midlands the Old Red Sandstone is missing, but it occurs again around the South Wales Coalfield, though here there is less conglomerate and more marl. South of the Bristol Channel, the Marine Devonian has been altered to slates by the Hercynian earth movements. The fossils of the marine Devonian are rather similar to those of the Silurian but the Old Red Sandstone contains little but fossil fish (Fig. 32h). Economically the rocks are of small importance.

THE CARBONIFEROUS SYSTEM.—The Upper Devonian is generally succeeded conformably by the Carboniferous. The Carboniferous system is subdivided as follows :—

Upper Carboniferous $\left\{ \begin{array}{l} \text{Coal Measures} \\ \text{Millstone Grit} \end{array} \right.$

Lower Carboniferous   Carboniferous Limestone Series

THE LOWER CARBONIFEROUS.—These rocks are widespread in Britain south of the Scottish Highlands, but their distribution was interrupted by two ancient land masses, the first, St. George's Land, extending from the

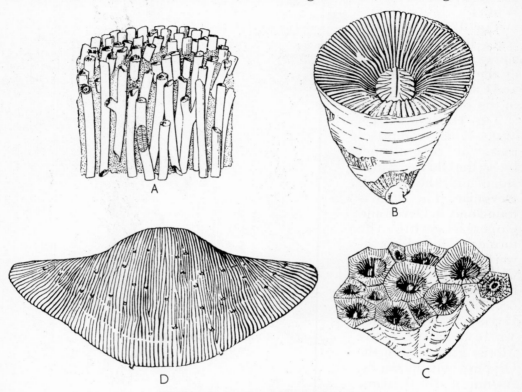

Fig. 34.—Carboniferous limestone fossils.

A, *Lithostrotion* (coral); B, *Dibunophyllum* (coral); C, *Lonsdaleia* (coral); D, *Productus* (brachiopod). (*Reproduced from* British Regional Geology: "*The Pennines and Adjacent Areas*", 1st Edition, H.M. Geological Survey. By permission of H.M. Stationery Office.)

Midlands about Leicester across St. George's Channel into Ireland and the other lying in the western parts of the Southern Uplands of Scotland. The Lower Carboniferous is by no means all limestone and shows great variations, particularly when traced from south to north. In Devonshire it is mostly absent. South of St. George's Land, around Bristol and South Wales, the rocks are limestones and shales. By means of their faunas they have been subdivided into a number of zones each named after a zone fossil (Fig. 34) and designated by a letter. These zones were first described in the Avon Gorge at Clifton and the succession there is as given in Table V.

TABLE V

SUCCESSION OF THE LOWER CARBONIFEROUS ROCKS IN THE AVON GORGE

Letter and zone	Zoological position of name fossil	Sub-zone	Rock	Thickness in feet
D Dibunophyllum	Coral	D_3	Grit	200
		D_2	Limestone	150
		D_1	Limestone with shale	400
S Seminula	Brachiopod	S_2	Limestone partly oolitic	370
		S_1	Limestone, oolitic and dolomitic	150
C Caninia	Coral	C_2	Shale	200
		C_1	Oolite, dolomitic limestone	200
Z Zaphrentis	Coral	Z	Limestone	370
K Cleistopora	Coral	K	Shale	400
				2,440

In southern Britain, including Kent, the rock successions are similar to the above. North of St. George's Land, massive limestones are again found in North Wales, the Peak of Derbyshire and to the east in Nottinghamshire and Lincolnshire where they have been proved in oil borings. In these districts the land was not submerged quite so early and the oldest known rocks belong to the S zone. To the north of the Peak district the limestones dip down under Upper Carboniferous rocks and when they reappear about Clitheroe and Skipton they contain a considerable amount of shale. This persists as far north as the line of the Craven Faults, which extend from Kirkby Lonsdale to Pateley Bridge. North of this latitude there are two regions; in one, north Lancashire and west Cumberland, the limestone preserves its massive character, but across the Craven Faults to the north and north-east another series of changes takes place. Immediately north of the faults the Lower Carboniferous is represented by a massive limestone about 400 ft. thick including the zones from C_2 to D_1 followed by the Yoredale Beds, a series of shales, sandstones and thin limestones belonging to the sub-zone D_2 and perhaps also to D_3. Northwards the massive limestone is split by shales and sandstones and coals begin to appear, till in Northumberland the succession of the Lower Carboniferous is as follows:—

			ft.
Bernician	{	Upper Limestone Series with Lickar Coals	1,000
		Middle Limestone Series	350
		Lower Limestone Series	650
		Scremerston Coal Series	400
Tuedian	{	Fell Sandstone	650
		Cementstone Series	1,150

The Limestone Series are rocks like the Yoredales with only thin beds of limestone. The coals are thin and poor and have been worked only locally.

In the Midland Valley of Scotland a rather similar sequence is developed, but with more coal and much volcanic rock. In the Lothians the succession is as follows:—

		ft.
Upper Limestone Series	.. ..	500
Edge Coal Series	.. ..	800
Lower Limestone Series	.. ..	500
Oil Shale Series ..	.. ..	2,500
Fell Sandstone ..	.. ..	1,500
Cementstone Series	.. ..	1,300

The Edge Coal Series is on about the same horizon as the Lickar Coals of Northumberland and the Oil Shale Series, which contains beds of oil shale from which oil is extracted, is of similar age to the Scremerston Coal Series. The Edge Coal Series contains important coals in the Lothians and Fife and elsewhere in Scotland. Over much of the country, particularly in the west and near North Berwick, great lava plateaux replace all the rocks up to the Oil Shale Series and the higher strata also contain the remains of small volcanoes that often interrupt the coal seams.

THE UPPER CARBONIFEROUS.—The Millstone Grit succeeds the Lower Carboniferous often with a marked unconformity. The name Millstone Grit is properly applied to the group of massive gritstones and shales which underly the Coal Measures of Lancashire and Yorkshire, but has been extended to cover all the rocks between the top of the Carboniferous Limestone or the Yoredale Beds and the base of the Coal Measures. The Millstone Grit was laid down in the delta of a river flowing from the north-east and bringing down debris from the Caledonian mountains. This delta was most persistent around the south end of the Pennine Chain where the series attains its greatest thickness. The delta was probably tidal, but only at certain horizons were marine conditions well established with the deposition of thin bands of shale often crowded with fossil goniatite shells. These shells (Fig. 35) have been used by Mr. W. S. Bisat[5] for the zoning and correlation of this formation. The general succession of the Millstone Grit in the north of the Lancashire and Yorkshire Coalfields is:—

Goniatite zones		Rock	Thickness in ft.
Gastrioceras	G_1	Rough Rock and associated shales	400
Reticuloceras	$\left\{\begin{array}{l} R_2 \\ R_1 \end{array}\right.$	Middle Grits and shales	800
		Kinder Scout Grit	400
Homoceras	H	Upper Sabden Shales $\left.\right\}$ Lower Sabden Shales $\left.\right\}$	1,500
Eumorphoceras	$\left\{\begin{array}{l} E_2 \\ E_1 \end{array}\right.$	Pendle Top Grits	2,000
		Upper Bowland Shales	400

As these rocks are traced northwards they become thinner and, in Scotland, are represented by not more than 1,000 ft. of the Roslin Sand-

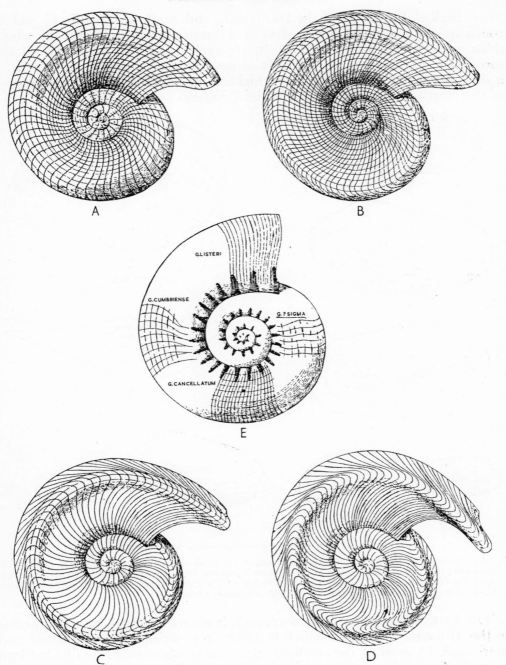

Fig. 35.—Goniatites used as zonal fossils in the Millstone Grits.

A, B, C, D, *Reticuloceras reticulatum*. A, type form; B, mutation α; C, mutation β; D, mutation γ;
E, composite diagram showing some of the chief types of ornament in *Gastrioceras*. (*Reproduced from
British Regional Geology: "The Pennines and Adjacent Areas," 1st Edition, H.M. Geological Survey. By
permission of H.M. Stationery Office.*)

stone Series. To the south in Derbyshire and Staffordshire the G and R zones are thick, but the lower parts of the series are thinner and the whole thins away to the south against St. George's Land. In South Wales the formation is composed of two beds of sandstone or quartzite separated by a shale series. The whole attains a thickness of 1,500 ft. in the western part of the North Crop of the South Wales Coalfield.

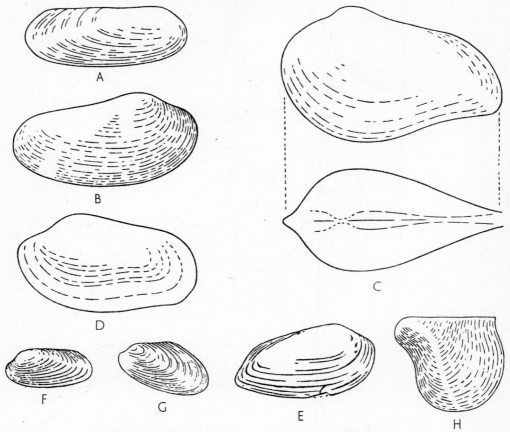

Fig. 36.—Upper carboniferous non-marine lamellibranchs.

A, *Anthraconaia lenisculata*; B, *Carbonicola ovalis*; C, *Carbonicola pseudo-robusta*; D, *Carbonicola communis*; E, *Carbonicola os-lancis*; F, *Anthraconaia pulchra*; G, *anthraconauta phillipsii*; H, *Naiadites quadrata*. (*Reproduced from* British Regional Geology: "*The Pennines and Adjacent Areas,*" 1st Edition, H.M. Geological Survey. By permission of H.M. Stationery Office.)

THE COAL MEASURES.—This formation is almost everywhere conformable to the Millstone Grit from which it differs in containing less sandstone and more coal. In most of the coalfields the Coal Measures can be divided into a productive series, grey in colour and containing workable coals, and an upper, red, non-productive series with few and poor coals. Like the Millstone Grit, the Coal Measures were laid down under deltaic conditions, but, for the most part, in fresh or brackish water. Incursions of the sea were short and infrequent and the "Marine Bands" are thin and sparse. Some of them are widespread and persistent as, for example, the Mansfield Marine Band of the Nottinghamshire Coalfield that has been recognised over the whole country and is represented by the Cefn Coed Band of South Wales and Skipsey's Marine Band of Scotland. Many, however, are less persistent and are frequently no more than a few feet of shale with the horny brachiopod *Lingula*. In consequence of their relative rarity they are useful in making correlation of coal seams over short distances, but for the correlation of the major divisions of the Coal Measures between different coalfields use is made of the non-marine lamellibranchs (Fig. 36) and fossil plants (Fig. 37). Several different systems of classification and nomenclature have been used, but the latest by Dr. Trueman[6] appears on the next page.

In referring to the zones it is usual to use only the species name, e.g., the modiolaris zone, and this practice is followed later. Since some account of the Coal Measures in the individual coalfields is given in a later section, this formation will not be further described here.

Fig. 37.—Fossil plants typical of the Coal Measures. (A—D, F, half natural size, E, natural size).

The Main Productive Measures.—A, *Neuropteris heterophylla* Brongn.; B, *Mariopteris musicata* (Schloth.); C, *Alethopteris lonchitica* (Schloth.). Upper Coal Measures.—D, *Sphenophyllum emarginatum* Brongn.; E, *Linopteris münsteri* Eichw.; F, *Alethopteris serli* Brongn. (*From* British Regional Geology: "*The Pennines and Adjacent Areas.*")

THE HERCYNIAN EARTH MOVEMENTS.—The Carboniferous period was followed by one of the great mountain-building episodes. In western Europe the main chain lay in the region of the English Channel and Brittany. Very intense earth movement affected the southern parts of the British Isles and in Devon and Cornwall, the Devonian and Carboniferous rocks are mostly in the condition of slates and were invaded by granites that were the source

CLASSIFICATION OF THE COAL MEASURES

Main divisions		Lamellibranch zones	Lithological divisions
Stephanian ..		Anthraconaia prolifera	Upper Coal Measures
Westphalian {	Morganian {	Anthraconauta tenuis Anthraconauta phillipsii	
		Carbonicola similis and Anthraconaia pulchra	Middle Coal Measures
	Ammanian {	Anthraconaia modiolaris Carbonicola communis	
		Anthraconaia lenisulcata	Lower Coal Measures
Namurian ..		—	Millstone Grit

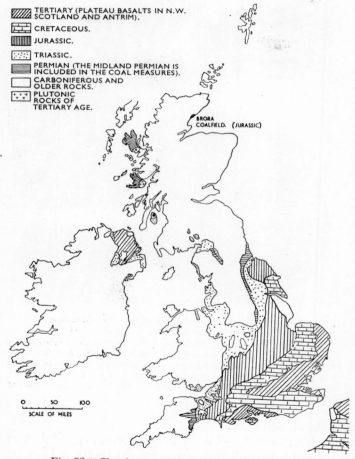

TERTIARY (PLATEAU BASALTS IN N.W. SCOTLAND AND ANTRIM).

CRETACEOUS.

JURASSIC.

TRIASSIC.

PERMIAN (THE MIDLAND PERMIAN IS INCLUDED IN THE COAL MEASURES).

CARBONIFEROUS AND OLDER ROCKS.

PLUTONIC ROCKS OF TERTIARY AGE.

BRORA COALFIELD. (JURASSIC)

SCALE OF MILES
0   50   100

Fig. 38.—Sketch map of the post-Carboniferous rocks.

of the Devono-Cornish metalliferous deposits. The intense earth pressures extended into South Wales, with overfolding and overthrusting especially in Pembroke. North of St. George's Land the effects are less marked and the Coalfield structures are less complex with gentle folding and normal faulting, but the separation of the coalfields (Fig. 33) took place at this time.

The Post-Carboniferous Rocks.—Fig. 38 shows the distribution of these rocks in the British Isles.

THE PERMIAN SYSTEM.—The Permian rocks occur in two facies, the Magnesian Limestone and the Red Sandstones and Breccias. The former crops out on the east of the Pennines, the latter in the Vale of Eden and in the Midland coalfields. In the last-named place they are difficult to separate from the Upper Coal Measures and they will be treated with that series. The Magnesian Limestone is a dolomitic limestone interbedded with red marls and associated with rock salt and gypsum. In Durham the limestone is about 600 ft. thick but southwards it is split up by beds of marl and thins out near Nottingham. From the Yorkshire border northwards it rests on a bed of unconsolidated sand of variable thickness. This is often full of water and behaves as a quicksand, so giving trouble in shaft-sinking. The limestone is also water-bearing. The Permian rocks of the Vale of Eden are thick and comprise the Penrith Sandstone with beds of breccia, the "Brockrams", which represent outwash deposits from screes of Carboniferous Limestone. The Permian was a desert period and fossils are few partly because of the unfavourable conditions and partly because organic structures do not survive the alteration of limestone to dolomite as has taken place in the Magnesian Limestone.

THE TRIASSIC SYSTEM.—The rocks of this system are subdivided as follows:—

3	Rhaetic	.. ..	Shale and limestone
2	Keuper	.. ..	Keuper Marl
			Waterstones
			Keuper Sandstone
1	Bunter	.. ..	Upper Mottled Sandstone
			Pebble Beds
			Lower Mottled Sandstone

The Triassic rocks crop out in a continuous band from the Tees to the south coast with a branch to the north-west through Cheshire and Lancashire to the north of the Lake District. The Bunter is a formation of red and mottled, open-grained sandstones much of them wind-borne with conglomerates of quartzite pebbles, the Pebble Beds, in the middle. The pebbles are larger and more numerous in the Midlands and become smaller and fewer northwards, pointing to a Midland origin. The Keuper Sandstone is similar to the Bunter, the Waterstones are interstratified beds of sandstone and marl and the Keuper Marls are a thick deposit of wind-blown dust accumulated in desert lakes and containing thick beds of rock salt. The thickness of the Triassic rocks varies from a maximum of about 5,000 ft. in Cheshire to a few hundreds of feet in the Midlands. They mainly form low-lying agricultural land. The Bunter is an important source of underground water, and has given trouble in this respect in shaft sinkings. The salt beds of the Keuper provide raw material for the alkali industries of Cheshire. The Rhaetic, though persistent is very thin, and of little importance.

THE JURASSIC SYSTEM.—The Jurassic rocks are subdivided as shown by the table at the top of p. 74.

The system crops out in a belt from the north coast of Yorkshire to the south coast in Dorset. The Jurassic rocks were mostly deposited in shallow water and show much variation. They are largely clays and oolitic limestones with some sandstones and shales in the Middle Jurassic of north-east Yorkshire. These last groups contain thin poor coals; they were laid down in shallow water and are called the Estuarine beds. The marine faunas (Fig. 39), include many ammonites and belemnites as well as other shells, and numerous remains of reptiles. The shales and clays make low-lying heavy land and

		South and Central England	North-east Yorkshire
Upper Jurassic	Purbeckian	Marls and limestones ..	Missing.
	Portlandian	Limestone, clay and sandstone	Missing.
	Kimmeridgian	Clays	Clays.
	Corallian	Limestone and clay ..	Sandstone and limestone.
	Oxfordian	Clays	Clays and sandstones.
Middle Jurassic	Bathonian (Great Oolite Series)	Limestones	Estuarine shales and sandstones.
	Bajocian (Inferior Oolite Series)	Limestones with Northampton Ironstone at the base	Estuarine shales and sandstones.
Lower Jurassic	Upper Lias	Clays	Shales.
	Middle Lias	Marlstone with Ironstones ..	Shales with the Cleveland Ironstone.
	Lower Lias	Clays with Ironstone at Frodingham	Shales and clays.

the limestones form uplands like the Cotswold Hills; whilst the Estuarine beds underlie the north-east Yorkshire Moors. The most important rocks economically are the ironstones (Fig. 9f). These occur at three horizons: the Northampton Ironstone at the base of the Middle Jurassic is worked in the counties of Northampton, Rutland and South Lincolnshire, the Middle Lias ironstone in the Cleveland district and in Oxfordshire and the Lower Lias ironstone at Frodingham in North Lincolnshire. Other materials of economic value in the System are the cementstones at the base of the Lower Lias, the building stones of the Oolites in the Middle Jurassic and the brick clays of the Oxford Clay, worked around Peterborough and Bedford.

THE CRETACEOUS SYSTEM.—The outcrop of these rocks is almost entirely confined to the south-east of England; their succession is the following:—

		South-east England	Bedfordshire	Lincolnshire	Yorkshire Coast
Upper Cretaceous	Chalk		Chalk	Chalk	Chalk
	Gault clay		Gault clay	Red Chalk	Red Chalk
Lower Cretaceous	Lower Greensand		Lower Greensand	Carstone Clays and Sandstones	Speeton Clay
	Wealden Beds				

The Cretaceous rocks were deposited on an old uneven land surface and the oldest beds are found only in the south-east parts of England and on the Yorkshire coast. In the Weald of Kent and Sussex they are sands and shales with ironstones deposited in a lake; in Yorkshire they are marine clays with a northern fauna. The Lower Greensand is a variable bed of glauconitic sand laid down in pockets only in certain areas and often missing. The Gault is clay and sand passing, in Norfolk, into the thin Red Chalk. The Chalk is the most persistent of the Cretaceous rocks, outcropping from Flamborough Head to the Dorset coast. Its lower beds are marly, but for the most part it is a white limestone with bands of flint nodules. The fossils of the Cretaceous are rather similar to those of the Jurassic. During Chalk times the ammonites died out and their place as zone fossils is taken by the echinoids (sea urchins). The Chalk outcrops make the Downs and the Wolds of Yorkshire and Lincolnshire; the sandy beds of the Wealden and the Lower Greensand give hilly pine-covered country. At present the Chalk is used for lime burning

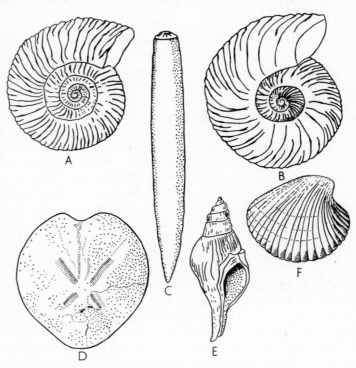

Fig. 39.—Mesozoic and Tertiary Fossils.

(A), *Parkinsonia* (Ammonite) Jurassic; (B), *Quenstedticeras* (Ammonite) Jurassic; (C), *Actinocamax* (Belemnite) Cretaceous; (D), *Micraster* (Echinoid) Cretaceous; (E) *Clavellites* (Gastropod) Eocene; (F), *Venericardia* (Lamellibranch) Eocene. (Figs. C to F based on drawings by the Geological Survey.)

and cement and is an important source of underground water. The Lower Greensand provides pure quartz sands for steel works and glass making and, in past times, the ironstones of the Wealden supported a flourishing iron industry.

THE TERTIARY SYSTEMS.—The only Tertiary system with deposits of any great extent in Britain is the Eocene. The Eocene rocks are developed in the London and Hampshire basins. In the former the thickness is about 1,000 ft. and in the latter as much as 1,500 ft. The rocks were laid down under marine conditions in the estuary of a river flowing from the west. The succession in the two areas is as shown in the table on p. 76.

The London Clay is about 400 ft. thick under London, but almost disappears in Dorset as it passes into the shallower parts of the estuary. The other beds all show evidence of approach to land in the westerly direction. The fossils of the Eocene are mostly marine shells, but some forms such as

	Hampshire Basin	London Basin
Barton Beds	Sands and clays	Missing.
Bracklesham Beds	Sands and clays	Sands and clays.
Bagshot Beds	Sands	Sands.
London Clay	Thin clay	Thick clay.
Woolwich and Reading Beds ..	Sands and clays	Sands.
Thanet Beds	Missing	Sands.

palm seeds and bones of monkeys suggest a tropical climate. The sandy beds form heath land and the London Clay heavy dairy land.

As raw materials the Tertiary rocks are unimportant, but the London Clay has provided a convenient medium for the driving of the London tube railways. In the north-west of the British Isles there were great manifestations of igneous activity. From a number of volcanoes floods of lava were poured out, parts of which now remain as the basalt plateaux of Antrim, Mull and Skye. At the same period there were intruded plutonic rocks which now form mountains like Goatfell in Arran and the Cuillins in Skye and also "swarms" of dolerite dykes.

The deposits of the later Tertiary systems are nowhere extensive in Britain. The Oligocene is represented by thin beds of clay, sand and limestone in the Isle of Wight and the nearby mainland, and by clays and lignites in the Bovey basin in Devon. The Miocene System is absent in this country. The Pliocene rocks occur along the east coast of Norfolk and Suffolk in the form of the "Crags", thin sandy beds full of shallow-water marine shells and as outlying patches on the Downs in Kent and in West Cornwall. The fossils of the later Tertiary rocks are mostly marine shells closely related to living species. They indicate a warm climate till the higher Pliocene period when the onset of cold conditions began.

The Alpine folding during Tertiary times had pronounced effects in Britain. In the south the anticline of the Weald rose and the Chalk was turned up vertical on the Hog's Back in Surrey and in the Isle of Wight. Along the Dorset coast Jurassic rocks were overturned and overthrust. In South Wales great disturbances such as the Vale of Neath Faults are of this date and, further north, the last uplift of the Peak, the updoming of the Lake District and the great fault system of Northern England, the Pennine, Dent and Craven Faults all took their present form during this time.

THE PLEISTOCENE OR GLACIAL PERIOD.—At the end of the Pliocene the climate became much colder, and glaciers spread over the country from the high ground and even across the North Sea from Scandinavia. They brought with them boulder clay, sand and gravel which was deposited in a haphazard manner over the country. These deposits profoundly modified the details of the topography, filling old valleys and diverting streams. Many of the coalfields have deposits of drift up to 100 ft. or more in thickness which in some instances fill wide valleys from which the coals have been removed by pre-Glacial erosion as in the "Team Wash" of the Durham Coalfield.

COAL AND THE COALFIELDS

The Origin of Coal.—Coal is a sedimentary rock of organic origin and has been described as a mass of mummified plants. Several fossil fuels are included under the word Coal: brown coal, lignite, bituminous coal and anthracite. Peat, though the first stage in the formation of most coals, has never been included under that name.

Practically all black coals, such as are worked in British coalfields, show banding of soft bright and hard dull coal ("brights" and "hards") parallel to the bedding and often, on the bedding planes, fragments of a substance rather like charcoal, "mineral charcoal". The banded coals were divided, by Dr. Marie Stopes,[7] into four constituents, Vitrain, Clarain, Durain and Fusain. The first two make up the "brights", the durain is the "hards" and the fusain is the "mineral charcoal". Examination with the microscope has shown that the bright vitrain streaks represent large pieces of wood or bark with their cells filled with a bright black substance originally introduced as a jelly; clarain is similar to vitrain, but made of plant debris such as leaves and twigs, and fusain is partly carbonised wood. Durain is composed of more highly carbonised material with a high proportion of spore-coats, both megaspores and microspores. The hards and brights are generally concentrated at more or less definite levels in a seam, though they are sometimes interbanded. Coals practically always rest on a seat-earth or fireclay containing plant roots, in which the bedding has been destroyed by the burrowing action of the roots. The normal roof of a coal is a shale full of fallen trunks of trees, the last trees of the coal-forming forest. Water-plants with roots in the bottom have a limiting depth for growth and, if this is exceeded, they drown and die. At present it is about 10 ft. and was probably similar in Carboniferous times. The history of the development of a coal seam was something like this: if silting in a lake basin or river estuary exceeds the rate of subsidence, the water shallows till plants are able to take root and grow. The vegetation becomes thick, movement of water is stopped and it becomes stagnant. By the decay of the accumulating vegetation the oxygen is used up and further decay is retarded. So peat composed of stems, twigs and leaves is formed and eventually gives a bed of "brights". If subsidence now exceeds the rate of deposition the plants are drowned and the region becomes open water. If the lagoon is shut off from mud-bearing streams accumulation of vegetable material will proceed, partly from spores and leaves blown on to the water and partly from vegetable mud eroded from the peaty banks. This, on consolidation, will give a band of "hards". If the rate of subsidence again decreases, plant growth will begin once more with the formation of more brights. With a further increase in the rate of subsidence, the depth of the water may exceed the critical figure and the plants will again be drowned. If mud is brought in from outside, a bed of shale with tree trunks will be formed, and, if coal growth is not renewed, this will be the roof of the seam. There are, of course, numerous variations on this cycle. The roof just described may be washed away and replaced by unfossiliferous mud or sand, and occasionally the coals themselves may be interrupted by "wash-outs". A wash-out may arise in at least two ways. There is no doubt that, in some instances, the peat has been removed by river erosion and the channel thus formed filled with sand or mud. On the other hand, the majority of wash-outs are difficult to explain in this way. In many the coal has been subject to faulting and crumpling and the seam is liable to be duplicated along the edges of the wash-out area, also the roof rocks are thrown into contortions, folded and faulted occasionally without any serious effect on the seam. It has been suggested that wash-outs of this type may have been caused by earthquakes, since similar phenomena have been observed on alluvial flats in regions where severe earthquakes have been experienced. After the coal is buried by overlying sediments a further series of changes takes place resulting in the increase in "rank" of the coal. In the term "rank" are summed up the chemical and physical properties of the coal, and, in general, the higher the rank the lower the oxygen and water content and the higher the carbon content and the calorific value. Changes in rank take place by the loss of CO_2 and water, resulting in a continuous rise in the carbon content and a fall in the oxygen content, the proportion of hydrogen remaining about the same. When the oxygen content of coal is plotted against the carbon content the analyses fall near to a band called by Professor Hickling the "Coal Belt". Coals of different properties have different carbon contents. The value for coking coals is variable, but for the Durham coking coals it lies between 84 and 89 per cent. Coals with more than about 93 per cent. carbon are anthracites (See Vol. 4, Chap. 6).

The reasons for increase in rank are not always the same. There is no doubt that the changes are brought about by rapid burial with accompanying increase in temperature resulting in a kind of stewing of the peat as may be seen in the Yorkshire Coalfield.[8] In other instances increase in rank has been promoted by the effects of intense earth movement as in the anthracite fields of Pennsylvania and South Wales where the highest rank coals are in the most disturbed areas. Again, as in Scotland, coals near large sills of igneous rock have been converted to anthracite by thermal metamorphism.

THE COALFIELDS OF GREAT BRITAIN

The Southern Coalfields.—South of St. George's Land (see p. 66) is a belt of coalfields, viz., those of South Wales, the Forest of Dean, Bristol, Radstock and Kent.

The South Wales Coalfield (Fig. 40) is a roughly oval area about 55 miles long and 20 miles wide with an extension into Pembrokeshire. The Coal Measures are divided into three series:—

    (3) The Supra-Pennant or Upper Coal Series.
    (2) The Pennant Series.
    (1) The Lower Coal Series.

In the east Nos. 1 and 3 are mainly shaly and coal-bearing while the

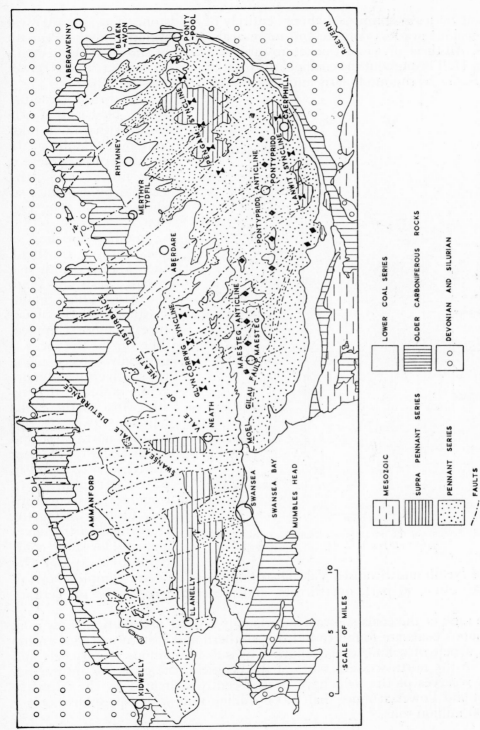

Fig. 40.—Map of the South Wales Coalfield. (*Lines after the maps of the Geological Survey.*) (Anticlines shown thus ◆, synclines thus ✕)

MESOZOIC

SUPRA PENNANT SERIES

PENNANT SERIES

FAULTS

LOWER COAL SERIES

OLDER CARBONIFEROUS ROCKS

DEVONIAN AND SILURIAN

SCALE OF MILES

0 5 10

79

Pennant Series is comprised almost entirely of sandstone. Towards the west the divisions are less definite and more coals are developed in the Pennant Series. All these divisions thicken towards the west as shown in the sections in Fig. 41. Throughout the coalfield the most important coals are in the Lower Coal Series in the modiolaris and similis-pulchra zones (p. 72).

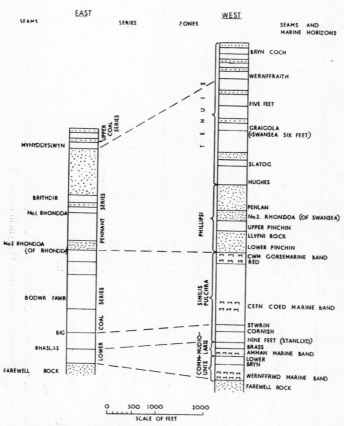

Fig. 41.—Sections of the South Wales Coalfield. (*After Geological Survey, Regional Geology, South Wales.*)

The broad structure of the field is that of a basin with minor folds and much faulting. In the eastern part there is one minor anticline flanked by synclines as shown on the map, Fig. 40.

Another anticline in the south of the field, the Mairos Anticline, passes westwards into the Moel Gilau Fault. Further west the structure is more complex. The dip of the rocks is generally steep along the south crop and more gentle in the north (Fig. 40). Most of the faults fall into two systems bearing north-west and north-east. The former are frequently found in pairs often making troughs; they were probably formed during the Hercynian earth movements. The latter comprise principally the Vale of Neath and Swansea Vale Disturbances. These are complex belts of faulting, often, in part, overthrusts, and are considered to be of Tertiary age.

The rank of the coals shows a surprisingly regular distribution. Low rank bituminous coals are found round the southern and eastern margins. Inside this is a belt of coking coals followed by sub-bituminous steam coals and finally in the north-western parts of the coalfield, the coals are anthracitic.

The reserves of the field have been recently estimated by the Ministry of Fuel and Power at more than 5,000 million tons with a possible increase of 3,000 million tons.

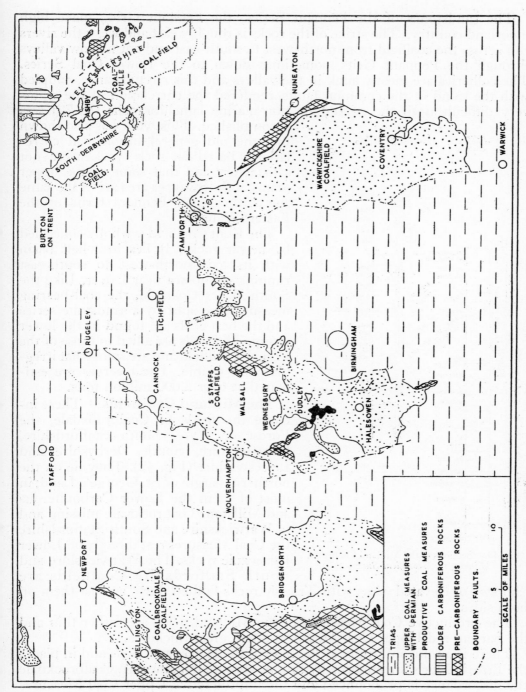

Fig. 42.—Map of the Midland coalfields of England. Igneous rocks in black. (*Lines from the maps of the Geological Survey.*)

SCALE OF MILES

0   5   10

TRIAS.

UPPER COAL MEASURES WITH PERMIAN

PRODUCTIVE COAL MEASURES

OLDER CARBONIFEROUS ROCKS

PRE-CARBONIFEROUS ROCKS

BOUNDARY FAULTS.

LEICESTERSHIRE COALFIELD

COAL-VILLE

ASHBY

SOUTH DERBYSHIRE COAL FIELD.

BURTON ON TRENT

NEWPORT

STAFFORD

RUGELEY

CANNOCK

LICHFIELD

TAMWORTH

NUNEATON

WELLINGTON

COALBROOKDALE COALFIELD

BRIDGENORTH

WOLVERHAMPTON

S STAFFS COALFIELD

WALSALL

WEDNESBURY

DUDLEY

BIRMINGHAM

HALESOWEN

WARWICKSHIRE COALFIELD

COVENTRY

WARWICK

The sandstones of the Pennant Series, the Pennant Grits, make high moorland country. The strike of the rocks is roughly east and west; the rivers run across the coalfield from north-west to south-east and cut narrow valleys through the Pennant Grits, sometimes down to the Lower Coal Series. The collieries are mostly sunk in the valleys and this circumstance, coupled with the trend of the common faults, rendered the correlation of the seams very difficult until the zoning by non-marine lamellibranchs (p. 72) was accomplished. This work has also shown that the old general lithological correlations, based on rock types, were not satisfactory and that some of the upper seams of the Swansea area are of the same age as the upper Pennant Grits of the Eastern Valleys.

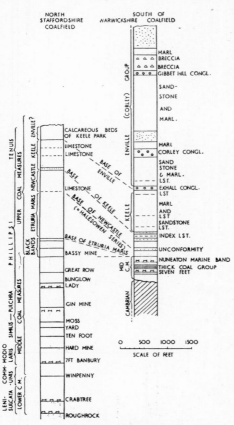

Fig. 43.—Sections of the Midland Coalfields.
(*Lines after Geological Survey.*)

The Kent Coalfield is wholly concealed by newer rocks. It lies in a half basin with its axis north-west to south-east running out to sea near Dover. Like the South Wales Coalfield, the coal-bearing measures are split by a sandstone series and the best coals are found in the lower group. The coals are allied to those of the French Coalfield and are somewhat irregular and friable. The reserves are estimated at over 2,000 million tons.

The Midland Coalfields.—These include the fields of Coalbrookdale, the Forest of Wyre, South Staffordshire, Warwickshire, South Derbyshire and Leicestershire (Fig. 42). They lie on the northern margin of St. George's Land; in most of them the Lower Carboniferous and Millstone Grit rocks are missing and in Warwickshire and South Staffordshire the Coal Measures rest directly on Lower Palaeozoic rocks. The Warwickshire and South Staffordshire Coalfields are "horsts" or elevated areas with Triassic rocks faulted down against them on both sides.

The productive Coal Measures in the Midland fields are rather thin and the barren, red Upper Coal Measures attain great thickness.

There is an unconformity at the base of the Halesowen Beds and in places the Etruria Marls are abnormally thin or absent altogether. In Coalbrookdale the discordance is pronounced and the unproductive Upper Coal Measures are separated from the Productive Coal Measures by a marked angular unconformity called the "Symon Fault".

The general succession of the Midland Coalfields is as follows:—

		ft.
Enville Group (Permian)	Red sandstone and marl with conglomerates	700 to 3,500
Keele Group	Red marls with spirorbis limestones	200 to 700
Halesowen Group ..	Grey sandstones and marl with poor coals	About 400
Etruria Marl Group ..	Red marl with green grits and spirorbis limestones	0 to 700
Productive Coal Measures	Grey shales and sandstones with coals	500 to 1,800

The Productive Coal Measures of the Midland Coalfields were laid down off the northern shore of St. George's Land which was undergoing a tilt to the north so that the sediments thicken in that direction. In the north also the coals are numerous and, when traced southwards, the lower seams die out against the old land, while the higher seams coalesce as shown in Fig. 44 to give thick coals, such as the "Thick Coals" of Warwickshire and South Staffordshire, up to 30 ft. in thickness. These represent a continuous growth of coal forest, since the subsidence just kept pace with the accumulation of the peat, while to the north it was intermittently more rapid.

The surface of St. George's Land was irregular and, though laid down continuously, the Coal Measures are interrupted by reefs of old

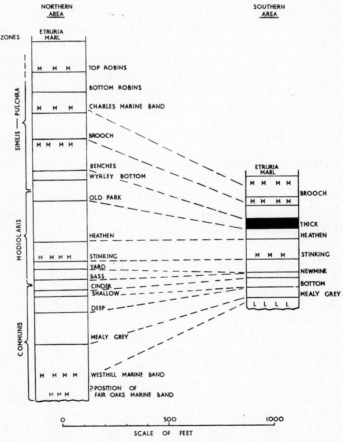

Fig. 44.—Section of the South Staffordshire Coalfield. (*After the Geological Survey wartime pamphlet, "Northern Part of S. Staffs. Coalfield".*)

rocks as at Dosthill in Warwickshire and Dudley and Walsall in South Staffordshire. The Leicestershire and South Derbyshire fields lie in two shallow basins separated by an upfaulted area around Ashby. Much of the southern and western parts of these fields is covered by Triassic rocks. The Warwickshire and South Staffordshire Coalfields have each a general basin structure broken by faults and on both sides of them the Coal Measures are dropped down by the so-called boundary faults and Triassic rocks are brought in contact with the Coal Measures. At the southern ends of these fields the Productive Measures thin out under thick barren red measures. To the north the Warwickshire Coalfield is bounded by faults; the northern boundary of the South Staffordshire field is concealed by the Trias on Cannock Chase and has not yet been fully explored. The Coalbrookdale Coalfield dips to the east under Upper Coal Measures and Triassic rocks; the question of continuation of the Productive Measures is uncertain on account of the "Symon Fault" unconformity, but they have been followed west of the "boundary fault" of south Staffordshire and may extend westwards to Coalbrookdale. Igneous intrusions occur in South Staffordshire and elsewhere and have damaged some coal. The rank of the coals in this group of coalfields is low, and coking coals in the modern sense are absent, though coke-making was first started in Coalbrookdale in 1709. Estimates of the reserves of this group of coalfields are:—

Leicestershire and South Derby	..	..		..	782 million tons	
Warwickshire ..	..	..	..	..	..	878 ,, ,,
South Staffordshire ..	..	..	..	..	1,233 ,, ,,*
Shropshire ..	..	..	..	..	..	126 ,, ,,

* Considerable extensions of the South Staffordshire Coalfield east of Cannock Chase have been proved lately.

The North Staffordshire Coalfield.—In this coalfield the Carboniferous system is complete and the Coal Measures rest on the Millstone Grit. The Upper Coal Measures are complete up to the Keele beds, but there is only a doubtful representative of the Enville Series. Below the Etruria Marls there is a group peculiar to this field, the Blackband Ironstone Series. The Keele Beds, Newcastle (Halesowen) Series and Etruria Marls are very similar to those of the southern Midland area. The Blackband Ironstone Series consists of marls with coal seams which have as their roofs blackband ironstones (Fig. 43).

The distribution of the coals in the measures is like that in Lancashire and Yorkshire rather than the southern Midlands. The best and most constant coals are found in the communis, modiolaris and lower similis-pulchra zones. The marine band associated with the Gin Mine Coal has been correlated with the Mansfield Marine Band of Nottinghamshire and with the Dukinfield Marine Band of Lancashire.

This field (Fig. 45), has a triangular shape with the apex pointing to the north; it is a syncline widening to the south and flanked by a steep anticline on the west side. As they widen, the folds pitch down to the south, and, while the nose of the fold to the north is enclosed by the Millstone Grit, to the south the Upper Coal Measures appear and spread more widely till covered by the Trias. The dips are steep and especially in the northern part of the westerly anticlinal area, where the beds approach vertical and are known as the "Rearers". The field is crossed by several large faults; the most important strike about NNW obliquely across the axes of the folds, Fig. 45, and in places they reach a throw of 500 yd. or more. Along the western boundary there is at least one fault trending NNE, parallel to the edge of the coalfield. On this side the coalfield has been thought to end against a fault throwing down to the west, the "Red Rock Fault", but the evidence for this fault is not certain. To the south the coalfield should extend under the Trias.

The latest computation gives the reserves of coal in the coalfield as 1,686 million tons.

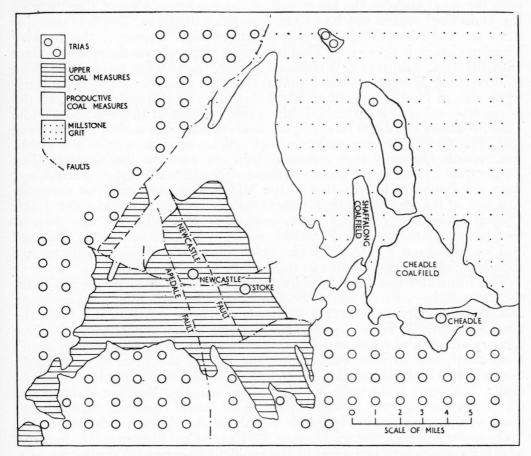

Fig. 45.—Sketch map of the North Staffordshire Coalfield. (*Lines from maps of the Geological Survey.*)

The North Wales Coalfield.—The Coal Measures of North Wales occur in a broad band on the east side of the outcrop of the older Carboniferous rocks. In Flintshire they dip to the north-east under the Dee estuary and in Denbigh to the east under the Trias of the Cheshire Basin. The succession is as shown on the next page.

					Maximum thickness in ft.
Erbistock Series (Keele Beds)	..	..	..	..	3,000
Coed-yr-Allt (Newcastle) Beds	..	..	..	..	500
Ruabon (Etruria) Marls	..	..	..	..	1,100
Middle Coal Measures	..	..	..	..	1,000 to 2,000
Lower Coal Measures	..	..	..	..	0 to 1,000
Millstone Grit					

The Lower Coal Measures contain no coals. The Middle Coal Measures of Flintshire are about 1,500–2,000 ft. thick; they are normal coal measures, with the good coals in the lower half of the sequence. One of these seams, the Main Coal, was as much as 13 ft. 6 in. thick in places. The field contains some small basins and in them a group of high measures, the Buckley Fireclay Group, is preserved. This is a series of purple sandstones and clays with fireclays, ganisters and siliceous clunch worked for refractories. The Middle Coal Measures extend under the Dee Estuary as far as Queensferry and at Neston a small coalfield occurs on the Cheshire shore. In the northern portion of the Denbighshire Coalfield around Brymbo the Middle Coal Measures are 2,000 ft. thick, the coals again being mainly in the lower half. The Coal Measures maintain their thickness some way to the south, but towards Oswestry they gradually thin out with the loss of coals. The Upper Coal Measures are similar to those of North Staffordshire but thicker; their main outcrop follows that of the Middle Coal Measures all along the east side of the Denbighshire Coalfield and they dip down under the Trias. During Coal-measure times some contemporaneous folding and erosion took place, particularly in Flintshire where wash-outs are rather frequent and where, about Flint, red rocks belonging to the Erbistock Series are found resting on low horizons in the Middle Coal Measures.

The Flintshire and Denbighshire Coalfields are divided by a great fault, the Bryn Eglwys Fault, along the line of which Carboniferous Limestone and Millstone Grit are raised to the surface. To the north of this fault, the Coal Measures lie in folds with axes trending roughly parallel to the Dee Estuary and one of these anticlines, the Horseshoe Anticline, swings round from south-east to south-west along the line of the Bryn Eglwys Fault. South of this fault the structure is complex and includes a number of curved faults, indicating a clockwise rotation of the country. Between Ruabon and Chirk the east-to-west Llangollen group of faults cross the coalfield, but south of this the structure is simple and the rocks dip east fairly constantly.

On account of the great thickness of the Upper Coal Measures it is doubtful whether there is any extension of the coalfield under the Trias to the east. The latest estimate of reserves of the known field is about 814 million tons down to 3,600 ft. in seams of 18 in. thick and over.

The Lancashire Coalfield.—(Fig. 46). This coalfield is triangular with a point to the north and an irregular base more or less parallel to the Cheshire border; it extends southwards into Cheshire south of Stockport. A faulted east-to-west anticline about the latitude of Chorley brings up the

Millstone Grit and divides the coalfield into two parts. The succession in the southern part of the coalfield is:—

		Thickness in ft.
Upper Coal Measures (Ardwick Group)	Red, purple and grey shales and marls with spirorbis limestones	0—800
Middle Coal Measures	Shales and sandstones with fireclays and coals	2,400—5,500
Lower Coal Measures	Similar but with rather more sandstone and only few coals	1,000—1,500

A general section of the coalfield is given in Fig. 47.

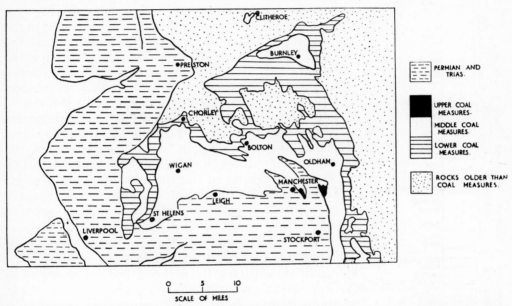

Fig. 46.—Sketch map of the Lancashire Coalfield. (*Lines after Geological Survey, Regional Handbook,* "*The Pennines and Adjacent Areas*".)

The Ardwick Group is found along the southern margin of the field. Its base is marked by an unconformity which in places cuts out as much as 2,000 ft. of Middle Coal Measures. The Middle Coal Measures are thicker in the south-eastern parts of this field than anywhere else in Britain; they may be roughly divided into a lower group corresponding to the communis, modiolaris and lower similis-pulchra zones with many workable coals, and an upper part, belonging to the upper similis-pulchra and phillipsii zones, that contains few workable coals except the Worsley 4 ft. and the Bradford group of coals at the top. There is only one well-defined marine band, the Dukinfield Marine Band, which is correlated with the Gin Mine Marine Band of North Staffordshire (Fig. 43).

The base of the Middle Coal Measures is taken at the Arley Mine at the bottom of the communis zone. Below this seam the Lower Coal Measures contain rather more sandstone and few coals and the only workable seams are the Mountain Mines. The Lower Coal Measures crop out to the north and east and round the central east-to-west anticline. The Middle Coal Measures form the surface along the southern margin and in a detached basin around Burnley.

On the north-west the coalfield is bounded by the Millstone Grit, on the west the Trias is faulted against the Coal Measures. To the south the Middle Coal Measures dip at about 1 in 5 under the Trias and soon pass to considerable depth. The field is intersected by numerous faults, mostly with a north-west to south-east trend, with a few running east and west. The north-west faults are strongest in the Wigan and Manchester areas where they break the edge of the coalfield. In the latter district the throws vary very rapidly and sometimes exceed 1,000 ft., e.g., the Irwell Valley, Pemberton and Bradford Faults. The Lancashire coals are not of very high rank. In the thick Manchester measures some of the lower coals of the Middle Coal Measures are coking coals, but in the Wigan area only the Mountain Mines have attained this rank. The Mountain Mines of the Burnley Coalfield are also Coking Coals. The latest estimate of the reserves of this field is just over 2,000 million tons down to 3,600 ft. in seams of 18 in. and over.

The Yorkshire, Nottinghamshire and Derbyshire Coalfield.—This is by far the largest coalfield in Britain; the exposed and concealed areas (Fig. 48) taken together are roughly oval in shape, about 70 miles from north to south with a maximum width of more than 40 miles, giving an area of over 2,000 sq. miles, about twice the size of the South Wales Coalfield. The Upper Coal Measures here are thin. They are not found at outcrop, but have been proved in the concealed coalfield in the basins of Maltby and Thurgarton where their maximum thickness is 600 ft. The succession is as appears in the table at the top of the next page.

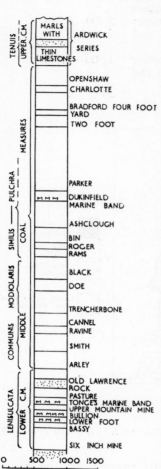

Fig. 47.—General section of the Lancashire Coalfield. (*Information from* British Regional Geology: "*The Pennines and Adjacent Areas*", H.M.S.O.)

The Middle Coal Measures are thicker in Yorkshire than in Nottinghamshire and Derbyshire, as indicated in Fig. 49, and in the structural basins than on the anticlinal areas between them. Sandstones occur throughout, but are most abundant in the upper measures where the coals are few and thin. The best coals occur in the lower portion, in the modiolaris and the

SUCCESSION OF THE YORKS, NOTTS AND DERBY COALFIELD

		Thickness in ft.
Upper Coal Measures	Red and purple marls and sandstones	200
	Grey sandstones and shales with a thin coal	100
	Red clays with green grits	300
Middle Coal Measures	Shales, sandstones, fireclays and coals, with the Silkstone Coal at the base.*	1,770–3,740
Lower Coal Measures	Similar with more sandstone and few coals	940–1,650

lower part of the similis-pulchra zone. The base is taken at the Silkstone Coal (Blackshale Seam of Derbyshire).* The Arley Mine of Lancashire is not on this horizon but on that of the Better Bed of West Yorkshire, and some of the Lower Coal Measures of Yorkshire are equivalent to the lower part of the Middle Coal Measures of Lancashire. In this field there are a number of marine bands; the two best known are the Mansfield Marine Band from 600–1,600 ft. below the top of the Middle Coal Measures, and that above the Halifax Hard Bed Coal near the base of the Lower Coal Measures, and equivalent to the Dukinfield and Bullion Mine marine bands of Lancashire respectively. The coals show variations in rank, both vertically and horizontally. In South Yorkshire, where the measures are thick, the higher seams

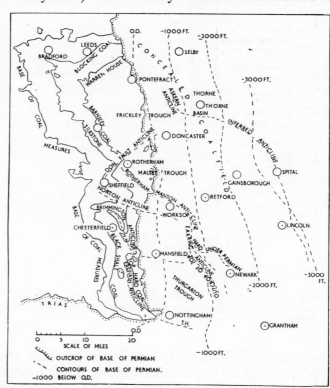

Fig. 48.—Sketch map of the coalfields of Yorkshire, Derbyshire and Nottinghamshire. (*Lines from the maps of the Geological Survey.*)

are of low rank and the coals below the Barnsley Bed have attained coking rank. In Derbyshire and Nottinghamshire, where the measures are much thinner, the coking coals are confined to the lower horizons, till, in the south of the

*The base and top of the Middle Coal Measures are now taken at the Clay Cross Marine Band and the Top Marine Band respectively.

coalfield, only the seams at the bottom of the Lower Coal Measures are of coking rank.

In pre-Permian times the Coal Measures were folded into several wide basins with anticlinal areas between them. These are the Frickley Trough and Selby Trough in the north and the Maltby and Thurgarton Troughs in the south. The exposed Derbyshire Coalfield, on the other hand, is traversed by a number of sinuous anticlines. One of the most pronounced anticlines in the coalfield is the Don Faults disturbance, a faulted anticlinal structure extending from Doncaster to Sheffield. The field is crossed by a

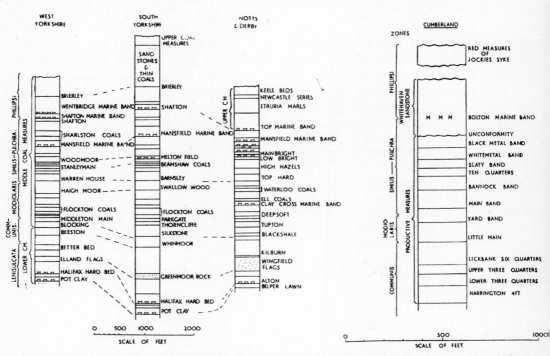

Fig. 49.—Sections of the Yorkshire, Derbyshire and Nottingham-shire Coalfields. (*Information from "Memoirs of the Geological Survey".*)

Fig. 50.—General section of Cumberland Coalfield. (*Based on Geological Survey, Regional Geology, Northern England.*)

number of faults mostly striking north-east or north-west and cutting the folds, except in the north where they turn more nearly east and west. The whole coalfield has later been tilted to the east and in that direction the Coal Measures are covered unconformably by the Permian, then by the Trias and finally by the Jurassic. The easterly dip takes the base of the Permian to 2,400 ft. at Gainsborough and to 3,000 at Lincoln. There is evidence that the Coal Measures are thinning to the east and that the coals are becoming fewer. The workable coalfield probably does not pass the Trent, but in the search for oil, coal seams were proved at great depth in borings in the longitude of Lincoln.

The latest estimate of reserves for this field is about 11,000 million tons.

The Cumberland Coalfield.—This coalfield lies on the north and north-west sides of the Lake District. The exposed field covers an area of 90 square miles around Whitehaven and Workington and has been followed under the sea for four miles; it may also extend to the north under the Carlisle Basin and link up with the Canonbie Coalfield just across the Scottish Border. The rocks are:—

Whitehaven Sandstone Group	Thickness unknown
Unconformity	
Middle Coal Measures	900 to 1,200 ft.

The productive Coal Measures (Fig. 50) are included in the communis, modiolaris and lower similis-pulchra zones; the coals are developed throughout and are of moderately high rank including steam, house, gas and coking coals. The Whitehaven Sandstone Group, red in colour, rests unconformably on the productive measures; the lower part is mainly sandy and the upper part shaly with thin coals and spirorbis limestones. About 100 ft. from the base lies the Bolton Marine Band which has been correlated with the Mansfield and Skipsey's marine bands (pages 89 and 95).

The Coal Measures dip to the north-west with minor folding, resulting in the preservation of the Whitehaven Sandstone Series north-east of Whitehaven and north of Workington. The field is much broken by faults mostly trending north-west and often making troughs in which the Whitehaven sandstone is preserved. These faults moved again in post-Permian times; they penetrate the Lower Carboniferous rocks and carry the haematite.

The latest estimate of reserves in the Cumberland Coalfield is 583 million tons.

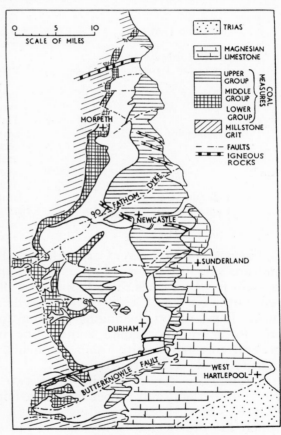

Fig. 51.—Sketch map of the coalfields of Northumberland and Durham. (*Based on Geological Survey, Regional Geology, Northern England.*)

The Coalfields of Northumberland and Durham.—These coalfields taken together cover a triangular area about 50 miles from north to south and up to 25 miles from east to west with extensions under the Permian rocks and the sea (Fig. 51). There are no upper red measures, and in the Lower Carboniferous, especially in northern Northumberland, coals begin to appear heralding the oncoming of Scottish conditions. Igneous rocks also appear in considerable force. The succession is as follows:—

		Thickness in ft.
Upper Carboniferous		
Productive Coal Measures ..	Upper Group with many sandstones and few coals	900
	Middle or Main Productive Group with the chief coals	650
	Lower or Ganister Group	250
Millstone Grit	Sandstones and shales with thin coals	300–600
Lower Carboniferous		
Limestone Group	Limestones, shales and sandstones with some coals principally in the south and the Haltwhistle district	1,600–4,000
Scremerston Coal Group ..	Shales, sandstones and limestones with several workable coals especially around Berwick	300–1,000
Fell Sandstone Group	Mainly sandstones	600–1,000
Cementstone Group	Sandstones and shales with bands of cementstone	500–3,000

The coals of the Lower Carboniferous (Fig. 52) are only of local importance and are very little worked. The Lower or Ganister Measures are thin and contain few thin coals. The Upper part of the Middle Coal Measures is not red, but is barren of workable coals. The main workable coals are contained in the lower 650 ft. belonging as usual to the upper communis, modiolaris and lower similis-pulchra zones. The non-marine lamellibranchs give a general correlation with other coalfields, but no equivalents of the known marine bands have been found.

Structurally the field falls into two main basins, a shallow one in Northumberland and a deeper one in Durham separated by the 90-fathom "Dyke", a north-east trending fault, a few miles north of Newcastle at which the dip begins to increase towards the south. There is also a third much smaller basin in the extreme south let in by the Butterknowle Fault. On the whole the measures dip to the east and have been followed for some distance under the sea. The faults mainly trend either east and west or north-east. Igneous intrusions are all dolerite dykes; they fall into two groups, one of late Carboniferous age striking north-east and the other Tertiary with a north-westerly trend. Apart from the great Whin Sill, in the Lower Carboniferous, sills are unknown. The Northumberland coals are all of low rank whereas in Durham most of the seams yield coking coal. The latest estimate of reserves is: Northumberland 1,760 million tons, Durham 3,000 million tons.

The Coalfields of Scotland.—The Scottish coalfields (Figs. 53–54) are situated in the Midland Valley. They differ from the English fields in the importance of the Limestone Coal Group and in the abundance of igneous rocks.

The Productive Coal Measures are everywhere coal-bearing, the Limestone Coal Group is variable, being most important in the east and north and to a lesser extent in the west, but with a barren area under the middle of the Central Coalfield. The Productive Coal Measures have been more extensively exploited than the Limestone Coal Group

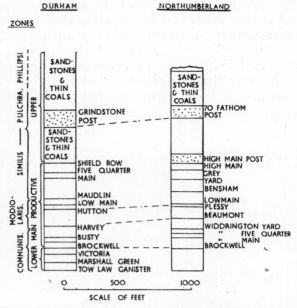

Fig. 52.—General sections of the Northumberland and Durham Coalfields. (*Based on Geological Survey, Regional Geology, Northern England.*)

which consequently provides the larger part of the reserves. Of these the Fife and Lothian Coalfields furnish the greater amount, and more extensive reserves may sometime be exploited beneath the Firth of Forth.

The general succession of the coal-bearing rocks is as follows:—

7. Barren Red Measures .. Reddish sandstones and marls.
6. Skipsey's Marine Band .. The equivalent of the Mansfield Marine Band of Notts.
5. Productive Coal Measures Normal coal measures with many coals, belonging to the communis, modiolaris and lower similis-pulchra zones.
4. Millstone Grit .. .. Sandstones, shales and fireclays, with volcanic rocks in Ayrshire.
3. Upper Limestone Group Sandstones and shales with limestones.
2. Limestone Coal Group .. Like No. 3 but with many coals in some districts and some volcanic rocks.
1. Lower Limestone Group .. Like No. 3.

Many small volcanoes were active during the deposition of the Millstone Grit and the Limestone Coal Group where they frequently interrupt the coal seams. In addition, intrusive sills and dykes are abundant throughout all the coalfields and have rendered much coal useless. If sills are not too close to a seam, they increase the rank of the coal and in this way anthracites have been produced.

The Scottish coals are mainly low-rank, free-burning coals, an important variety being the splint coals that were formerly used for iron smelting. In the north-western area of the Central Coalfield they have attained the rank of coking coals and locally of anthracite, due probably to the heating of the measures by numerous igneous intrusions.

The coal-bearing rocks have been folded into three major basins separated by anticlinal areas of older rocks, the Ayrshire basin, the Central basin, including Stirlingshire and the Douglas Valley and the East Fife-Lothians basin. The larger structures have been further subdivided into smaller units.

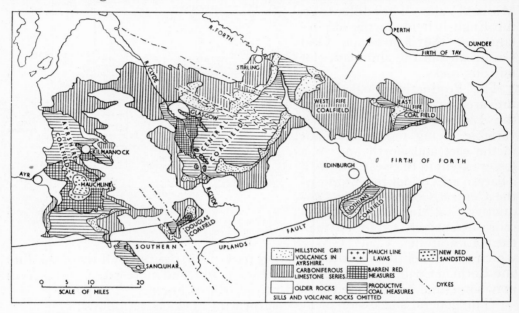

Fig. 53.—Sketch map of the Scottish coalfields. (*Lines from the maps of the Geological Survey.*)

The faults are often closely spaced and make an intricate pattern. In the deeper parts of the basins the Barren Red Measures overlie the Productive Coal Measures which, in their turn, are surrounded by a rim of Lower Carboniferous rocks including the Limestone Coal Group, which, in West Fife and East Lothian, covers wide areas. In the Mauchline Basin of the Ayrshire Coalfield, the Red Measures are covered by volcanic rocks and sandstones of Permian age and here all the coals must lie deeper than 3,000 ft. In the Central Coalfield the Coal Measures coals are generally less than 1,500 ft. deep and the Limestone Coals are all within 3,000 ft. of the surface. The Lothian Coalfield is an elongated basin with steep dips on the west side, so that in places the Limestone coals are vertical (Edge Coals) in contrast to the Flat Coals of the Coal Measures along the axis of the fold. The basin is deep and on the coast the lowest coals may lie at 4,500 ft. This deep basin is continued across the Firth of Forth and on the Fife shore the lowest coals are probably as deep as 4,800 ft.

Apart from Glacial Drift which is everywhere present and often thick, there is little concealment of the coalfields by post-Carboniferous rocks. The only case is that of the Mauchline Basin in Ayrshire. There are, however,

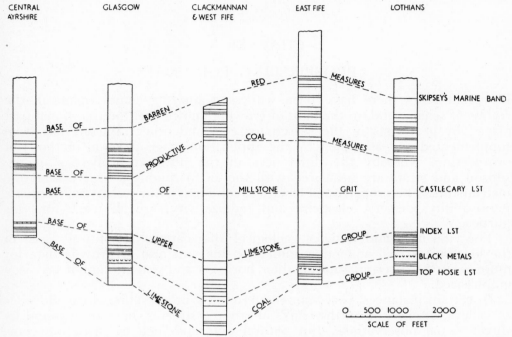

Fig. 54.—Sections of the Scottish coalfields. (*After Scottish Home Dept. Report on Scottish coalfields.*)

considerable areas of undersea coal off the Ayrshire coast and under the Firth of Forth.

The latest estimate of reserves by the Scottish Coalfields committee is:—

	Estimated available	Possible additional reserves
	tons	tons
Productive Coal Measures ..	1,412,000,000	1,344,000,000
Limestone Coal Group ..	2,012,000,000	2,629,000,000

REFERENCES

[1] *Bull. U.S. Geol. Surv.*, No. 770, 1924, p. 34.   [2] Blyth. *Geology for Engineers*, p. 97.

[3] Faulkner, R., and Phillips, D. W. Cleavage induced by mining. *Trans. Inst. Min. Eng.*, 1935, Vol. 89, p. 264.

[4] Holmes, A., *Proc. Geol. Soc., Glasgow*, 1947, Vol. 21, p. 117.

[5] Bisat, W. S. The Carboniferous Goniatites of the North of England and their Zones. *Proc. Yorks. Geol. Soc.*, 1924, Vol. 20. p. 40.

[6] Trueman, A.E., *Q.J.G.S.*, Vol. 103, 1947, p. lxv.

[7] Stopes, M. C. On the Four Visible Ingredients in Banded Bituminous Coal. Studies in the Composition of Coal, No. 1, *Proc. Roy. Soc. (B)*, Vol. 90, 1919.

[8] Mott, R. A. Coking resources in the Yorkshire, Nottinghamshire and Derbyshire Coalfields. *Trans. Inst. Min. Eng.*, 1945, Vol. 104, p. 446.

CHAPTER 3

PROSPECTING FOR COAL

In recent years there have been witnessed amazing achievements in the realms of science and, in the light of growing knowledge, the traditional part played by geologists in the search for coal and other minerals has been supplemented and amplified by the application of geophysical methods of prospecting, whereby the differences in the physical properties of the subsoil and strata are measured with the aid of highly sensitive scientific instruments. The properties of electrical conductivity or resistivity, magnetic permeability, density, elasticity and radioactivity, are all used for this purpose.

The vital need and value of geological information, not only to assist in the location of coal and other mineral fields, but also to provide data for more accurate determination of their horizons and extent, cannot be over-emphasised.

In certain instances, coal seams outcropping in sea cliffs, along the sides of valleys, ditches, or on the banks of eroding streams, have been found by direct visual observations. But natural outcrops such as these are comparatively rare and thus other indications of the presence of coal must be sought.

APPLICATION OF AERIAL PHOTOGRAPHY TO GEOLOGICAL RECONNAISSANCE

In prospecting virgin coalfields, aerial photography will, in future, play a very important part. An unexplored unmapped region can be photographed rapidly from the air and a topographic map can be built up by examination of stereoscopic pairs. It is frequently possible to make deductions concerning the geology of an area directly from the aerial photographs and, in this way, a great deal of valuable information may be gained before ground parties set out to map the new terrain.

As both geological maps and aerial photographs are horizontal projections, they are amenable to the same interpretative treatment. It is therefore necessary to have an understanding of the interpretation of geological maps before a study of aerial photographs is undertaken. There are two ways of interpreting geological maps, the first by relating the geological contacts to the topographic contours, and the second by studying the outcrop patterns. The latter method is of most use in studying large-scale reconnaissance maps, but both methods are needed for detailed maps.

Under favourable conditions dip and strike of beds, folding, faulting and unconformity may be detected and some conclusions may be reached regarding the nature of the various rocks. In areas where the rocks are largely exposed, differentiation between the various rock types is greatly simplified. In most parts of the world, however, there is some superficial cover on the bedrock. Where the soil is mainly derived from the bedrock, different shades of soil from different beds may be distinguishable on the aerial photograph. Different soils give rise to different natural vegetation, often emphasising tonal differences on the photographs.

The inclination of bedding may readily be determined from a contoured aerial photograph by studying the relation between the outcropping bands of rock and the topographic contours. The strike may be determined by selecting two points on a given contact at the same elevation. The line joining these two points will be a line of strike. Horizontal beds are easily recognised from their correspondence to the contouring, while vertical beds cross the country without deflection by topography. Folding may be detected by tracing rock contacts but it may not always be possible to distinguish between an anticline and a syncline. The area must have moderate relief so that dip of beds may be determined. On a level plain interpretation of geology is very much restricted. An unconformity may be distinguished from a fault by an examination of the dip of the boundary plane but it may not be possible to detect the difference between an unconformity and an overthrust.

Topographic features due directly to the geology may be interpreted from aerial photographs in the same way as when encountered on the ground. Hard bands of rock tend to stand out as escarpments while streams often erode softer beds and are guided by the strike of those beds. Igneous dykes usually stand out above the softer surrounding rocks, although in some cases they are eroded into trenches when the surrounding rocks are harder. At times stream valleys are eroded along fault lines.

In a virgin area, the preliminary aerial survey will be followed first of all by a topographical survey. Guided by the information derived from the aerial photography, a geological party will follow the surveyors, putting geological information on the map. The geological party will almost certainly encounter various problems which they cannot immediately solve, for lack of rock exposures. A geophysical party, following the geologists, would be able to complete gaps in the information, tracing faults, rock outcrops, etc. Finally, the findings of the geologists and geophysicists would be examined by a competent mining engineer, to decide upon the feasibility of further exploration by boring and, should the coal seams located prove an economic proposition, their development and exploitation.

DIRECT PROSPECTING METHODS

Coal seams are frequently overlaid by a water-bearing sandstone and underlain by an impervious seat earth or fireclay. Under favourable conditions, therefore, a line of springs or a belt of damp ground may indicate the presence of a coal seam (Fig. 1). The belt of damp ground may be discernible by the marshy vegetation growing on it. Coal seams and associated clays often contain some iron pyrites which is readily decomposed, giving iron-bearing springs at the outcrops. The weathering of coal will often give a soil of darker colour than the normal one from the surrounding rocks and small pieces of coal may be visible in the soil, particularly in ground which has been ploughed over.

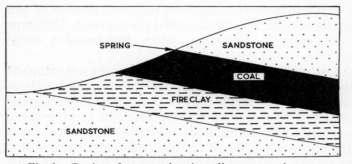

Fig. 1.—Section of strata and spring adjacent to coal seam.

In an area where coal is suspected to be present, and favourable indications have been found, some method of rapidly proving its existence and extent is needed, and if the cover is shallow, a trial trench may be dug across the supposed outcrop. If a better idea of the thickness and quality of the seam is required, it is preferable to drive a small exploratory drift in the coal, sink a trial shaft, or put down one or more shallow borings a few yards in from the outcrop. The use of a bulldozer to clear away the overburden may prove quicker, cheaper, and provide facilities for obtaining information over a wider range. An older but more destructive method of clearing the overburden is known as " hushing ". In order to apply it, a stream was dammed on a hillside and, when sufficient water had been accumulated, the dam was suddenly opened and the water allowed to rush over the adjoining land. The surface soil was thereby washed away, exposing any coal seams, mineral veins, etc.

GEOLOGICAL AIDS TO PROSPECTING

The modern tendency is for direct methods of exploration to be guided by a study of the local geology, thereby avoiding as much unproductive work as possible. In the Northern Hemispheres, the Upper Carboniferous rocks, containing plant material, are usually coal-bearing. In the Southern Hemispheres, rocks which contain certain fossil plants, for example, Glossopteris and Sigillaria, usually carry coal seams. The possibility of coal occurring in rocks later than the Carboniferous system depends on the type of sediment. Coal seams were laid down on the margins of shallow seas and associated rocks are usually of shallow water or estuarine type, fine-grained sandstone and shales. Superficially similar rocks of an earlier age are, however, common in this country but are not coal bearing. A brief examination of the fossil content of these rocks would suffice to show that there was no prospect of coal occurring. For example, some of the Coal Measures of this country are associated with reddish sandstone, while certain Devonian and Triassic measures are of a similar colour. If the red rocks are Devonian then the Coal Measures must have been eroded from the area. If, however, the red rocks are Triassic, then the Coal Measures may lie beneath and deep boring may be profitable. Shafts have sometimes been sunk for coal in black shales of Ordovician and Silurian age which had been mistaken for Coal Measures. Here again, examination of the fossil content would have saved unnecessary expenditure.

Fossils such as those found in the Coal Measures do not persist throughout the whole series but often have quite a limited vertical range in the succession. One form predominates for a time and is then replaced by another which, in turn, dies out. Thus it has been possible to divide the Coal Measures into zones on a basis of their fossil content.

Careful identification of the fossil remains of a stratum often enables one to place it correctly in the succession. Bands of marine remains, due to flooding of the Coal Measures areas by the sea, are particularly valuable as datum planes, as marine incursions would always be widespread. Those marine shales, such as the Mansfield Marine Band in the Midlands, are very valuable in correlation between different coalfields.

Recognition of rhythmic deposition of the Coal Measures is important. Coal seams were laid down during a period when conditions were static and vegetation was able to grow in the estuarine areas. The areas were then depressed and shales deposited on top of the vegetation. This was followed by sandstone and later by more vegetation of the coal-forming type. No two units of the rhythmic succession are ever identical. The unit associated with a particular coal may exhibit easily recognisable features which distinguish it from other units. Usually these units are constant over a whole coalfield and provide useful means of correlation. Seams may often be identified in boreholes or shaft sections by this method.

In a local prospecting of the Coal Measures, once the horizon has been established by means of the fossil content of the rocks, it may be possible to determine, with a fair degree of accuracy, the number of coal seams likely to occur in depth in that area.

CONCEALED COALFIELDS

After the Coal Measures were laid down and consolidated, they were folded into domes and basins. Prolonged erosion of the area then took place before the Permian and later rocks were laid down. Thus the anticlinal areas were removed and only the synclinal basins remained. The overlying rocks rest unconformably upon the Coal Measures. These combined facts introduce many problems into coal prospecting in this country. The extent of the exposed coalfields in Britain is now well known but, in most of these areas, the Coal Measures dip under newer rocks. In some cases, as in the Lancashire Coalfield, the dip is very steep, and the concealed coalfield cannot be followed very far. In the Yorkshire and Nottinghamshire Coalfields, however, the dip is less steep and the coal has been located at workable depth several miles east of the Permian-Carboniferous junction, (Fig. 2). Prospecting in these areas has been limited to deep boring which is very expensive and also provides somewhat limited information. The dip of the rocks under the unconformable

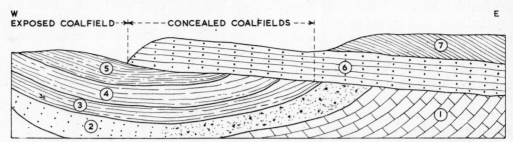

Fig. 2.—Diagrammatic section across exposed and concealed coalfields of Nottinghamshire.
1. Carboniferous Limestone; 2. Millstone Grit; 3. Lower Coal Measures; 4. Middle Coal Measures; 5. Upper Coal Measures; 6. Permian; 7. Trias.

cover is not constant and faulting is common. Some of the more important faults persist through into the Permian measures above and this fact has sometimes been useful in determining the deeper structures.

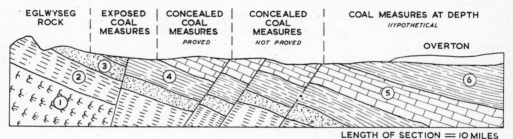

Fig. 3.—Section across Denbighshire Coalfield.
1. Pre-Carboniferous; 2. Carboniferous Limestone; 3. Millstone Grit; 4. Coal Measures; 5. Barren Red Measures; 6. Trias.

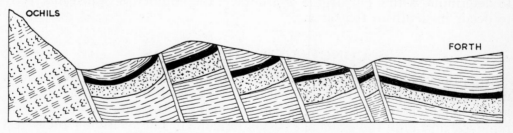

Fig. 4.—Section across Clackmannan Coalfield.

In some cases the geology has been favourable to the preservation of considerable areas of Coal Measures at a workable depth when the dip was very steep. In the Denbighshire and Clackmannan Coalfields, a system of step-faults has kept the measures at an accessible depth, (Figs. 3 and 4).

A careful study of the geological history of the area was responsible for the discovery of the concealed Kent Coalfield. During the latter part of last century it was realised that beneath the Mesozoic rocks there were probably synclinal areas of Coal Measures. Deep borings were put down and the results amply justified the expenditure. It is likely that other Coal Measure areas exist in the East and South of England, under cover of newer rocks, which could be discovered by a geologically guided boring programme.

In the past, on account of the speed and relative cheapness, many boreholes were put down by the percussive method. Unfortunately, all data regarding inclination of strata, structures and fossil content were destroyed in this method of boring.

Even in modern rotary systems, similar difficulties could arise but are overcome by the application of relatively recent developments which are now a regular routine in oilfield prospecting and drilling. Dipmeters are used which give information from which the amount of dip and the direction of dip of the formations crossing the borehole may be determined.

A photoclinometer or other type of borehole

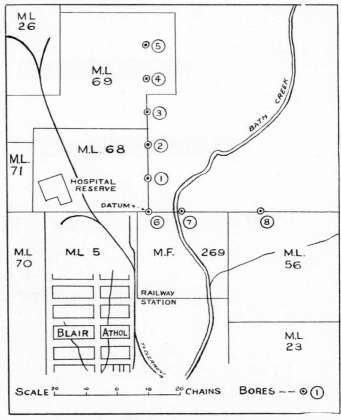

Fig. 5.—Portion of Blair Athol Coalfield, showing positions of Government Bores Nos. 1–8.

surveying apparatus may also be applied where necessary to obtain a record of the deviation and direction of deviation of the borehole from the vertical.

Side-wall coring may also be of value in soft formations to produce a core. The apparatus consists of a percussion core-taker or gun (p. 137) which fires hollow bullets into the formation at the chosen horizon, thereby providing relatively small cores. A mechanical core taker can be applied in the harder formations.

Electrical well logging can be applied for location of coal seam horizons.

By means of a wire-line core barrel (p. 133) it is possible to obtain a small core in the centre of a rock or other full-size drilling bit.

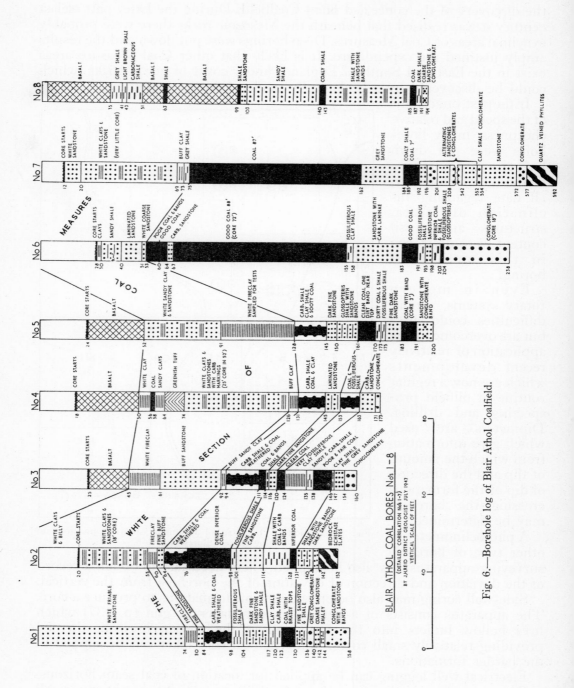

Fig. 6.—Borehole log of Blair Athol Coalfield.

BLAIR ATHOL COAL BORES Nos 1-8

(DETAILED CORRELATION Nos 1-7)
BY JA.REID DISTRICT GEOLOGIST JULY 1947
VERTICAL SCALE OF FEET

102

All borings for coal should be by methods which yield cores from which much valuable information may be obtained. Diamond borings in Coal Measure strata may, in certain instances, record in the cores 90 per cent. or more of the depth bored and cores of coal seams may be secured to depths of 6,000 ft. or more.

This is not always possible, however, and even with diamond drilling for cores the recovery is sometimes insufficient to enable complete conclusions to be drawn. There is evidence of this in recent work done in Australia. The case is cited to show the layout, systematic operations and results obtained.

In the *Queensland Government Mining Journal* (Vol. 49, No. 557, March, 1948) reference is made to the systematic prospecting of the Blair Athol Coalfield, where eight boreholes were put down by diamond drilling to determine the limits of the economic coal on the north-eastern side of the basin. Fig. 5 is a plan showing the positions of the boreholes. The District Geologist examined the cores of the boreholes and compiled the logs, (Fig. 6).

It was hoped to core the complete section of the seam for the purpose of sectional sampling, to study any variation and arrive at the average composition of the seam as a whole. This objective was frustrated by insufficiently complete core recovery.

In a contribution to the discussion on a recent paper on Exploratory Boring (*Trans. Inst. Min. Eng.* Vol. 114, 1954, p. 75), Mr. Tom Gledhill, referring to the authors' mention of the difficulties encountered in obtaining satisfactory cores from coal seams, indicated that most of the difficulties had been eliminated by the use of the split-core barrel and that the device had been given a thorough trial in drilling 17 seams, representing over 50 ft. of coal, with a total recovery of not less than 90 per cent.

A further review of progress is included in the chapter on Boring.

PROSPECTING FOR OPENCAST COAL SITES

Very early coal-getting in this country was restricted to areas near outcrops, but soon deeper seams were worked by shafts and the outcrop areas were left undisturbed. In recent years, with the high demand for coal, attention has again been directed to the considerable reserves of coal situated within 60 ft. or so of the surface. In this country, in the first instance, prospecting for shallow coal is guided by a careful study of the existing 6-in. Geological survey maps, colliery working plans, abandoned mine plans, records of mining engineers with knowledge of the area, and local information. Consultations are also made with collieries havings workings in the vicinity. On the geological maps all the known and conjectural outcrops are marked and all the known faults. The nature of the local topography must also be taken into consideration in conjunction with the geology, the most important points being the dip of the seams and the dip of the land surface. The presence of faulting may limit the size of the site so that it would be unprofitable. Other important non-geological points, which may be obtained from the map and ground reconnaissance, will be the presence or absence of roads, railways, buildings and other artificial structures.

Once a site has been selected as suitable on the grounds of geological and other evidence, a preliminary boring programme is carried out. A shallow pit is usually sunk so that a pillar sample may be taken for analysis. If the analysis of the coal seam indicates that it is worthy of exploitation, the site

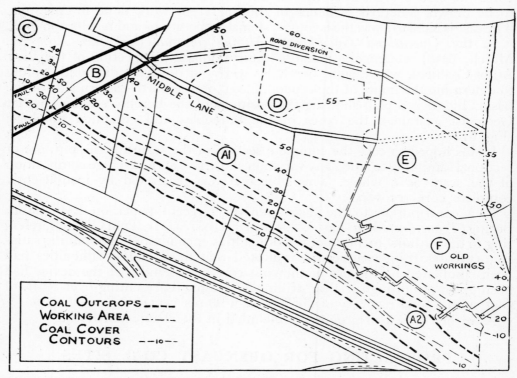

Fig. 7.—Nostell opencast site with overburden contours.

is drilled systematically. The area is pegged out to a grid of 100-ft. squares and is drilled at approximately 200-ft. intervals on the strike lines and 100-ft. on the dip. Surface levels are taken at each intersection of the grid and correlated to ordnance datum.

Information to be derived from the boring covers various points. First, the true dip and strike of the seam or seams may be determined and the presence of any folding of the strata or splitting of seams. The approximate thickness of the coal seams will be ascertained. The presence of faults will be indicated and the strike and throw can be determined. Also, some information may be obtained relating to the presence and extent of possible worked-out areas.

From this information, a detailed site plan is drawn up on a scale of 1/2,500 and overburden contours at 10-ft. intervals sketched on to it (Fig. 7), and sections to a scale of 1/500 are prepared. The economic area of working can then be delineated and a fairly accurate estimate made of the available tonnage, overburden ratio, geology and other relevant information regarding faults, etc. This, together with a consideration of the quality of the coal and accessibility, determines whether or not opencasting will be an economic proposition.

PROSPECTING BY GEOPHYSICAL METHODS

After correlation of all the existing evidence usually provided by the geologists, it may prove economical to supplement the geological and other data by some form of geophysical exploration, either direct or indirect, as explained later, prior to embarking on a drilling programme.

By this means the prospecting areas may be delineated within limits, thereby providing a more definite control in the siting of the boreholes, with a view to obtaining the maximum amount of information regarding the extent, depth, thickness and quality on the most economical basis.

A geologist can easily locate exposed geological structures by inspection or mapping, and geophysical methods are not required, but it is advisable to apply them where the structures are concealed, and remarkable successes have been achieved by their application. Much of the information so provided might be difficult or impossible to obtain by other methods and geophysical surveying provides data which will assist in the location and reduction of the number of boring sites and the cost of exploration.

Electrical Resistivity.—The particular method of geophysical surveying to be applied depends upon the difference in physical properties exhibited by rock formations. Thus the electrical resistivity method has been applied extensively and proved of value in the location of concealed faults, dykes, different types of rock contacts and mineral veins, etc., at shallow and moderate depths.

Magnetic Method.—The magnetic method, the oldest and probably the cheapest of geophysical methods, has had a wide field of application in metalliferous prospecting to locate iron ore rich in magnetite, ilmenite, pyrrhotite or other strongly magnetic minerals ; and in coal-mining areas for the location and mapping of concealed dykes and sills.

Seismic Method.—Seismologists, in their investigation of the sub-soil, make use of the different velocities of waves through the different constituents of the earth's crust. These variations in wave velocity result from the unequal elastic properties of rocks. The seismic system affords a valuable means of tracing buried features where geological evidence is limited, and for the location of faults, fissures, dykes, anticlines and synclines connected with mineral and other deposits.

Gravitational Method.—Considerable attention has been focused upon the gravitational method in the investigation of various types of structures in search of coal, oil, natural gas, salt, ores, etc.

The attractive force which the earth exerts on a body tending to cause the body to move towards the earth's centre, is termed gravitation and this force is measured in the gravitational method since its variations afford information of the rock masses.

It is evident that no one method is universally applicable, but in some cases only one method may offer prospects of success : in other cases, where conditions are such that location of the structure is possible by more than one means, then one serves as a check on the other.

It is of the greatest importance in geophysical prospecting to have close co-operation between the geophysicist and the mining geologist.

Resistivity Methods.—Direct current or alternating current may be used in this system. Alternating current is, however, most commonly applied and one of the principal types of instrument is the Geophysical "Megger" Earth Tester.

The methods of using the four-electrode system of resistivity surveying and the mathematical principles have been expounded in several articles. The three chief methods of application of the four-electrode system are:—

(*a*) The step-traverse method.
(*b*) The expanding electrode method.
(*c*) The single electrode-probe method.

Of these, the first method, that of taking successive readings along a traverse-line with a fixed electrode interval has been applied in surveying over a mineralised area in Derbyshire.

The empirical rule formulated by Gish and Rooney for depth penetration by the four-electrode method, i.e., that the depth to which the resistivity is measured is equal to the distance between the electrode stakes, is put to use in the expanding-electrode method of surveying. Thus if the electrodes are placed close together and a reading taken of the resistivity, and further readings are then made as the electrode interval is successively increased, the resistivity of the ground to increasing depths is obtained. Thus horizontal discontinuities, which result in a vertical change in resistivity, are recorded. In this way the average resistivity of the ground, down to any required depth, can be measured and, when plotted in graphical form, enable the depths of geological discontinuities to be determined.

The single-electrode probe method, which consists in exploring the field around one of the two current electrodes, is a more flexible means of taking field measurements than the expanding-electrode method and the results are approximately the same. One current-electrode is placed over the position where it is desired to explore, while the second current-electrode is placed at a distance of four to five times the depth it is required to probe. The potentials near the first current-electrode are then explored along any straight line passing through it.

Of the direct methods of location the electrical-resistivity method appears likely to meet with some measure of success. In its dry state, coal is almost an insulator and, even *in situ*, retains a very high resistivity. Associated shales are of very low resistivity but sandstones have quite high resistivities and may sometimes approach coal in electrical properties. Direct-resistivity measurements have been carried out in areas where the coal was at shallow depth and first results show moderate success for the method. The coal was found to be normally of higher resistivity than either the shale or the sandstone, except when approaching within a few feet of the surface, where the coal was weathered.

At the present time the resistivity method is only applicable to shallow depth determinations up to two or three hundred feet, but it may well be developed as an aid in this type of work. The large amount of boring now in operation for locating and proving shallow coal could be reduced to a number sufficient for checking the electrical results, and provide data for calculating the amount of coal available.

Resistivity measurements may be of considerable value indirectly in the location of faults. In faulting of Coal Measures, where sandstone may be thrown against shale, there is a good resistivity contrast for location by the electrical method.

In cases where the surface rocks on either side of a fault are the same, the underlying rocks may be different at some point, and this difference can be detected by the electrical-probe method of depth measurement. Electrical-resistivity methods are therefore of considerable value in coal prospecting, particularly in areas of shallow seams where much detail is required.

The application of the electrical-resistivity method of geophysical surveying was carried out recently with a view to ascertaining its value in prospecting for coal seams at shallow depths.

In the Billingley (Yorkshire) area a fair correlation was found between the depths of the coal seams indicated in the boreholes and the depths indicated by geophysical probes.

At Nostell, West Yorkshire (Fig. 8), the method appears to have been more successful. The seams indicated in the boreholes appear to give rise to identifiable features on the resistivity curves (Fig. 9).

The probe method was used in this survey and the curves illustrated are a function of depth plotted against resistivity. Thus sharp changes in resistivity appear as peaks on these curves and identification of the highly resistive coal seams is facilitated.

By comparison of the resistivity results with the borehole logs it is seen that the coal seams frequently give rise to high resistivity values, often with a marked decrease in resistivity immediately below the seam. The high resistivity characteristic of the coal seams may be considerably modified by their moisture content and by the mineral content of the underground water. These factors should, however, affect the surrounding rocks as well, reducing or possibly, in some cases, eliminating any marked variation in resistivity between the various rocks. Resistivity surveying has also been found useful in outlining areas underlain by abnormal thicknesses of unconsolidated deposits. In the Chester-le-Street and Bearpark areas in Durham, the positions of the pre-Glacial river channels of the Rivers Wear and Browney were located by a series of parallel constant-electrode spacing traverses over these areas, and resistivity contour maps were built up. These showed in both areas the existence of two distinct types of unconsolidated material, a clay of low resistivity and patches of dry sand of high resistivity. Coal Measures resistivities lay between these two extremes. The buried river channel was in general marked by a zone of low resistivity.

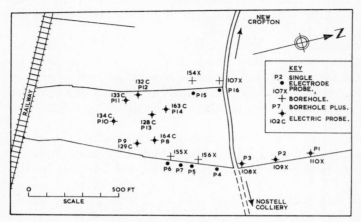

Fig. 8.—Area plan of boreholes and probes at Nostell, West Yorkshire.

LOCATION OF A COAL SEAM HORIZON. — A very important application of earth resistivity surveying is that known as " electrical coring". The system has been successfully applied in locating oil-bearing horizons and also coal-seam horizons, and it is possible to correlate wells or bore holes by their "resistivity log" in much the same manner as it is possible by the sample log obtained by mechanical coring.

In the last few years there has been a great expansion in the techniques of borehole logging and a variety of methods has been evolved. Most of these are based on electrical resistivity but radioactive methods are in use for difficult cases, where, for example, highly conducting mud is present in the borehole or it has been necessary to put in a steel casing. All these logs are obtained by continuous recording methods while the system of electrodes or radioactive measuring device is slowly lowered down the borehole. As a rate of recording of several hundred feet an hour may be used, it is possible to obtain a log of any borehole for coal in one day.

The result of a resistivity survey of a borehole drilled near Estevelles by the Compagnie des Mines de Courrieres (France) affords a striking example of the information obtainable and proves that this method may be of direct use in prospecting for coal. Fig. 10 illustrates the location of a coal seam horizon by resistivity measurements. The coal was very brittle and the driller's report merely indicated traces of coal. The conclusion drawn from the electrical survey was that the high resistance peak corresponded to a coal seam located within a layer of soft material. The position of the seam was checked by further drillings and, by sieving the matter from the borehole, the coal drillings indicated a seam three metres thick.

Magnetic Methods.—Magnetic surveys for prospecting were formerly carried out by means of a crude pocket compass or a dip needle. In recent years, however, sensitive and delicate magnetic field balances such as magnetometers and variometers have been devised for earth magnetic work.

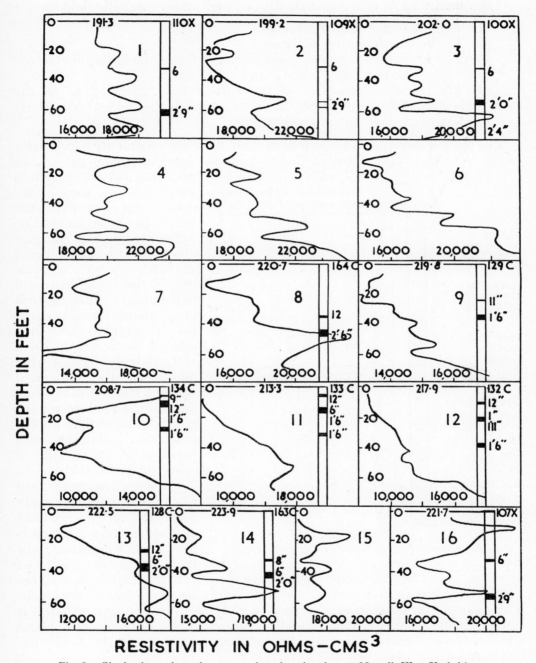

Fig. 9.—Single-electrode probe curves plotted against logs at Nostell, West Yorkshire.

The quantitites or elements met with in the earth's magnetic field are :—

    (1) The magnetic declination.
    (2) The magnetic dip or inclination.
    (3) The horizontal component of the earth's field, which may be referred to as the horizontal force ; and
    (4) The vertical component of the earth's field, referred to as the vertical force. Of these, the vertical force is the element commonly used in magnetic prospecting.

The more recent types of instrument such as the variometer are particularly sensitive to local differences in the vertical and horizontal components. In practice, traverse lines parallel to one another are usually set out over the area to be investigated. The differences in scale readings observed on the instruments at each point on a traverse line or the same expressed in gammas (1 gauss, the unit of magnetic force, is equal to 10^5 gamma) are then plotted on a graph on a vertical scale against distances on the horizontal scale as measured between instrument stations on the ground. Anomalies on the profiles indicate the presence of dykes, sills or other magnetic bodies.

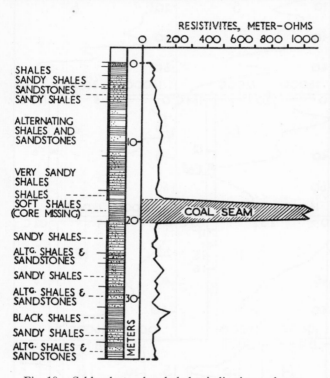

Fig. 10.—Schlumberger borehole log indicating coal seam.

In some instances, coal prospecting is severely hampered by the presence of igneous rocks in the coalfield area. These may take the form of either intrusive rocks or contemporaneous lava flows. In the first instance, the occurrences are in the form of vertical dykes or mainly horizontal sills. The dykes often outcrop on the surface and their position underground is comparatively easy to predict. Near the edges of the dyke the coal seams are " cindered " but on driving through the dyke the seam is usually encountered at the same horizon (Fig. 11).

In cases of doubt the position of igneous dykes may be located by geophysical magnetic surveying. Sills are not so easy to locate in advance and, if intruded near a seam, may cinder the coal over a wide area. Underground magnetic observations in conjunction with surface work may help in such cases.

The most troublesome phenomenon is the occurrence of contemporaneous lava flows which originated from a volcano in the coalfield area. In some cases volcanic action continued throughout the period when coal was being formed, and frequently the coal-producing vegetation was overwhelmed by a lava flow or by deposits of ash. The distances to which coal seams can be followed in such circumstances is unpredictable and only boring or direct exploration will give the required information.

A volcano of this type occurs between the coal-fields of Bathgate and Bo'ness in West Lothian. When followed

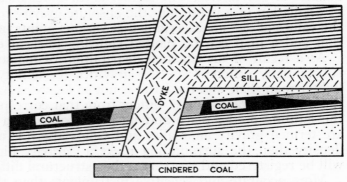

Fig. 11.—Intrusive dyke and sill with cindered coal.

towards the volcanic centre the seams become replaced by volcanic ashes and lavas.

Seismic and Gravitational Methods.—The tracing of hidden geological formations by the seismic method depends upon the fact that elastic earth waves, generated at the surface impinging upon a layer or structure in which the waves travel with higher velocity, are reflected to the surface or return to the surface after refraction through the higher velocity medium. Waves may also be reflected by lower velocity media. The usual method of producing the elastic waves is to fire a buried charge of explosive and record, with suitable recorders, the time of arrival of shock waves at different points. Although at one time the practice was to use mechanical seismographs, electrical types have now replaced them. In general, the following types of seismograph have been used.

    (1) *Electromagnetic:*—(*a*) Induction (constant air gap), (*b*) Reluctance (variable air gap).
    (2) *Capacitative:*—(*a*) Tuned circuit, (*b*) Grid coupled.
    (3) *Pressure:*—(*a*) Carbon microphone, (*b*) Contact accelerometer, (*c*) Piezo-electric.

The indirect seismic and gravitational methods of geophysical surveying may be of value in determining the extent of a coalfield. In areas where the basement of the Coal Measures, i.e., the underlying formation, is of markedly different elastic quality to the Coal Measures themselves, the seismic method may be used to determine the depth of this basement over a wide area. In many areas, where coal seams are overlaid unconformably by newer rocks, the depth of the unconformity might be determined and the extent of the coalfield at workable depth estimated. Seismic methods are capable of recording discontinuities at considerable depths and are likely to be of value in making observations of a general nature about the extent of a coalfield. At present the method is not suitable for detection of coal seams in detail, the results being too complicated to interpret.

Gravity variations are determined by using either a pendulum, torsion balance or gravimeter. The former is the older method and from the period of oscillation of a pendulum the absolute gravity may be determined. Thus the values of "g" are ascertained at various points in an area under investigation and a map can be plotted showing lines of equal gravitational force.

As a result of the unequal distribution of masses of rock of various and substantially different specific gravities (certain types of salt deposits are lighter than shale and the latter is not so heavy as basalt) in the earth's crust, the measured value of "g" differs from that corresponding to the normal for the latitude of the place and its height above sea level. These differences are termed gravity anomalies and where there is a mass of rock of higher density than the surrounding rocks a "gravity high" or positive anomaly will be registered and *vice versa*: thus structural differences may be detected.

More accurate and sensitive instruments than the pendulum have been evolved for investigations of this nature. It is not necessary to know the actual value of "g"; a knowledge of the variations which occur in the direction and magnitude of the attractive force, as a result of differences of density, is sufficient. These slight variations may be measured by a torsion balance, and the Eötvös balance, and others of the same principle, were formerly widely used.

Coal has a relatively small density in comparison with its surroundings and so the gravimetric method might be expected to be suitable for the location of coal deposits. If the coal is very thick it may be detected on its approach to the surface by a diminution of the gravitational field. Either the faulted edges of the deposit or the outcrop area would be most easily located. In either event, at shallow depths the electrical-resistivity method would probably be both quicker and cheaper. Also, where folding occurs the gravitational effects of the folding might mask that of the coal seam. In cases, however, where the seam is steeply inclined, it may be detected even if it does not outcrop.

The location of the Onakawana lignite in Northern Ontario provides an interesting example of the value of the gravity method. Compared with the surrounding rocks, the lignite had a very low density. A geological section of the area is shown in Fig. 12. By extensive drilling the area had been outlined to within a few square miles and the densities of the various materials ascertained from the borehole samples. Gravity traverses taken across the area revealed distinct regions of low gravitational attraction above the deposit and it was possible to estimate the thickness of the seam at its centre.

In this survey, variations in the thickness of the overburden (clay and muskeg) although small in comparison with the rocks immediately below it, produced irregularities in the results for which allowances had to be made. This was due to the upper layer being much nearer the instrument.

The torsion balance may be used to determine the folding in the heavier strata and thus show where the coal approaches nearest the surface. Fault lines may frequently be detected gravimetrically. The first investigations on these lines were undertaken by Professor R. Schumann during 1919 to 1921 in the great Vienna Basin of the Hungarian Plain. In this area the structure of the underlying rocks is greatly masked by the sedimentary covering, but, with the aid of an Eötvös balance, Schumann was able to make certain deductions concerning the folding of the lower, heavier strata. He also was able to show the position of a sharp fault cutting across the area.

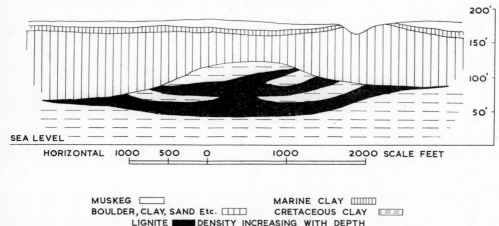

Fig. 12.—Section through Onakawana Lignite in Northern Ontario.

The place of the torsion balance has largely been taken by the modern lightweight gravimeter, mainly owing to increased speed of working and ready portability. The best of these meters will measure differences in the value of "g" to 0·01 milligals (1 milligal equals 0·001 cm/sec/sec). By making use of the high order of accuracy, it has been found possible to locate comparatively small changes in structure in the Coal Measures, where a suitable density variation exists. In an area surveyed in the Anthracite Coalfield of South Wales, residual anomalies of between 0·5 and 0·75 milligals were found to be related to folds, faults and overthrusts in the Coal Measures. The necessary density contrast in this case was provided by the increasing density with depth of the fine mudstones, caused by compaction. The problem of concealed coalfields is a more difficult one, but surveys now being carried out in West Yorkshire appear likely to meet with some success.

It is evident that geophysical methods will take their place alongside the more conventional methods of prospecting, resulting in a more rapid and more economical survey of coal-bearing regions.

BIBLIOGRAPHY

The Principles of Geophysical Surveying, Professor Henry Briggs, *Colliery Engineering*, May, 1930.

Gravitational Method of Prospecting, Captain H. Shaw, M.Sc., F.Inst.P., and E. Lancaster Jones, B.A., *Colliery Engineering*, June, 1925, p. 265.

Prospecting for Coal, A. Nelson, F.G.S., *Iron and Coal Trades Review*, September 26, 1947.

Coal in Great Britain, Walcot Gibson.

Earth Resistivity Surveys in Coal Measure Strata, J. T. Whetton, M.C., M.Sc., *Trans. Inst. of Mine Surveyors*, Vol. 14, 1934.

Aerial Photographs, Their Use and Interpretation, A. J. Eardley, *Harpers Geoscience Series*.

Application of Electrical Resistivity Measurements to the Location of Coal Seams at Shallow Depths, Professor J. T. Whetton and J. O. Myers. *Report to Directorate of Opencast Coal Production, Ministry of Fuel and Power.*

Electrical Coring, a Method of Determining Bottom-hole Data by Electrical Measurements, C. and M. Schlumberger and E. G. Leonardon, Technical Publication No. 462, *The American Institute of Mining and Mechanical Engineers.*

A New Contribution to Sub-surface Studies by means of Electrical Measurements in Drill Holes, C. and M. Schlumberger and E. G. Leonardon, Technical Publication No. 503, *The American Institute of Mining and Metallurgical Engineers.*

Gravitational and Magnetic Surveys of the Onakawana and Grand Rapids Siderite Deposits, F. H. Miller, *Canadian Journal of Research*, Vol. 10, April, 1934.

The Search for New Coalfields in England, A. Strahan, Lecture to Royal Institution of Great Britain, March 17, 1916.

The Coal Supply of Britain, W. W. Watts, *Q.J.G.S.* (1912), Vol. 68.

The Concealed Coalfield of Yorkshire and Nottinghamshire, W. Edwards, *Mems. Geol. Surv.*, 1951.

The Geological Aspects of Planning and Exploration in the Coalfields, J. K. Allen, *Trans. Inst. Min. Eng.*, Vol. 107, 1947.

A Gravimeter Survey in the Bristol and Somerset Coalfields, A. H. Cook and H. J. S. Thirlaway, *Quart. J. Geol. Soc.*, Vol. 107, 1951.

The Application of Resistivity Methods in Establishing the Base of Water-bearing Rocks in the Cannock Chase Coalfield, E. J. Polak, *Geophysical Prospecting*, Vol. 1, No. 3, 1953.

The Application of Gravity Surveying to Colliery Planning, Professor J. T. Whetton, J. O. Myers and I. J. Watson, *Trans. Inst. of Mine Surveyors* Vol. 33, 1953.

A Resistivity Investigation into a Washout Feature in Coal Measure Strata, G. M. Habberjam and Professor J. T. Whetton, *Geophysical Prospecting*, Vol. 2, No. 1, 1954.

A Resistivity Investigation of Glacial Deposits Near Bearpark, County Durham, G. M. Habberjam and Professor J. T. Whetton, *Proc. Yorks Geol. Soc.*, Vol. 29, Part II, 1954.

Developments of the Technique of Borehole Logging, C. and M. Schlumberger and Louis G. Bordat, *Trans. Inst. Min. Eng.*, Vol. 114, Part 6, March, 1955.

Gravity Surveying in the East Carmarthenshire Anthracite Coalfield, Professor J. T. Whetton, J. O. Myers, and I. J. Watson, *Colliery Engineering*, April–July, 1955.

Gerrestrial Magnetism and Atmospheric Electricity, Gish and Rooney, Vol. 30, 1925, p. 104.

CHAPTER 4

BORING

EXPLORATION by boring provides data and information relating to the existence, extent, depth, thickness, inclination and nature of coal seams and the intervening strata. It serves to confirm and amplify the knowledge gained from preliminary reconnaissance, geological observations and geophysical investigations. Boring is, however, an expensive operation, and to minimise the number of holes to be drilled in an exploration scheme, and place them to the best advantage within the area, efficient methods of preliminary prospecting are essential.

In addition to prospecting and formation testing, boreholes are used in coal mining for a variety of purposes, including:—

(1) Shaft sinking; in special cases the shaft itself being bored and constituting a large diameter borehole. (See Chapter 5.)

(2) For the insertion of tubes in which the cooling mixture is circulated around the circumference of a shaft being sunk by the freezing process.

(3) In the process of cementation to facilitate the injection of cement into the ground.

(4) To convey material used for the stowing of wastes.

(5) To drain off gas from a coal face, the adjacent strata, a fissure or cavity, and water or gas from old workings.

(6) For the passage of haulage ropes, electric cables, steam pipes, water pipes, drainage, ventilation purposes, fire fighting and testing of dam sites.

(7) Blasting and water infusion. (See Chapters 8 and 9.)

Drilling apparatus and techniques have undergone wide improvements, particularly as regards the type of cutting-bit, the amount of pressure on the bit, the rate of rotation and the types of core barrel and core catcher. Thus there has been a great improvement in the physical type and proportion of core recovered for examination and complete cores are now obtained not only of hard sandstone, but also soft shales and fireclays, and it is not unusual to get cores of up to 90 per cent. of coal seams bored through.

Various methods have also been applied to provide checks and collect supplementary information, such as careful measuring of the rate of penetration by means of a continuous recorder; the resulting graphs indicating rock junctions and, as coal is penetrated more easily than other carboniferous rocks, the position and thickness of coal seams can be checked with some accuracy. Various physical characteristics of the strata are also measured, indicating their nature and location; thereby providing more precise correlation data of the different horizons.

CLASSIFICATION OF BORING METHODS

The method of boring to be adopted in any particular instance depends upon the objective, the depth of the hole, the direction in which it is being bored, and the nature of the ground through which it must pass. Methods in use at the present time may be divided broadly into percussive and rotary systems according to the type of motion by which the drilling tool is actuated.

1. Percussive Methods.—In these methods the penetration of the ground is achieved by a succession of blows made by the boring tool which is of the chisel type. Between the blows the tool is rotated slightly to alter the position of the cutting edges relative to the ground and to maintain the circular shape of the hole. The rate of penetration is dependent upon the nature of the ground, the weight of the tools, the height to which they are raised on each stroke, the type of the cutting bit and the number of blows struck per minute. The tools may be suspended either by rods or by a wire cable.

Fig. 1.—Portable percussive drilling rig.

(*a*) BORING WITH RODS.—The rods may be of wood or of steel and successive lengths are added as the depth of the hole increases. The simplest application is in shallow seam prospecting when holes are bored down to depths of about 40 ft. by hand. A steel chisel bit is raised and allowed to fall through a stand pipe about 4 ft. in length fixed in the ground at the top of the hole and the sludge produced during drilling is removed by a simple sludger. Such operations as these are carried out for shallow borings in soft overburden and strata where power drilling is not required and where the transport of such equipment would damage agricultural land.

Where the coal is at depths of more than 40 or 50 ft. it is preferable to use some form of power drilling, usually a compressed-air drill. A portable percussive drilling apparatus of this type is illustrated in Fig. 1. The actual drilling unit is an ordinary compressed-air jackhammer equipped with a hand-operated rope feed. A small reciprocating pump, which is also driven by compressed air and which is mounted on the drilling rig, provides a stream of water for flushing out the hole during drilling operations. The machine is capable of drilling to a depth of about 150 ft. Apart from such machines and from hand drilling rigs, percussive boring with rods is rarely used to-day, although it was formerly used to a very large extent for the drilling of deep holes.

(*b*) CABLE OR CHURN DRILLING.—The drilling bit in this method, suspended by a rope or cable, is actuated by a beam action or eccentric device. The necessary rotation is imparted to the bit by the natural spin of the cable. It has been evolved from the method of boring with rods which it has now almost entirely superseded as the percussive method for deep drilling.

It is a relatively cheap method and, compared with rotary methods, it has the advantage that the tools can be withdrawn from the hole very rapidly. It is, however, restricted to the boring of vertical holes and is not suitable for drilling through very hard formations. Furthermore, cable drilling does not lend itself to accurate and continuous sampling of the rocks being drilled.

2. Rotary Methods.—As the name implies, the boring tools used in these methods are rotated and they crush, cut or abrade the rock. The rate of drilling depends upon the nature of the rock, the pressure exerted by the drilling bits and rods (either by their own weight or by a special feeding arrangement), the number of revolutions of the bit per minute and the type of drilling bit. The simplest form of rotary drilling is by the use of hand

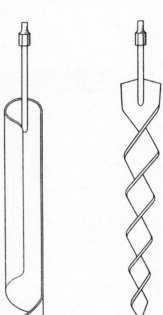

Fig. 2.—Hand augers (diagrammatic).

augers such as are shown in Fig. 2. These are attached to rods and rotated by means of a simple crossbar. Where the overburden is soft these tools are quite useful but the operation is very laborious. For deeper holes up to 100 ft. in depth a rotating table of the type shown in Fig. 3 is more suitable. The outer casing is equipped with a cutting shoe and is rotated, whilst the chopping bit within the casing is raised and dropped by hand. Thus it is really a combination of both rotary and percussive methods. To achieve high drilling speeds, and to bore holes to any great depth, however, three power-driven rotary methods are available:—

(*a*) HYDRAULIC ROTARY DRILLING.—Metal bits of various designs are used in this method of drilling, the rods to which the bits are attached being rotated through bevel gearing driven by an internal-combustion engine or electric motor. The fragments of rock which are cut and ground away are removed from the borehole by a mud-laden fluid pumped down the hollow drilling rods. This has the advantage of being a continuous process and high boring rates can therefore be achieved. An accurate record of the strata bored through, however, is difficult to obtain, and it is customary when boring through the actual coal seams to adopt some device whereby a cylindrical core sample of the seam can be obtained. Hydraulic rotary drilling is now widely used for the drilling of both shallow and deep holes. Almost all types of formation or strata can be drilled and the bits are relatively inexpensive.

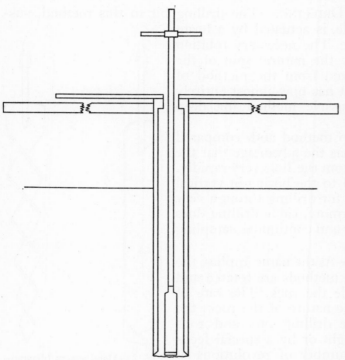

Fig. 3.—Drilling platform with rotary platform (diagrammatic)

(*b*) DIAMOND DRILL-ING.—The abrasive power of the diamond is made use of in this method, the diamond being mounted in a circular or annular steel bit or crown. The rods are similar to those used for hydraulic rotary work, but in this instance the cuttings are removed by either a stream of water or a mud-laden fluid. One of the major advantages of this method is that core samples can readily be obtained throughout almost the whole length of the bore when an annular bit is used. The hardest of rocks can be drilled and the holes may be drilled in any desired direction, including vertically upwards. The bits used are expensive, especially if the diameter of the hole is large, but small-diameter holes are best bored by this method. Within recent years the diamond method has been used for all types of drilling, and all depths of holes.

(*c*) CHILLED-SHOT DRILLING.—In this method chilled shot of high-carbon steel is passed with water through the hollow drill rods and grinds away the strata by means of a drilling shoe or boring crown. The action is that of crushing and abrading. Whereas this method is suitable for core drilling it is not suitable for very hard ground or soft ground in which the shot might become embedded. In highly fissured ground there is always the danger that the shot may be lost. Again, the system is not applicable to holes which have to be bored at an angle greater than 35 degrees from the vertical. It is, however, used under certain conditions and, in some cases, has proved to be relatively cheap compared with other methods. It is particularly useful for holes of large diameter where cores are required and the cost of diamond bits is prohibitive.

CABLE DRILLING

The cable or churn drilling system was formerly widely used in the drilling of deep oil-wells, and large stationary rigs of American design such as the "California" or "Canadian" rigs were relatively common. Such large installations are not now used to any great extent and the modern application consists of light or medium weight mobile rigs capable of drilling to depths of about 1,000 ft., with occasional heavy-duty rigs for depths of the order of 3,000 ft. In addition to these there are certain special applications such as combination rigs using both cable and rotary drilling.

Drilling Tools.—The tools normally used in cable drilling are illustrated in Fig. 4, and comprise a drilling bit A, stem B, jars C and socket D. The over-all length of a string of tools of this type is 28 ft. 6 in., and for drilling an 8-in. hole to a depth of 800 ft. the weight would be 2,000 lb. The weight of the tools to be used is, however, governed by the diameter of the hole, the depth to be bored and the hardness of the rock. In hard ground tools must be heavy and of fairly large diameter. This is necessary to strike a harder blow and reduce the amount of play or swing at the top of the tools. Thus the heavy weight and reduction of swing tend to maintain the hole more nearly vertical.

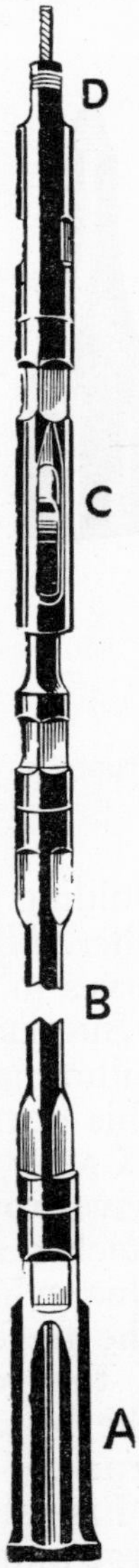

In deep drilling the initial diameter of the hole must be large to allow of reduction by lining or casing as the depth of the hole increases, and a reasonable diameter at the ultimate depth.

DRILLING BITS.—Bits normally have a screwed joint pin at the top, and below the collar of this joint the bit is of square or rectangular section to allow the application of a wrench. This is a feature common to all cable drilling tools. The various types of bit in common use are illustrated in Fig. 5. The spudding bit is wider than that used for drilling the general body of the hole and is used at the outset to penetrate the loose or soft overburden so that a conductor pipe or guide pipe may be set through which subsequent drilling proceeds. Normally this is followed by the ordinary or regular bit, but in the case of hard fissured rock the "Mother Hubbard" bit is sometimes adopted as its squarer shoulders tend to reduce deviation. Where a hole has already deviated, the star or cruciform bit is used to rectify it, or in inclined strata to

Fig. 4.—String of cable-drilling tools.

counteract the tendency of the hole to follow the bedding planes. The cutting edges of all bits are hardened or case hardened.

DRILL STEMS.—Above the bit a drill stem is used to add weight to the blow and assist in keeping the hole vertical. The drill stem is made at least 12 ft. in length and in certain cases is equipped with wings.

DRILLING JARS.—The additional weight of the drill stem is necessary as the full weight of the tools and cable is prevented from bearing down on the bit as it strikes the ground, thereby avoiding heavy stresses. This is achieved by drilling jars, inserted in the string of tools above the drill stem. The two parts of the jar telescope or slide within each other, the distance of travel either way being limited to from 4 in. to 8 in. The jar is not allowed to telescope completely on the downward stroke, thus

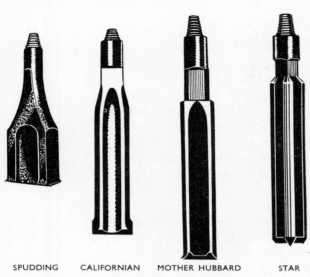

SPUDDING   CALIFORNIAN   MOTHER HUBBARD   STAR

Fig. 5.—Types of cable-drilling bits.

avoiding breakages which might result from the two members striking each other. The sharp jerk which the jar gives to the bit on the upward stroke also serves to prevent the bit from sticking in the hole.

SINKER-BAR.—On large rigs a sinker-bar is sometimes inserted above the drilling jars mainly in order to increase the momentum of the upward blow. This device is similar to the drill stem, but is shorter and lighter.

CABLE SOCKET.—The uppermost member of a string of tools is the swivel rope socket. This consists of an inner portion to which the rope is attached and an outer cylinder to the bottom of which the tools are screwed. This cylinder also has a hole in the top through which the cable passes. The freedom of motion between these two sections is such that the twist of the rope is utilised to rotate the tools between consecutive blows. The bit as a rule averages one complete revolution for every three blows struck.

FISHING TOOLS.—In addition to the tools normally used in drilling, a large number of special devices are used to release jammed tools or to recover tools lost in the borehole as a result of breakages during drilling. A number of these fishing tools are illustrated in Fig. 6. The jar bumper is used to release tools which have become jammed in the hole but are not broken. It is threaded over the cable and passed down the hole on a light line to strike downwards against the locked tools. When a sharp upward blow is needed to effect the release, fishing jars which are telescopic and resemble the drilling jars illustrated in Fig. 4, are used on the end of the recovery line.

The latch jack and the bit hook are used to recover a string of tools broken above the drilling jars or just above the bit. Various types of socket such as the horn socket or slip socket are dropped over the broken tools to take a frictional grip sufficient to allow of their being drawn out of the hole. To cut a rope just above a line of tools which have become jammed, a wire

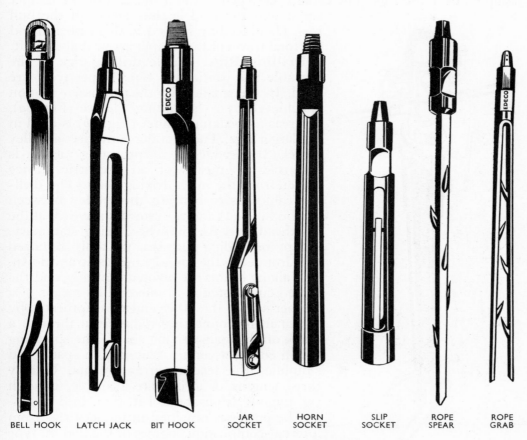

| BELL HOOK | LATCH JACK | BIT HOOK | JAR SOCKET | HORN SOCKET | SLIP SOCKET | ROPE SPEAR | ROPE GRAB |

Fig. 6.—Fishing tools used in cable drilling.

rope knife is used and to recover tools with a length of rope attached, rope spears are used having a number of projections known as "wickers" which pierce the broken rope and enable it to be drawn to the surface.

Drilling Cables.—Manila ropes, which were formerly used in churn drilling, have now been entirely replaced by steel cables. The diameter of the cable is $\frac{5}{8}$ in. for rigs drilling down to depths of about 600 ft. and $\frac{3}{4}$ in. for those drilling to 1,000 ft. These cables invariably have a left-hand lay so that the spin of the cable which tends to rotate the drilling tools also tends to tighten the joints between them. Feeding of the cable is achieved on the smaller portable rigs by means of a hand-operated worm gear which turns the bull reel on which the drilling cable is coiled. The bull reel is provided with a plate-type friction clutch which is open during drilling when the reel is being turned by hand, and is closed for hoisting the tools from the hole, under power of the driving unit. On the larger rigs, however, a temper screw such as that shown in Fig. 7 must be used because of the beam action adopted on these rigs. The cable is clamped at the lower end of the temper screw and the load is thus taken off the bull reel. Hand feeding is used in this case also and the total travel of the temper screw is about 6 ft.

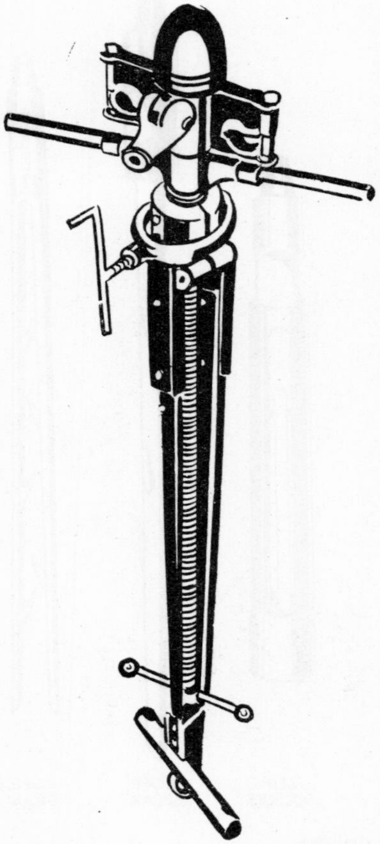

Drilling Rigs.—Cable drilling rigs of the portable and stationary type respectively are used. In the smaller rigs the percussive motion is achieved by a "spudding" device (Fig. 8a), whereas a "walking beam" (Fig. 8b) is used in the larger rigs. The spudder comprises a pulley wheel (2) to which a reciprocating motion is imparted by means of an eccentric device driven from the main driving shaft. The drilling cable passes beneath this pulley between the bull reel (1) and the crown sheave (3) at the masthead, and the bullwheel being stationary, except for feeding purposes, the tools are raised and dropped as the spudder moves up and down.

Walking beams are pivoted centrally, and the cable being fastened to one end by means of a temper screw, the other end is reciprocated by a pitman or connecting rod, driven through a crank on the main driving shaft. The spudding action effects a certain economy in space, and simplifies the feeding arrangements. Usually three lengths of stroke are available for each rig, ranging from about 1 ft. 6 in. to 3 ft.

The power is obtained in modern rigs from internal-combustion engines of the fuel-oil type or more rarely the petrol type, or where electric power is available by electric motors. Horse-powers range from about 5 in the case of

Fig. 7.—Method of actuating and feeding cable drills.

very light prospecting rigs to about 75 on the largest stationary rigs. The rigs shown in Fig. 9a and 9b are powered by a diesel engine. The spudder or walking beam, the bull reel, sand reel and casing reel are all driven through plate clutches from the main shaft or more usually from a counter-shaft with a chain drive. The sand and casing reels carry cables from which the sludger, used for removing cuttings from the hole, is suspended and for slinging the casing which is sometimes used for lining the boreholes. All three are driven through gearing to give rope speeds of about 150 ft.

per min. for the tool cable and the casing line and 350 ft. per min. for the sand line to facilitate rapid cleaning of the hole and the minimum of delay in drilling.

The masts of the smaller rig are usually telescopic for ease of transport. Modern masts, and the derricks of larger rigs are of all steel construction.

Sampling Cable Drilled Boreholes.—The cable-drilling system is most frequently used where an accurate record of the strata drilled through is not necessary. Normally all the information available is that provided by the cuttings brought up in the bailer. This is a steel tube 10 ft. or more in length with a loop or "bail" at the upper end and a non-return valve at

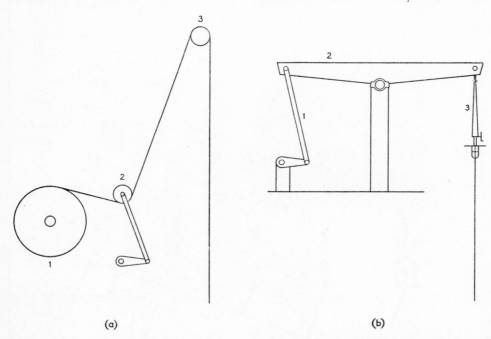

Fig. 8a.—Small drilling rig for spudding.
1, Bull reel; 2, pulley; 3, crown sheave.

Fig. 8b.—Large drilling rig with walking beam.
1, Pitman; 2, walking beam; 3, temper screw.

the lower (Fig. 10a). It is suspended from the sand line and the tools having been withdrawn from the hole it is lowered to the bottom and there moved up and down several times a distance of a few feet to assist the entry of the sludge or cuttings. These are retained in the bailer and brought to the surface where the sludge is washed away and the coarser cuttings examined.

Where a more accurate sample is required, as when passing through a coal seam, a core barrel (Fig. 10b) is used. This consists of an inner barrel or core tube which remains stationary at the bottom of the hole, and an outer barrel provided with an annular cutting edge, which is raised and lowered in the same manner as the ordinary tools. The core formed in the inner barrel is broken off by a spring-loaded clip as the barrel is withdrawn from

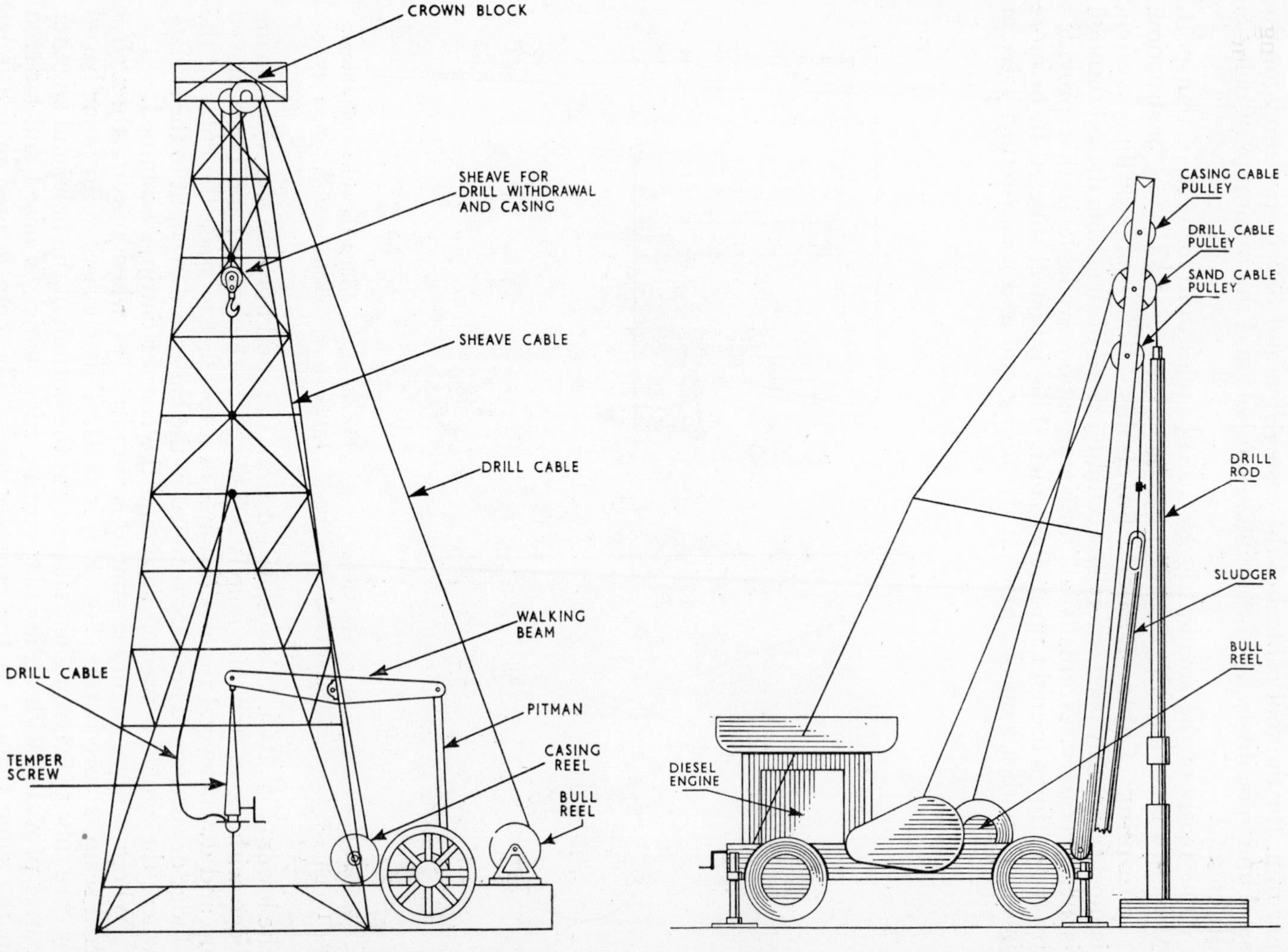

CASING CABLE PULLEY
DRILL CABLE PULLEY
SAND CABLE PULLEY
DRILL ROD
SLUDGER
BULL REEL
DIESEL ENGINE

CROWN BLOCK
SHEAVE FOR DRILL WITHDRAWAL AND CASING
SHEAVE CABLE
DRILL CABLE
WALKING BEAM
PITMAN
CASING REEL
BULL REEL
DRILL CABLE
TEMPER SCREW

Fig. 9a and b.—Cable drilling rig.

124

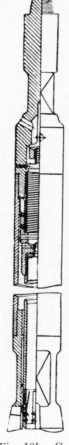

the hole. Such a core is definitely superior to a bailer sample which is difficult to examine and which may contain extraneous loose material fallen from the sides of the hole.

Lining Boreholes.—It is frequently necessary to line boreholes, either temporarily to prevent the collapse of the walls during drilling, or permanently if the hole is to be used for pumping or other purpose. Such materials as cast iron, brass, asbestos and cement have been used under various conditions, but steel tubes with threaded joints are most commonly used. The dimensions of tubing are laid down in British Standard Specifications, and in the Specifications of the American Petroleum Institute.

The first length of casing inserted in a hole is fitted with a casing shoe such as that shown in Fig. 11a. An elevator, shown in Fig. 11b, is attached to the casing so that it may be raised above the hole prior to being lowered into it. In order to support the casing during drilling, use is made of a pipe ring or "spider" (Fig. 11c). The spider is a heavy steel ring with a tapered bore within which are fitted a number of wedges serrated to grip the pipe, the whole ring resting on the conductor or large diameter pipe which is normally inserted at the top of the hole.

In the event of the casing having to be driven into the hole, especially heavy piping is used and the driving is carried out with the drilling tools, a shoe or clamp being attached to the lower end of the drill stem for this purpose. Special bits or reamers are used when it is necessary to enlarge the hole beneath the casing. These tools take the place of the bit and are equipped with expanding wings or

(a)   (b)   (c)

Fig. 10a.—Bailer used in cable drilling.

Fig. 10b.—Core barrel used in cable drilling.

Fig. 11.—Casing fittings.

cutters, which collapse when the reamer is being lowered through the casing and are then forced out by springs to take out the extra ground beneath it.

Various types of reamers are also used for straightening holes or for cutting away ground over and around tools which have become fast in the borehole.

Speed and Cost of Cable Drilling.—The amount of time expended in cleaning out a cable drilled hole is quite considerable even with shallow holes. With deep holes it is proportionately more, until finally a limiting economic depth is reached. The result is that cable drilling is mostly confined to shallow work.

An example of the extremely low cost of cable drilling for this type of work in 1949 is given below. The figures relate to a light petrol-driven machine drilling 6-in. diameter blast-holes for quarry work. The holes were bored to a depth of 110 ft. and the rate of advance was 8 ft. per shift through limestone:

	s.	d.	
Labour (Rig operated entirely by one man)	2	0	per ft.
Depreciation	—		,,
Stores, petrol, etc.	1	0	,,
TOTAL COST ..	3	0	,,

HYDRAULIC ROTARY DRILLING

The hydraulic rotary system of boring is extensively used for boring to depths ranging from one hundred to several thousands of feet, and a very wide variety of rigs are available. Where reasonably full information is required at a large number of sites rather than exact information from relatively fewer holes, the system finds its best application For this reason it is at present being used for large scale coalfield exploration in this country. It indicates the depth of each seam and by special application complete cores can be obtained over limited distances, such as through a coal seam or even through small groups of seams. Rather more expensive than cable drilling, it is cheaper than diamond drilling, and although the very hardest rocks present some difficulties it can be used in most formations and certainly in harder ground than that to which cable drilling is applied.

Drilling Bits.—The most popular forms of bit, from the very large variety available for use with this system, are illustrated in Fig. 12. Fishtail bits (Fig. 12a) with two, three or four wings are used for drilling through relatively soft formations, the number of wings increasing as the hardness of the formation increases. A solid bit suitable for rather harder rocks is the so-called diamond bit (Fig. 12b) but in hard rocks, especially at depth, roller bits are most commonly used. These bits (Fig. 12c and 12d) combine both cutting and crushing actions and the rollers may be two, three or four in number and are usually conical in shape. In this type of bit the teeth are varied according to the nature of the rock. For drilling through soft formations the rollers have relatively few teeth which are cut deep and widely spaced. The number of teeth increases with increasing hardness and they are cut less deeply and placed closer together. Bi-cone bits are favoured for use in

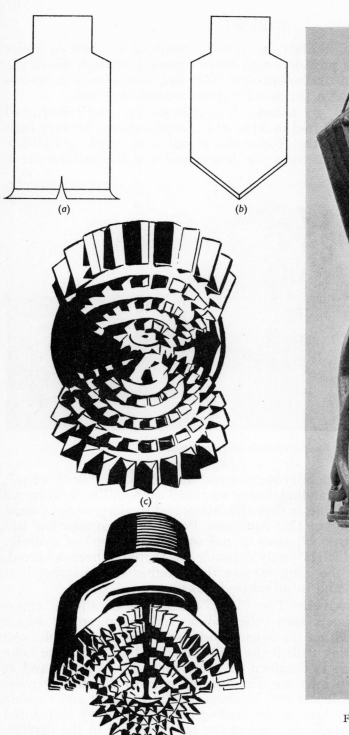

(a)   (b)

(c)

(d)

Fig. 12.—Rotary drilling bits.

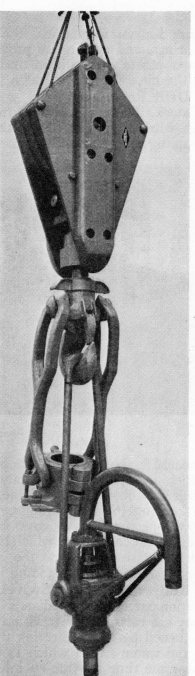

Fig. 13.—Water swivel.

more broken formations. Rollers are usually mounted on ball or roller bearings, and all bits are provided with water channels through which the water passes from within the hollow drill rods and serves as a lubricant to the bit, returning through the annular space around the rods.

Drill Rods.—Drill rods are hollow, circular in section, and constructed of steel. They are manufactured in 30 to 50-ft. lengths except for very light rigs when they may be shorter. Taper thread joints are used to facilitate coupling and uncoupling. Between the lowest rod and the drilling bit is

Fig. 14.—Draw-works and rotary table.

situated a short length of heavier section rod known as the "drill collar", which is capable of withstanding heavy torsional stress. The lowest rod itself may be of a larger diameter than the others and its purpose is to assist in keeping the hole straight. The American Petroleum Institute has laid down specifications to cover all sizes of rod used in this type of drilling; a degree of conformity which is highly desirable has therefore been achieved. All rods are enlarged at the joints to give them higher tensile strength at these points of weakness and to minimise breakages.

Kelly and Water Swivel.—The "kelly" is a rod of square cross-section attached immediately above the drilling rods by means of which they are rotated. It fits within the square bushings of the rotary table, and is turned by them, carrying with it the drill rods and bit. Above the kelly is the water swivel which is designed to allow the kelly to rotate and at the same time provide an inlet for the water or mud to the drilling rods. The swivel is fitted with heavy ball-bearings, totally enclosed and capable of withstanding the heavy load of the drilling column. A heavy loop fitted to the swivel serves to attach the load to the pulley blocks in the derrick. A water swivel is illustrated in Fig. 13.

Fig. 15.—Light rotary prospecting rig.

Fig. 16.—Heavy large stationary rig
for rotary drilling.

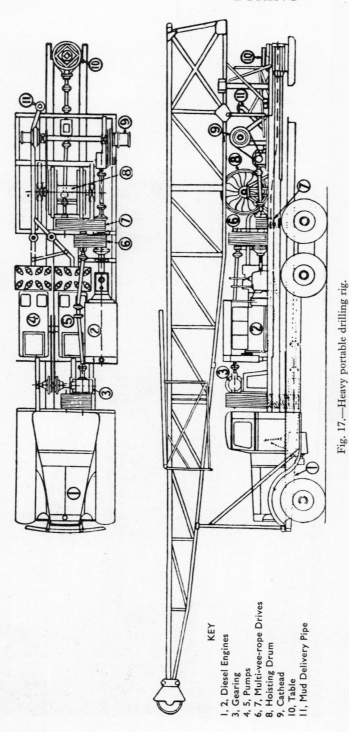

Fig. 17.—Heavy portable drilling rig.

KEY

1, 2, Diesel Engines
3, Gearing
4, 5, Pumps
6, 7, Multi-vee-rope Drives
8, Hoisting Drum
9, Cathead
10, Table
11, Mud Delivery Pipe

Rotary Table.—
The draw-works and
rotary table of a large
rig are illustrated in
Fig. 14. The 4-cylinder
diesel engine develops
85 h.p. at 1,500 r.p.m.,
and is equipped with a
friction clutch and gear-
box, with four forward
speeds and one reverse
speed for hoisting or
rotating. The main
drum is driven by gear-
ing through a flexible
coupling whilst the
auxiliary drum has a
chain drive. The rotary
table is also driven by
means of a chain,
through a short hori-
zontal shaft with a bevel
pinion which meshes in
the horizontal bevel
wheel of the table itself.
The bushing of the
bevel wheel is tapered
to receive the kelly
bushings.

Drilling Rigs.—Hy-
draulic rotary rigs vary
considerably in size and
type, but the two most
common types are illus-
trated in Figs. 15 and 16
which illustrate a light
prospecting rig and a
heavy stationary rig re-
spectively. The pros-
pecting rig is capable of
drilling to a depth of 600
feet and is driven by a
Ford-10 petrol industrial
engine. It is mounted
on a rubber-tyred trailer
and is completely self-

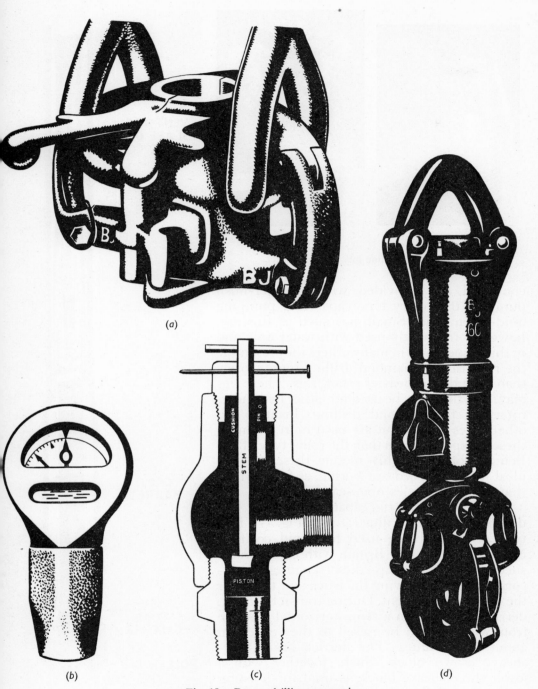

Fig. 18.—Rotary drilling accessories.

(*a*) Casing hook. (*b*) Mud pressure gauge. (*c*) Shear relief valve. (*d*) Drill-rod elevator.

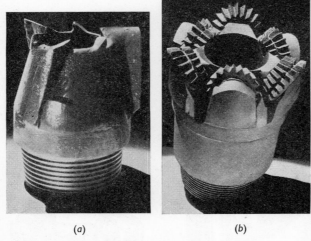

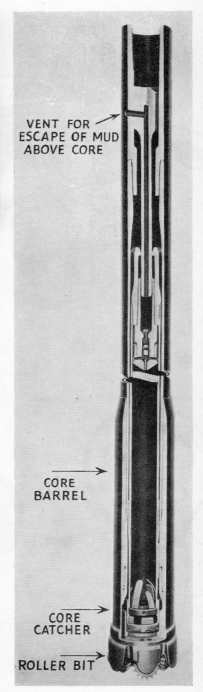

VENT FOR
ESCAPE OF MUD
ABOVE CORE

(a)   (b)

Fig. 19.—Rotary drilling bits and core barrel.

CORE
BARREL

contained and provided with a water-flush
pump of the rotary type capable of pumping
mud-laden fluid. Small rigs such as this are,
however, frequently used with water only and
in this respect and in many others they resemble
the rigs used in diamond drilling more closely
than they do the heavier rotary rigs. These rigs
may, as in this case, be used for either hydraulic-
rotary or for diamond drilling. Fishtail and
other types of solid bit are used more often on
these prospecting rigs than the roller type of bit.
Being light and highly mobile these rigs are
ideal for high-speed test boring, as for example
that which precedes open-cast mining.

A heavy portable rig, capable of drilling to a
depth of 3,000 ft., is illustrated in Fig. 17. This
type of rig is being used for rapid coalfield
exploration in Great Britain with considerable
success. Two 150-h.p. diesel engines are incorporated, one driving the truck and the other
the drilling equipment. During transit the 57-ft.
derrick is carried in a semi-horizontal position
from which it can be raised to the vertical in
about five minutes. The derrick has a four-
sheave crown block which, together with a
lower three-sheave block, is used for hoisting
rods and casing, and supports the rods during
drilling operations. A $\frac{7}{8}$-in. wire rope is used

CORE
CATCHER

ROLLER BIT

Fig. 19 (c)

and a weight-line indicator is attached to the "dead line" portion of this rope. This is the part of the rope between the derrick floor, to which it is attached, and the crown sheave. The rope passes around the sheaves of the crown and travelling blocks and finally to the main winch. The indicator enables the driller to control the weight on the drilling bit.

The casing hook which is attached immediately below the travelling block and carries the swivel, kelly and drill pipes is shown in Fig. 18a. This hook has two side lugs to which the drill rod elevator (Fig. 18d) can be attached when it is necessary to withdraw the rods. During withdrawal slips or jaws are fitted into the central bushing to hold the pipe column whilst a joint is being made or broken.

Two horizontal reciprocating pumps are used for the mud flushing and are driven from the main motor by chain drives. Each pump has a displacement of 126 gals. per min. On the delivery manifold of these pumps is a shear relief valve (Fig. 18c). Excessive mud pressure shears a shear pin and releases the pressure to avoid damage. The valve is set to shear at 700 lb. per sq. in. In conjunction with this valve a mud-pressure gauge (Fig. 18b) is used to inform the driller of the pressure within the circulating system.

Drilling speeds achieved with this type of rig averaged 110 ft. per day down to 1,000 ft., 80 ft. per day down to 2,000 ft. and from 40 to 50 ft. per day through coal measures to depths between 2,000 and 3,000 ft.

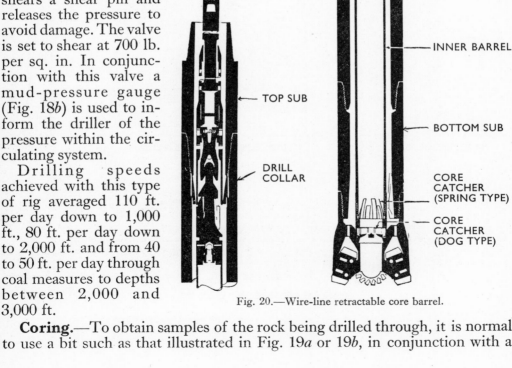

Fig. 20.—Wire-line retractable core barrel.

Coring.—To obtain samples of the rock being drilled through, it is normal to use a bit such as that illustrated in Fig. 19a or 19b, in conjunction with a

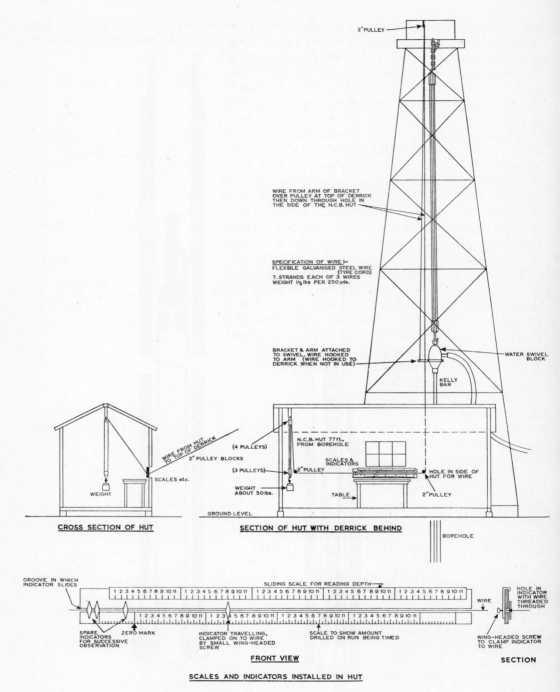

Fig. 21.—Apparatus used to record the rate of penetration.

134

core barrel as shown in Fig. 19c. This equipment is attached to the drill rods in the normal manner and to extract the core the drilling rods are withdrawn from the borehole. This laborious operation may be avoided by the use of wire-line retractable core barrels. This type of core barrel is illustrated in Fig. 20. A narrow core barrel is incorporated within the lowest drill pipe and when the barrel is full, it is withdrawn by means of a wire line lowered within the drilling pipe. A special latching device or "overshot" on the end

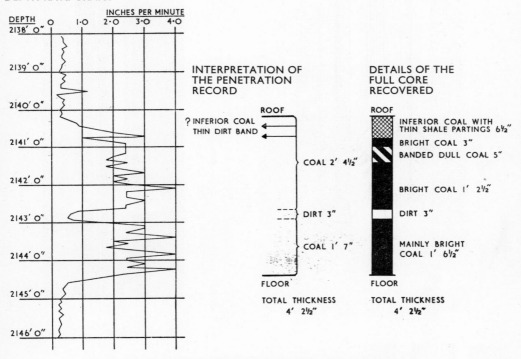

Fig. 22.—Comparison of penetration record with core recovered.

of the line detaches the core barrel (which is normally securely held in place above the drilling bit) and lifts it within the drill rods to the surface.

Fig. 21 illustrates a simple type of apparatus used in the North-eastern Division of the National Coal Board to obtain the thickness and section of coal seams in boreholes. It has been found of considerable value where incomplete cores have been recovered. In all cases the interpretation of the penetration record has agreed very closely with the core obtained, thus demonstrating its reliability and accuracy.

The apparatus consists of a fine wire with one end hooked on to a bracket clamped to the water-swivel block of the drill. The wire passes over a brass pulley at the top of the derrick, to another pulley, along the indicator board, over a third pulley and then to two pulley blocks. The weight attached to

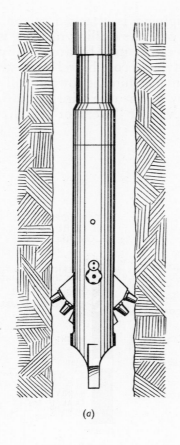

(a)

(c)

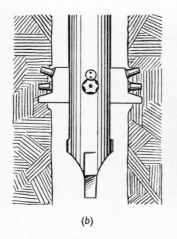

(b)

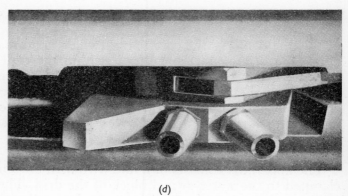

(d)

Fig. 23.—Side-wall sampler.

(a)

Fig. 24.—Percussion core takers and samples.
(a) Samples.   (b) Six-shot sample taker.   (c) Thirty-shot
sample taker.

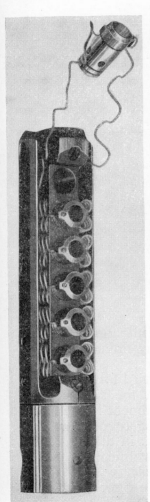

the lower pulley block keeps the wire in tension
and the indicators, through which the wire has
been threaded, are fitted with small wing-headed
screws so that they can be clamped to the wire.
The number of pulleys in each of the blocks is
determined by the maximum travel of the water-
swivel block and the available height in the hut.

At the commencement of drilling the first indicator is clamped to the wire at the zero mark
and timing is begun by using a stop watch or a
watch with a large second hand. As the indicator
passes each inch mark the time is noted and
when the first indicator reaches the end of the
scale the second indicator is clamped to the wire
and the first unclamped. The indicator board
shown in Fig. 21 is equipped with four sliding
indicators each of which can travel 4 ft. so as to
time a run of 16 ft. When the timing is complete
the individual times for each inch drilled are
converted into the rate of penetration and these
figures are plotted against the depth, as shown
in Fig. 22.

The coring tools described so far are designed
to take cores during drilling. For the purposes of
sampling from the sides of holes already drilled
other devices known as "side-wall samplers"
may be used. The side-wall sampler manufactured by Baker Oil Tools Inc. of America is illustrated in Fig. 23a, b, c and d. The tool is lowered
into the borehole with its blades in a collapsed

(b)

(c)

position. At the required point the sampler is halted and hydraulic pressure built up within the drill rods. This forces out the blades into contact with the drill wall. The drill rods are then allowed to weigh down on the sampler, forcing the blades into the wall of the borehole and forcing a core into each of the sampler tubes. Pump pressure is then released and the rods withdrawn as the core blades collapse.

Another interesting device is the Percussion Core Taker used by Schlumberger Drilling Services which is illustrated in Fig. 24. This is a "gun" which fires hollow bullets into the formation. The bullets are held to the gun by wires and are retracted from the ground by raising the gun out of the hole.

Fig. 25.—Mud pump for counterflush system.

The explosive charge is such that the bullets are driven well into the wall of the hole so that the cores are not contaminated by the clay lining the hole. Both of these methods are rapid and relatively inexpensive.

Schlumberger also use a diamond side-wall corer for hard formations. A small diamond bit extends diagonally downward from the side of the instrument and is driven by an electric motor. The instrument is anchored in the hole when each core is cut, the anchor arm being released by the rotation of the electric motor. The cores, which are $\frac{3}{4}$ in. in diameter and from 2 in. to $2\frac{3}{4}$ in. in length, are stored within the instrument, it being possible to take up to nine cores on one trip in the borehole.

Mud Flushing.—The use of water laden with mud instead of clear water is the principal characteristic of the hydraulic-rotary system of drilling. It has the following advantages:—

(1) The high specific gravity of the mud assists in supporting the sides of the borehole. This is of particular importance when drilling through weak ground.

(2) It serves to keep back any gas, water or oil under pressure, encountered during the drilling operations.

(3) As its specific gravity is higher it is more efficient than clear water in raising the broken material to the surface.

(4) When the circulation is stopped it sets into a gel and holds the cuttings in suspension instead of allowing them to fall back to the bottom of the hole.

In addition it serves, as does clear water, to cool the drilling bit, and in the case of roller bits to lubricate them during drilling.

THE CIRCULATING SYSTEM.—Driven by a pump, as described on p. 133, the mud passes through the manifold and up the stand pipe within the derrick and thence to the swivel through a high-pressure flexible hose and down through the kelly and drill rods to the bit. It passes out of the circulating ports in the bit and carries the broken material to the surface through the annular space around the drill rods. At the surface it flows out of a pipe from the conductor into a fine sieve which extracts the chippings for examination and allows the mud to return to the mud pit for re-circulation by the pump. This is the most common system, but a counterflush system is used by the Werf Conrad Co. of Holland in which the mud travels in the reverse direction. The pump used in this system is illustrated in Fig. 25. Each unit consists of a duplex mud pump with interchangeable steel liners and rubber-sleeved pistons, driven by a 4-cylinder diesel engine with friction clutch and V-belt transmission. The pump displacement is 110 gals. per min. and the working pressures are 410 lb. with 5-in. pistons or 1,135 lb. with 3-in. pistons.

PROPERTIES OF THE MUD FLUID.—The importance of the physical properties of the mud cannot be overstressed. It must be sufficiently fluid to flow readily and require the minimum amount of pumping. A low viscosity from 20 to 22 viscosity units or centipoises may therefore be essential. Again, to give the maximum support to the sides of the hole and to raise the cuttings rapidly, a high specific gravity is necessary. Specific gravities ranging from 1·05 to 2·3 have been used under various conditions, the latter being used only when very high pressures of gas or water are encountered. A more usual figure is about 1·3. The mud must also set readily into a gel which supports the cuttings when for any reason the pump is stopped. This change of consistency from a fluid when in motion, to a gel in the static state, is known as the thixotropy of the mud and must, like the specific gravity and viscosity, be carefully controlled. Finally, the mud has to be protected against the extraction of water from it when drilling through porous ground. This is necessary to prevent the mud from thickening as the water is removed and forming too heavy a coating on the sides of the borehole.

CONTROL OF MUD PROPERTIES.—The control of these essential properties

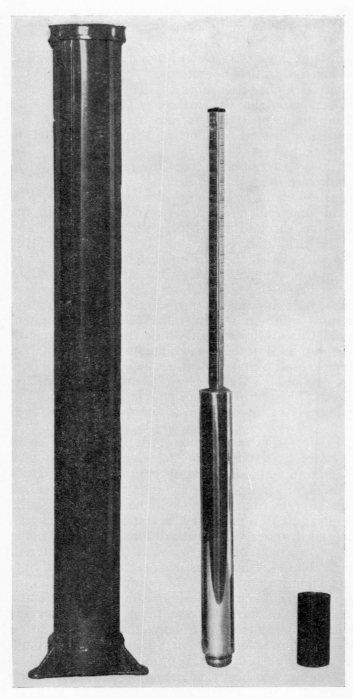

Fig. 26a.—Simple hydrometer for specific gravity tests of mud.

of the mud calls for a high degree of skill and, to ensure success, the tests should be done in the field. This is necessary as the requirements vary according to the ground being drilled through. Thus, when boring through clay, the cuttings themselves become mud and affect the properties of the fluid; in sandstone the mud tends to lose water; in sands a high specific gravity is necessary, and so on. In addition to these factors, the proper control of the properties of the mud becomes increasingly difficult as the hole deepens.

The tests carried out in the field are simple but effective. The apparatus used is illustrated in Fig. 26a, b, c, d and e.

SPECIFIC GRAVITY.— This may be determined by means of a simple hydrometer (Fig. 26a) or with a mud balance, comprising an arm with a small vessel at one end and a moveable weight at the other (Fig. 26b). The vessel is filled with mud, the weight adjusted and the density read off from the graduations on the weighted arm. In order to increase the specific gravity, barytes (specific gravity 4·3 to 4·6) or

alternatively haematite (specific gravity 4·9 to 5·3) is added as required.
VISCOSITY.—The time taken for a fixed quantity of mud to run out of a

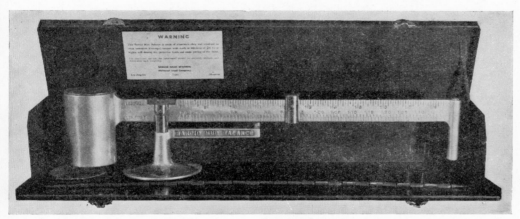

Fig. 26b.—Balance for specific gravity tests of mud.

funnel (Fig. 26c) under the force of gravity is taken as a measure of the
mud's viscosity. Alternatively a Stoamer viscometer in which a spindle is
rotated in the mud by weights through gearing is used (Fig. 26d). The
weight required to give the specified rate of rotation
is a measure of the viscosity and gel strength of the
mud. The viscosity is reduced when necessary by the
addition of water and increased by adding bentonites
which are fine-grained plastic clays.

PERMEABILITY.—A small steel cylinder with a filtering
device in its base (Fig. 26e) is partially filled with mud
and air or other gas passed in at a pressure of 100 lb. per
sq. in. for a given length of time. The water expelled
through the gauge in a given interval, together with the
compactness and thickness of the remaining mud cake
indicate the manner in which the mud will behave
under pressure in a borehole.

The essential colloidal properties of the mud are
sometimes achieved by the addition of bentonite which
retards the sedimentation of the other solids in the mud.
In deep holes, however, owing to the high temperatures, the mud may develop excessive gel strength and
cause difficulty in the re-circulation after pumping has
been stopped. This difficulty is overcome by the use of
sodium tannate.

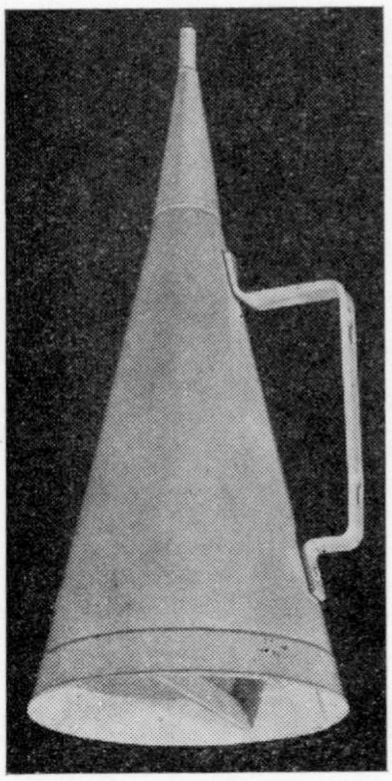

Fig. 26c.—Funnel used in
measuring viscosity of
mud.

In addition to these physical properties of the mud which must be varied
and carefully controlled to meet the changing requirements, the purely
mechanical effects of lining the borehole with mud and cooling the drilling

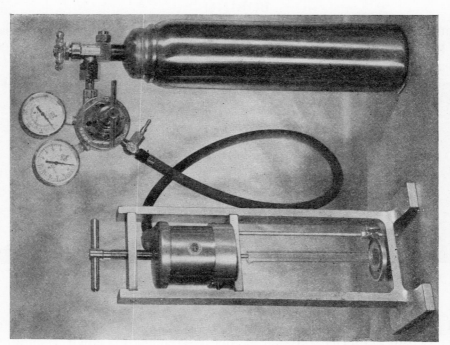

Fig. 26e.—Apparatus for inspecting behaviour of mud under pressure.

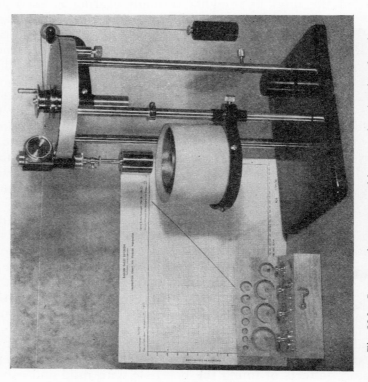

Fig. 26d.—Stoamer viscometer used in measuring viscosity of mud.

142

bit must be carefully supervised. The rate of circulation has to be regulated to allow the mud to settle on the borehole walls with, as near as possible, the exactly right effect, providing a coating which is neither too thick, due to slow velocities, nor yet too thin. Water, having a greater specific heat than clay, is of greater value than mud for cooling the bit and, consequently, a fluid which is not overburdened with solid matter is best for this purpose. A high circulating velocity also improves cooling effects.

Rotary Air-blast Drilling.—Rotary air-blast drilling machines have now been introduced in quarries, open-cut metalliferous-ore mines and open-cast-coal sites in America, Britain and France. Water is not always available, or only in limited quantities, for use alone or mixed as a mud fluid, therefore air or steam is used.

It is claimed that the penetration rate is higher than in comparable orthodox borings by from 40 to 200 per cent. and with an improvement in bit life of between 36 and 300 per cent. Since the air has to lift the $\frac{3}{8}$-in. cuttings produced by a roller-bit, the consumption is high and of the order of 600 cu. ft. per minute. Where loss of mud circulation is severe owing to fissured formations and inadequate water supply, it is considered that air can compete with the ordinary means of cooling the bit and removing drilling debris; it will not, of course, afford any protection to the walls.

In general, however, it is only in shallow holes such as blast holes that air or steam is used. Here the effect of water on such minerals as gypsum and anhydrite should be noted, for the drilling debris is converted to plaster of paris if circulation fails. With sodium and potash deposits, water also is deleterious to cores and the drilling fluid must be saturated with similar or associated salts. The use of alcohol has been proposed for drilling ice and it is by no means unusual to use oil as a base for mud in oil-well drilling.

Records kept over the first five weeks on a Northumberland opencast-coal site showed the average penetration rate to be in the neighbourhood of 50 ft. per hour. Throughout this period the average depth of hole was 51 ft., the strata consisting of broken sandstone for about 12 ft., under which the sandstone was progressively harder, each hole culminating in shale. The bits were $7\frac{3}{8}$ in. diameter and bit life was estimated as being nearly 1,800 ft.

Better figures, for both penetration rate and bit life, are at present being obtained at other opencast-coal sites in Britain where the rock formations are softer, and bit life figures of 16,000 ft. to 21,000 ft. have been reported. Drilling costs (1955) are said to vary between 1s. 1d. per foot to 1s. 11d. and as such are from one-third to a half of the cost previously incurred.

Drilling Speeds with the Hydraulic Rotary Method.—As mentioned previously, the speeds which can be achieved with rotary drilling depend upon a number of factors. The nature of the ground and the type of bit are of great importance and, although the design of the bit is varied for different hardnesses of ground, the nature of the ground has also a pronounced effect upon the drilling speed, as can be seen from the following figures which have been obtained in practice:—

Nature of ground						Drilling speed in yd. per hour
Soft surface formations ..	..	..	..	..	..	10 to 20
Medium shales ..	..	..	..	..	..	3 to 16
Hard shales	..	..	..	..	..	2 to 10
Hard limestones ..	..	..	..	..	..	1 to 3
Very hard quartzite	..	..	..	..	..	$\frac{1}{3}$ to 1

These speeds were obtained with roller type bits of various designs.

Drilling Costs For Hydraulic Rotary Method.—The high initial cost (approximately £20,000) is a prominent feature of deep drilling with a hydraulic rotary truck-mounted drill. This figure, which includes the cost of 4,000 ft. of drill rods, necessitates a very high drilling speed to reduce the cost of capital depreciation per foot of hole to a minimum. The portability of the rig is also of prime importance and such rigs are usually capable of drilling 2,000 ft. in a period of three weeks.

The following figures refer to a large portable rig on hire in 1949, and include 10 per cent. contractor's profits, the contract for the work being on a "cost plus" basis. The hole was 1,925 ft. deep and $8\frac{5}{8}$ in. initial diameter, no cores being taken throughout the whole depth:—

Item					Cost per ft.
					s. d.
Wages, fares and transport	..	..	..	..	18 0
Rock bits ..	..	..	..	..	2 10
Plant hire ..	..	..	..	..	11 9
Miscellaneous (including casing)	..	..	..	2 4
					34 11

The cost of hiring the plant is based on its depreciation over three years. Wage rates in this case were high, as the labour required on these, and diamond rigs, is necessarily more skilled than in cable or chilled-shot drilling. The cost is that of boring a single hole only at an average drilling speed of 213 ft. per week and 113 ft. per week through sandstones and limestone respectively. For a number of holes a lower cost would be achieved.

DIAMOND DRILLING

Although it is more than eighty years since diamonds were first used for the tipping of drilling bits, it is within the last three decades that this type of drilling has been most widely applied. The manifest advantages of diamond drilling have led to its use for all types of boring, for all sizes and depths of boreholes both above and below ground, and a wide variety of rigs are available. The two main disadvantages are high capital cost of equipment and risk of loss of diamonds. The ease with which coring is carried out makes diamond drilling one of the most important methods where accurate records of the strata are required.

Diamonds.—There are two types of diamond used in drilling operations.

1. BLACK DIAMONDS.—Black diamonds or "carbons" which are an amorphous form of pure carbon, almost black in colour and of granular structure. These stones are largely obtained from South America, and although not as hard as the crystalline forms, are exceedingly tough and difficult to fracture. They are accordingly adopted for drilling in the hardest rock. The stones vary from one to four carats in weight.

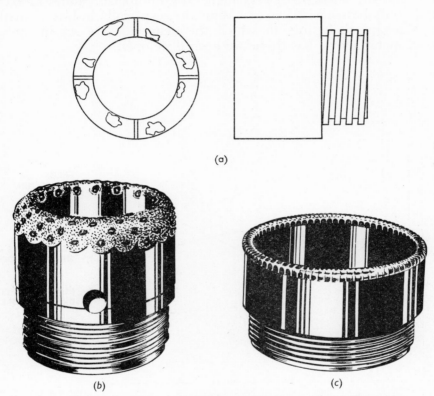

Fig. 27 *a*, *b* and *c*.—Diamond drilling bits showing setting of diamonds.

2. BORTS.—These are white diamonds of imperfect crystalline form. Although actually harder than the black diamonds, borts fracture far more readily in hard ground. South Africa is the main source of this type of diamond, and those used for drilling are very much smaller than the black diamonds, ranging from five to fifteen or more to the carat. Borts are also relatively inexpensive, being about one-quarter the price of carbons, per carat.

Diamond Bits.—Bits set with black diamonds usually have from six to eight stones set in a soft steel bit as shown in Fig. 27a. Horizontal holes are drilled around the circumference of the blank bit to take the outer stones and vertical holes for the inner ones. These holes are trimmed by hand chisel to fit the stones, and the metal of the bit is caulked around each carbon to hold it in place. The largest stones are set around the outside of the bit and the arrangement is such that all the ground to be cut away comes into contact with one or other of the diamonds.

When using borts a larger number is required and the bits may be either hand set as with carbon bits or mechanically set. The hand-set bits may have as many as 70 stones set as indicated in Fig. 27b, but the process is laborious and the setting cost very high. Any number of stones in excess of this could only be set with extreme difficulty, especially in bits of small diameter. Mechanical setting, in which the diamonds are set in molten or powdered metal alloys, has therefore been developed.

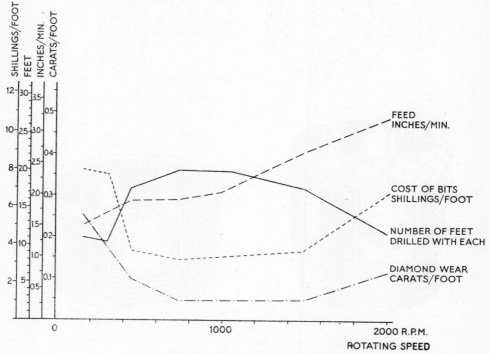

Fig. 28.—Wear of diamond drilling bits.

The most recent development in the setting of bort bits is the use of thin inserts. In this type of bit the diamonds are placed in their correct positions in a mould with powdered metal. This powder is then pressed and sintered and the complete inserts formed are fastened radially to the drilling bit by soldering. Up to 700 diamonds may be set in a $5\frac{3}{4}$-in. bit in this manner. The stones are set evenly and consequently wear away evenly when drilling, and it is claimed for these "Korbelite" bits (Fig. 27c) that the diamonds are held so securely that they wear away before becoming dislodged.

Wear of Diamonds.—The rate at which the diamonds in a bit wear depends upon a number of factors, the principal of which are:—

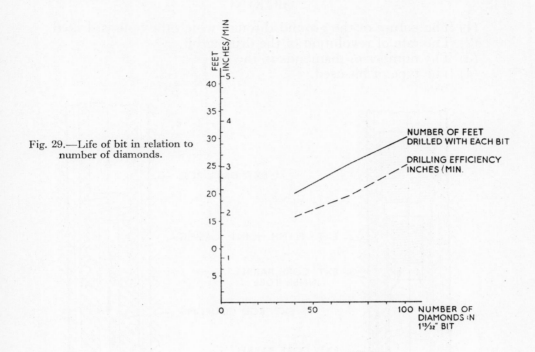

Fig. 29.—Life of bit in relation to number of diamonds.

NUMBER OF FEET
DRILLED WITH EACH BIT

DRILLING EFFICIENCY
INCHES (MIN.

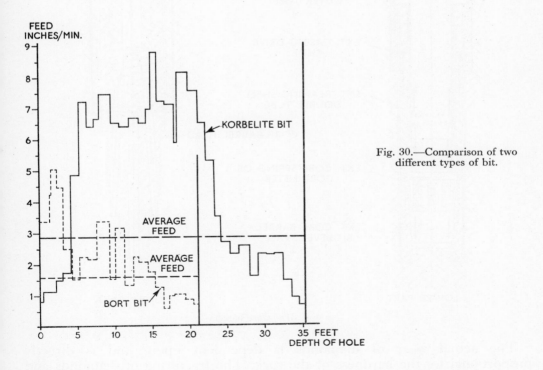

Fig. 30.—Comparison of two different types of bit.

147

(1) The nature of the ground through which the hole is drilled.
(2) The rate of revolution of the drilling bit.
(3) The number of diamonds in the bit.
(4) The type of bit used.

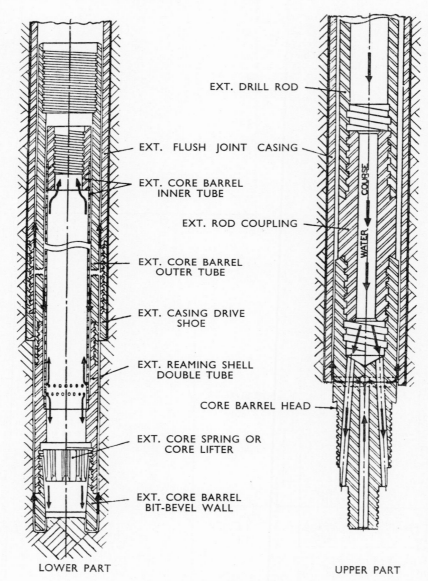

EXT. DRILL ROD

EXT. FLUSH JOINT CASING

EXT. CORE BARREL
INNER TUBE

EXT. ROD COUPLING

EXT. CORE BARREL
OUTER TUBE

EXT. CASING DRIVE
SHOE

EXT. REAMING SHELL
DOUBLE TUBE

CORE BARREL HEAD

EXT. CORE SPRING OR
CORE LIFTER

EXT. CORE BARREL
BIT-BEVEL WALL

WATER COURSE

LOWER PART   UPPER PART

Fig. 31.—Core barrel.

The actual wear of diamonds is dependent upon, and is directly proportional to, the hardness of the rock. The fracturing of diamonds and their loss is, however, more likely to occur in broken and fissured ground.

The relation between wear and speed of rotation can be seen from Fig. 28, which shows the wear of a bort type of bit when drilling through granite. It will be noted that the heaviest wear occurs at low speeds and that the optimum speed for this type of rock is in the neighbourhood of 1,000 r.p.m. The drilling rate increases with increasing speed of rotation from 1·5 in. per min. at 200 r.p.m. to over 3 in. per min. at 2,000 r.p.m. Other costs besides that of diamond wear are therefore inversely proportional to the speed.

The life of a bit varies with the number of diamonds. This is illustrated in Fig. 29. The graph is for hand-set bort bits drilling in granite at a constant speed of 740 r.p.m. Not only is the life of a bit lengthened considerably as the number of stones increases, but drilling efficiency also improves steadily. Thus a strong argument is presented in favour of mechanically set drill bits in addition to their low cost.

Finally the comparison between the insert type of bit and the ordinary hand-set bort bit is illustrated in Fig. 30. The drilling time in granite at 740 r.p.m. was taken for each complete run of the feeding thread.

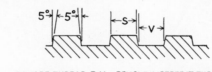

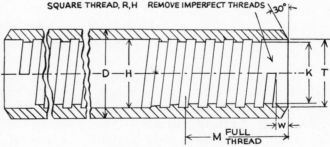

Fig. 32.—Drilling rod joints.

The insert bit with the larger number of small stones proved to have almost twice the speed of the ordinary bit.

Core Barrels.—Not infrequently diamond drills with solid bits instead of annular bits are used when cores are not required, but the diamond drill is generally applied when high-speed coring is desirable. A type of core barrel used is illustrated in Fig. 31. The outstanding features of this core barrel are the reaming shell, which is set with diamonds to maintain the gauge of the hole, and the core lifter. The latter is, in its most common form, a split ring of wedge-shaped section. As the tools descend it allows the core being formed to slip past, but when the barrel is withdrawn from the hole its wide upper periphery bites into the core and breaks it off. Single and double core barrels differ in that the latter have an inner barrel which does not rotate, and therefore protects fragile cores from wear by rotating parts or circulating water. The core barrel is attached to the drill rods by a ferrule with male threaded joints at either end.

Drilling Rods.—The dimensions of the rods used in diamond drilling, together with all other fittings are specified by the United States Bureau of Standards, in a voluntary trade specification. The most common sizes

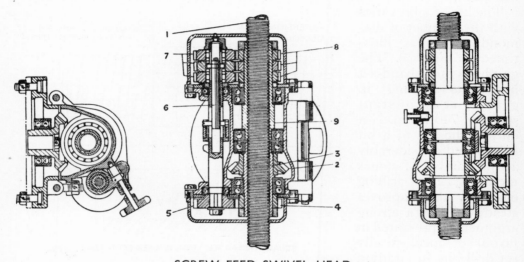

SCREW FEED SWIVEL HEAD

Fig. 33.—Differential screw feed.

of equipment are those which give cores $\frac{15}{16}$ in., $1\frac{5}{16}$ in., $1\frac{5}{8}$ in. and $2\frac{1}{8}$ in. in diameter, but larger cores are easily obtainable with special fittings. The type of joint used and their general design are shown in Fig. 32.

Feeding Arrangements.—There are two devices in common use for the feeding of drilling rods in diamond boring. The smaller machines are usually equipped with a differential screw feed, whilst on the large rigs hydraulic feeding is adopted. Both methods are necessarily intermittent with a fixed travel at one setting.

THE DIFFERENTIAL SCREW FEED.—This type of feed is illustrated in Fig. 33. A hollow shaft (1) which is threaded on the outside passes over the drilling rods and is attached to them by means of a chuck. The bevel pinion (2) turns the shaft (1) through the sleeve (3) running in three splines along the length of the shaft. It is rotated itself, from the main drive through a bevel wheel. Also driven by the bevel pinion (2) is the spur wheel (4) which drives the pinion (5) and the countershaft (6). Mounted on the countershaft are three

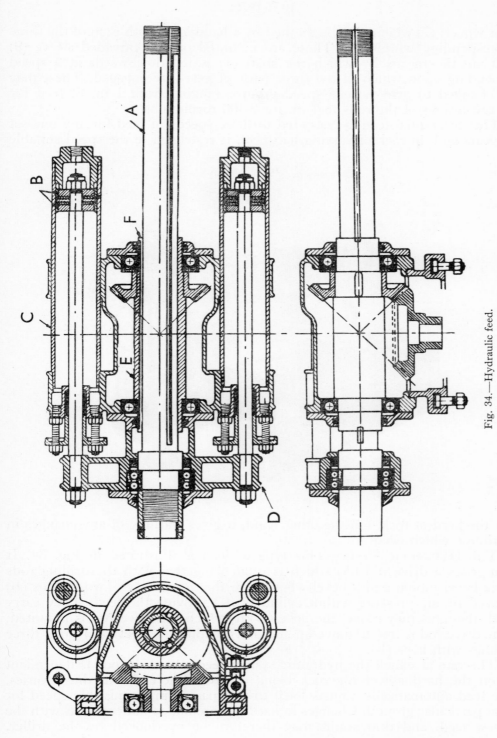

Fig. 34.—Hydraulic feed.

151

gear wheels (7) which may be meshed by a hand lever with each of the three corresponding wheels (8). These are mounted on the threaded sleeve (9) and are the means by which the shaft (1) is fed downwards at a speed depending upon which of the three pairs of gears are engaged. These may be changed to give various speed groups, ranging from 1 in. of feed for 50 revolutions of the rods to 1 in. for 2,400 revolutions.

The differential feed is restricted to three speeds of feed for any one set of gears and, in rock of varying hardness, is restricted to the speed suitable

Fig. 35.—Diamond drilling rig.

for the hardest rock. On the other hand, it gives warning of any changes in hardness which occur.

THE HYDRAULIC FEED.—This type of feed is illustrated in Fig. 34. It comprises a drive rod (A) which is rotated together with the drilling rods by a bevel pinion and a bevel wheel from the main drive. Two pistons (B) moved by air pressure within cylinders (C) provide the feed. They carry with them, as they move, the yoke (D) in which the drive rod is mounted. The drive rod is free to move up and down within the sleeve (E) along three splines with keys (F).

The rate at which the hydraulic system feeds the drill rods is dependent upon the hardness of the rock being drilled. Where the hardness varies, the feed automatically adjusts itself to the maximum permissible speed for that particular ground. Changes in hardness are not so noticeable as with the screw feed, and thin seams may therefore be overlooked by the driller.

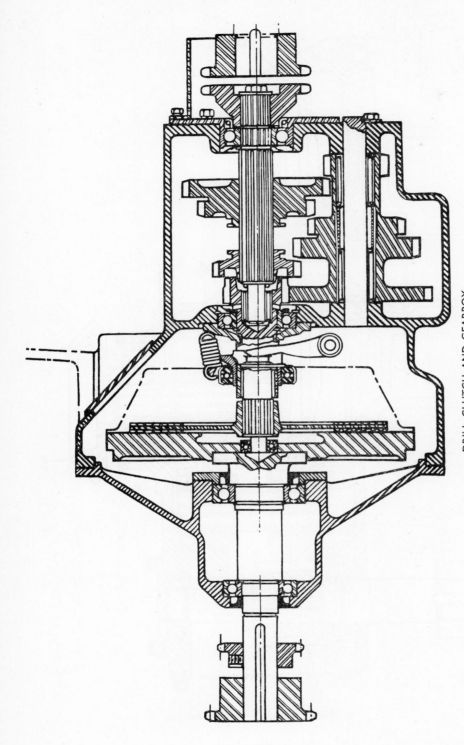

DRILL CLUTCH AND GEARBOX

Fig. 36a.—Transmission unit of diamond rig.

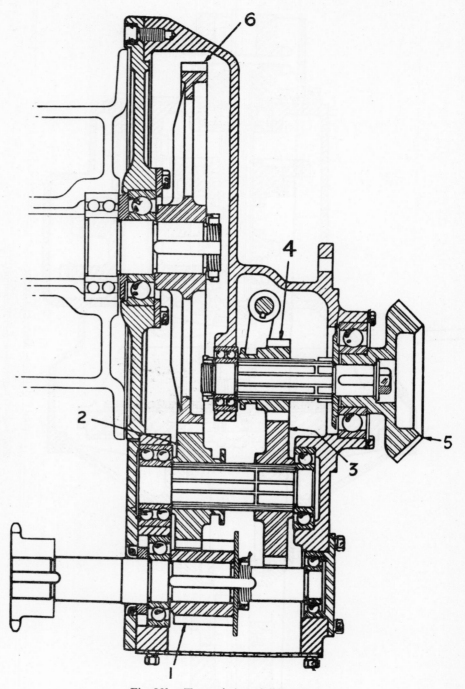

Fig. 36b.—Transmission of diamond rig.

Diamond Drilling Rigs.—A very wide variety of diamond drilling rigs are available, ranging from very small hand-operated machines to large stationary rigs capable of drilling holes to depths of over 10,000 ft.

A modern portable rig, designed to drill to depths of 1,750 ft., is illustrated in Fig. 35. The rig may be driven by a petrol engine or a diesel engine, or by an electric or a compressed-air motor. It weighs rather less than a ton and is 8 ft. in length, the over-all width and height being 3 ft. 6 in. and 4 ft. 4 in. respectively. Fig. 36a illustrates the drill clutch and gearbox.

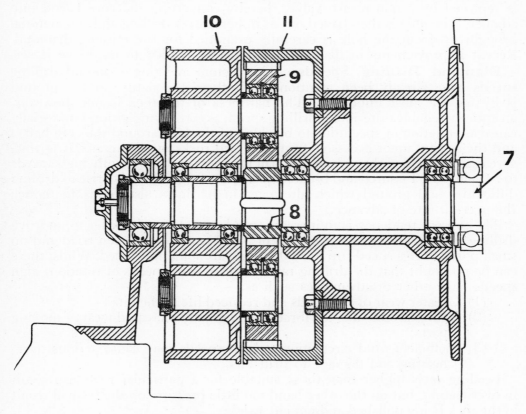

Fig. 36c.—Transmission of diamond rig.

The clutch, which is operated by a hand lever, is of the friction type and the gearbox provides four speed changes. Bit speeds of 190, 390, 700 and 1,200 r.p.m. can be obtained by engaging the appropriate gears. The swivelhead drive is carried out through the spur and pinion gears (1), (2), (3) and (4) and the bevel wheel (5) shown in Fig. 36b. The sliding gear (2) may also be meshed with the gear wheel (6) which drives the drum shaft (7) in Fig. 36c. This shaft rotates the gear wheel, (8) the planetary gears (9), the planetary clutch wheel (10), and the internal gear (11), which is attached to the hoisting drum. This drum has a capacity of 211 ft. of ½-in. rope and hoisting speeds of 45, 100, 170 and 290 ft. per min. The oil pump for the hydraulic feed is driven by means of a chain from the main driving shaft.

Loss of Diamonds.—The chief difficulty in diamond-drilling operations is the loss of diamonds in the borehole. This may result from wear of the metal in which the diamonds are set or through breakage of the stones themselves. The usual method of recovery is to fill a blank bit or crown with wax and lower it into the hole. The diamond becomes embedded in the wax and is retrieved. When the bottom of the hole is not clear, the cutting bit is replaced by a non-return valve, thereby converting the core barrel into a bailer. The hole is then bailed out as in percussive drilling and the material brought up from the hole is carefully examined for the missing diamond. Recent improvements in diamond setting have tended to minimise losses.

Diamond Drilling Speeds.—The factors affecting diamond drilling speeds have already been mentioned. Of these the nature of the ground is by far the most important. The hardness of the rock is not, however, an entirely reliable criterion of drilling speed, as soft caving ground may easily cause a reduction of speed due to blocking of the hole around the core barrel and the setting up of excessive friction. Hard rocks may, in contrast to this, core easily provided they are of uniform hardness and allow quite high speeds to be achieved. Fissured and broken rocks quite frequently give rise to drilling difficulties and ground which alternates in hardness also tends to reduce the over-all rate of advance.

The present tendency is to increase speeds of rotation in order to improve drilling speeds. On large rigs speeds of 3,000 r.p.m. have been tried and on small portable rigs speeds up to 5,000 r.p.m. are sometimes used. Whilst there can be no doubt that the drilling rates increase with speeds of rotation, high speeds have other disadvantages such as:—

(1) Greater wear of diamonds and reduced life of the bits.

(2) Heavy stresses due to vibration and greatly increased wear of moving parts.

(3) Inefficient mud circulation at high speeds may cause serious over-heating and damage to drill bits.

Feeding rates higher than those suitable for a particular rock also result in overheating, but on the other hand too little pressure on the bit will result in the rock being polished and not cut away.

Diamond Drilling Costs.—An example of the cost of boring by diamond methods which is comparable with that given earlier for hydraulic rotary drilling is given on p. 157. This hole was bored to a depth of 1,739 ft. and a 3-in. core was taken throughout. The average drilling speed was 174 ft. per week and the over-all speed 75 ft. per week. The diamonds were purchased for £5 per carat.

In this particular instance the diamonds were later replaced by stellite-tipped metal bits and a great reduction of cost was thereby effected. It was found that in the ground being drilled (largely limestone) the hard-metal bit costing 5s. rendered the same service as £30 worth of diamonds.

It is necessary to recover the diamonds from a worn bit in order to maintain

Item					Cost per ft.	
					s.	d.
Allowance for clearing site	..	..	..	..		11·6
Labour, fares, etc. (inclusive 10%)	..	..	..	16	8
Transport and sundries	..	..	..	..	4	8
Core crowns, diamonds, etc.	..	..	..	..	2	3
Consumable stores	..	..	..	..	..	1	5
62 ft. surface casing.	..	..	..	..	..	8·7
Plant hire	..	..	..	..	..	5	2
					31	10·3

as low a drilling cost as possible. This is done by dissolving away the matrix in which the diamonds are set with the aid of concentrated acid. The use of acid is, however, rather slow, particularly when the matrix consists of a highly resistant alloy. Electrolytic processes have therefore been devised in which the drilling crown is used as an anode. The electrolyte varies according to the metal in the bit, e.g., copper sulphate for brass and nitric acid for bronze, and the matrix being eaten away the diamonds are freed.

CHILLED-SHOT DRILLING

This method of drilling is far less widely used than cable, hydraulic, rotary or diamond boring but, in addition to its use for holes of normal diameter, it has had a field of application in the boring of shafts of small diameter for ventilation and other purposes. It most closely resembles diamond drilling, but, for general boring purposes, it suffers from the following disadvantages:—

(1) It is not suitable for boring holes less than 4 in. in diameter.

(2) Inclined holes cannot easily be bored by this method.

(3) It is restricted to certain types of ground.

(4) Power costs are higher than with diamond drilling.

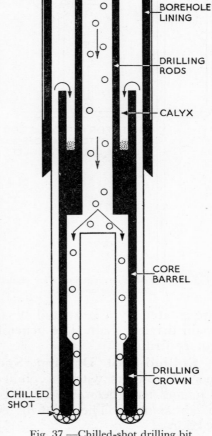

Fig. 37.—Chilled-shot drilling bit (diagrammatic).

Drilling Bit.—The cutting tool used in chilled-shot drilling is illustrated in Fig. 37. With few exceptions, chilled-shot drilling is used when cores are required and the bit is annular, with a rounded edge and diagonal slots, to allow the flushing water to flow without carrying away the shot. Above the bit is the core barrel to which the rods are screwed and above the barrel an inverted tube or barrel known as a "calyx". The shot is fed into the hollow drill rods with the flushing water and passes beneath the bit where it is ground into the rock. Cuttings are washed up outside the core barrel and the heavier particles settle back into the calyx. This settling is due to a sudden reduction in the velocity of water as it passes into the less restricted passages above the calyx. No core lifter is used but the core is broken off by jamming it within the barrel with shot or flint pebbles.

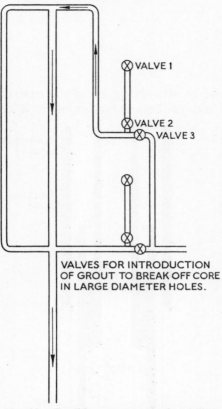

ARROWS INDICATE PATH OF SHOT CARRIED BY WATER.

VALVE 1

VALVE 2
VALVE 3

VALVES FOR INTRODUCTION OF GROUT TO BREAK OFF CORE IN LARGE DIAMETER HOLES.

Fig. 38.—Feeding arrangements for chilled shot (diagrammatic).

Feeding the Shot.—The arrangements for introducing the shot into the water stream are shown diagrammatically in Fig. 38. The shot is fed in through valve 1 with valve 2 closed. Valve 1 is then closed and valves 3 opened and, subsequently, valve 2, when the shot is swept with the water through the swivel into the hollow rods. The size of the shot used ranges from $\frac{1}{8}$ in. downwards and quantities which vary according to the hardness of the ground and may be as high as 5 lb. per ft. of hole drilled for a hole 12 in. in diameter.

Chilled-Shot Rig.—Chilled-shot drilling is normally used in boring relatively shallow holes, and the boring rigs are therefore of the light and medium type rather than the heavier types. Powered by an electric motor or oil engine the drills are rotated by a kelly and bevel gearing which are chain driven from the main driving shaft. The general arrangements resemble those of hydraulic rotary drilling.

Chilled-Shot Drilling Speeds and Costs.—Boring speeds over a period of years with the chilled-shot method of drilling in the North of England have been quoted as being 43 ft. per week, with 200 ft. per week as a maximum. The following figures refer to holes bored through a general section of:—

> 0 to 1,000 ft. red sandstone.
> 1,000 to 1,200 ft. conglomerate.
> 1,200 to 1,500 ft. limestone.

A 6-in. diameter core was always taken and core recovery was about 95 per cent. 14 hours or 1¾ shifts per day were worked. For a hole 1,858 ft. deep in the immediate post-war years the costs were as follows:—

Item					Cost per ft.	
					s.	d.
Wages. 1. Whilst boring	..	..	..	..	14	6
„ 2. Deadwork ..	..	..	..	..	3	6
Maintenance ..	..	..	..	..		6
Depreciation ..	..	..	..	..		—
Stores, transport, shot, etc. ..	..	..	..	..	6	8
					25	2

UNDERGROUND BORING

It is often necessary in all types of mining to drill holes for exploratory and other purposes from sites within the mine itself, and such operations need separate consideration, although the principles involved are similar to those of surface borings. A large number of our older collieries were originally sunk to a particular seam without any systematic preliminary boring from the surface, and information relating to lower seams was meagre. Underground borings were therefore considered necessary to prove these seams. Furthermore, in any colliery, supplementary prospecting by boring from within the workings as they progress is highly desirable. Finally, difficulties due to geological disturbances such as faults and washouts can often be successfully surmounted only by exploratory boring.

In addition, boring is carried out underground for cementation, ventilation and to drain off gas and water (see Vol. 3, Chap. 7).

Special Requirements.—Holes bored underground are not as a rule deep, their depth being measured in tens or hundreds of feet, rather than in thousands. Machines are not therefore large and, since they have to operate in confined spaces and be readily portable, they are constructed as light and compact as possible. In a coal mine the power supply may be only compressed air and boring machines are designed accordingly.

Portable Underground Rigs.—Diamond drilling is most commonly used in underground boring rigs, one of the reasons for its adoption being the relatively small diameter of the holes required. The machines are generally mounted on a heavy steel post which can be erected and made secure between the roof and the floor, and is so designed that the hole can be drilled in any required direction. Differential screw feeds are normally applied but, in some instances, hand feeding along a thread screw, similar to that used in drilling for blasting purposes, is used. Electricity or compressed air may be used and horse-powers range from 1 to about 7·5. Drills which are capable of boring up to 500 ft. usually require only one man for their operation, but, from 500 to 1,000 ft., crews of two men are usual.

Fig. 39.—Portable compressed-air drill.

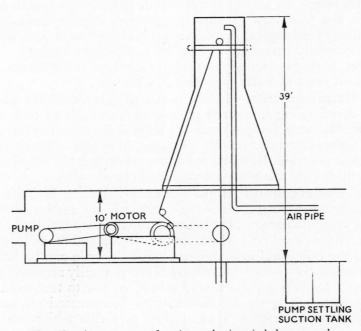

Fig. 40.—Arrangement of stationary boring rig below ground.

A typical portable drill for underground work is illustrated in Fig. 39. This drill is driven by compressed air and is equipped with a water-flush system and a mechanical device for withdrawing the drilling rods. It is capable of drilling a $1\frac{1}{2}$ in. hole to a depth of 500 ft. and yielding a core $\frac{7}{8}$ in. diameter.

Stationary Underground Rigs.—Stationary rigs are not much used underground since space is rarely available for their accommodation and it is not often necessary to bore to a greater depth than that which can be dealt with by a portable rig. Occasionally, however, the necessity arises for their use, and an example is illustrated in Fig. 40. Put down by such a rig for the purpose of proving seams, a hole was bored to a depth of 1,300 ft. The first 97 ft. was bored by the percussive method and the remaining 1,203 ft. by means of rotary diamond drilling.

Some of the difficulties of using a large rig below ground can be seen from the excavation (29 ft. in height, 8 ft. in width) required above the boring room to form the brick-lined pulley chamber. This was further complicated by the two embrasures necessary to form a ropeway on one side, and to allow the drill rods to be raised and lowered on the other side.

The initial diameter of the hole was $9\frac{1}{4}$ in. and the final diameter $4\frac{1}{4}$ in. The total depth of 1,300 ft. was bored in seven months, one very serious delay being encountered, prior to which the average drilling speed was 300 ft. per month. The labour employed was one driller and two labourers on each shift and boring was continuous throughout the 24 hours.

DIRECTIONAL DRILLING

It is sometimes necessary to drill a hole in a particular direction other than on a straight line. In boring for coal the most probable need for this is when a hole becomes deflected to a marked degree from the vertical and it is required to bring it back to the vertical or alternatively to deflect a hole to give a satisfactory core from a seam already passed through.

There are three general methods of altering the direction of a hole whilst it is being drilled. These are, respectively, the use of special bits or reamers, of knuckle joints above the bit and of a whipstock. A removable whipstock which is threaded over the drill rods is illustrated in Figs. 41 and 42. In effect the whipstock constitutes a deflecting guide which directs the bit and rods in the direction required.

OUT-TO-SEA BORING

Techniques that have been developed and applied in boring for oil have in recent years been introduced into coalfield boring, since boring for oil off the sea coasts and in large lakes has been successful in different parts of the world.

Important reserves of coal extend under the sea in Northumberland, Durham, off the Fife coast, under the Firth of Forth, and in areas of lesser importance.

In 1953 the National Coal Board put in hand a project to explore the possibility of out-to-sea boring to prove reserves of coal under the sea.

The boring tower (Plate facing this page), the first of its type to be built, with the other equipment to prove undersea coal, was completed in 1955 at St. David's Harbour on the Firth of Forth. The technique for boring and

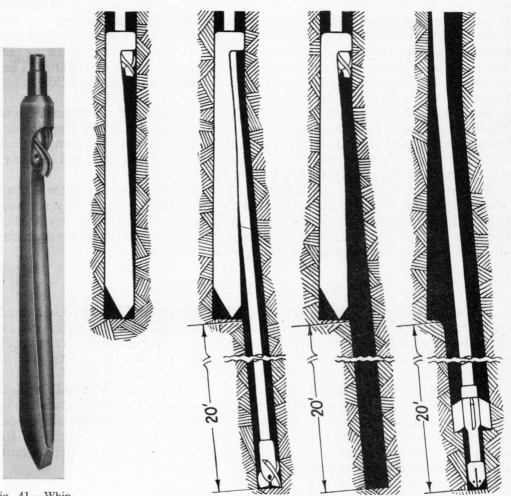

Fig. 41.—Whip-stock or deflecting guide.

Fig. 42.—Deflecting guide in position; deflection of hole in progress and completed ready for normal boring.

recovery of cores is similar to that for land operations except that a 24-in. tubular casing, 160 ft. long, shields the driving rods down to the sea bed. The tower accommodating the drilling platform is designed for use in water up to depths of 20 fathoms at low tide, and constructed to remain steady in bad weather. The structure is claimed to be capable of withstanding an 80-m.p.h. gale and waves up to 30 ft. high.

OUT-TO-SEA BORING TOWER

Tower used by the National Coal Board for proving under-sea coal in the Firth of Forth.

(Craelius Co. Ltd., London)

A BORING RIG IN USE BELOW GROUND

EQUIPMENT.—The boring tower is built of fabricated steel tubes mounted on heavy steel box girders, X-shaped in plan, each of the two members forming the X being 163 ft. long, 3 ft. wide and 7 ft. deep. These are hollow and the water can be extracted from them when the tower has to be floated. On the top of the tubular steel tower is a timber-surfaced octagonal steel deck of about 86 ft. diameter, located some 130 ft. above the box girder base. The drilling rig, which is 54 ft. high, is built on this deck, and accommodation is provided for the stacking of 90 tons of tubular casing for the borehole. A two-ton mobile crane is provided, also a small workshop. Under the main deck there is another deck for accommodating 25 men, and in addition an office, mess, recreation room, power generator and store rooms. The drilling rig has its own generator. Fresh water is provided by a distillation plant.

MOVING INTO POSITION.—The tower with its equipment weighs about 500 tons and is about 185 ft. high from the underside of the base to the top of the drilling rig. Two steel pontoons are used to float the tower and enable it to be towed by tugs to its sea position. Each pontoon is 170 ft. long, 17 ft. 6 in. wide and 7 ft. deep. They are locked in position on each side of the tower by tubular steel spars. The pontoons carry the tower on four sets of heavy twin hawsers, one end of which is attached to the top of the base girder and the other to a large pulley block from which ropes are connected to electrically-operated winches housed within the pontoons and powered from the tower generators. When the boring site is reached, the tower is slowly lowered on to the sea bed by the winches. Once the tower is securely grounded, the lowering ropes are cast off and the pontoons towed away. The cost of the boring tower is estimated to be about £180,000.

PROGRESS.—Two boreholes have been completed in the Firth of Forth. No. 1 hole cut the complete succession of the Millstone Grit, Upper Limestones, Limestone Coal Measures into the top of the Lower Limestones at a total depth of 3,161 ft. The average drilling speed was in the region of 125 ft. per week. No. 2 hole cut the Upper Coal Measures from the top seam to the top of the Millstone Grit at a total depth of 1,802 ft., with a drilling speed of some 180 ft. per week. The figures taken out to date indicate that the cost of out-to-sea drilling is approximately three times that of land drilling.

The 5-ft. seam was encountered at a depth of between 2,914 ft. and 2,930 ft. in No. 1 borehole, but was found to be fragmented and incomplete. The hole was therefore re-cemented to 2,845 ft. and a $3\frac{1}{2}$-in. diversionary cut was taken, starting at 2,640 ft. depth. The wedge-block method was used for the deflection which was taken to 2,935 ft. To ensure the safety of future underground workings it was essential to seal the borehole after all the information had been obtained. Part of the casing was recovered and the hole was sealed by pumping a thick slurry of ferrocrete cement through the drill rods. The cementing was done in stages following the withdrawal of a section of casing, and was completed in two months.

REFERENCES

J. T. Whetton, The surveying of boreholes, *Trans. Inst. Min. Eng.*, Vol. 79, 1930, p. 309.

J. C. MacRae and L. H. Leighton, The radiographic examination of coal cores, *Trans. Inst. Min. Eng.*, Vol. 112, Pt. 6, 1953, p. 500.

R. F. Goosens, Recording the rate of penetration during drilling, *Trans. Inst. Min. Eng.*, Vol. 112, Pt. 6, 1953, p. 497.

R. Peele (ed.), 3rd. ed., *Mining Engineers' Handbook*, Vol. 1, Wiley & Sons, New York, 1941.

W. E. Netzeband, Charm drilling practice in Tri-State Lead-Zinc District, *Min. Cong. Jour.*, January 1935.

J. E. Brautly, *Rotary Drilling Handbook*, Russell Palmer, New York, 1936.

W. H. Jeffrey, *Deep-well Drilling*, Galf Publishing Co., Texas, 1925.

C. W. Otway, Mud-flush boring, *Trans. Inst. Min. Eng.*, Vol. 108, 1949, p. 348.

G. A. Robinson, Diamond core drilling—some practical aspects, *Mine & Quarry Eng.*, Vol. 19, 1953, pp. 416 and 455.

J. B. Murdoch, Jnr., *Methods and Equipment used for Controlled Directional Drilling*, Eastman Oil Well Survey Company, U.S.A., 1949.

K. Carlsten, *Methods and Equipment used for Obtaining Oriented Cores*, Eastman Oil Well Survey Company, U.S.A., 1949.

Off-shore Boring in the Firth of Forth, National Coal Board Production Department Information Bulletin No. 56/172, London, 1956.

Drilling for Coal at Sea, National Coal Board, Headquarters, London and Scottish Division.

Acknowledgement is also made to the following for information supplied:

Schlumberger Drilling Services, U.S.A.
Werf Conrad Co., Holland.
Baker Oil Tools, Inc., of America.
Craelius Co., Ltd., London.
Joy Manufacturing Co., Sullivan Division, Pittsburg, U.S.A.
National Lead Co., Ltd., Houston, U.S.A.

CHAPTER 5

SINKING

THE word "shaft" as used in the following account of sinking methods refers to a vertical shaft. It is often used in U.S.A. and elsewhere to refer to entrances and openings into a mine which are not vertical. In coal-mining practice in Great Britain, however, inclined shafts are rarely used. A roadway driven from the surface to a shallow seam, or from one seam to another, and having a low gradient compared with an inclined shaft in a metal mine, is usually referred to as a drift.

Shafts are necessary in mining enterprises where the mineral to be won is at some distance below the surface of the earth. Through them men and minerals are wound in cages or skips to the surface and materials taken underground. They house water pipes, power supply pipes and cables, etc. Shafts are also the medium through which the ventilating current enters and leaves the mine.

There is a limit to the depth from which mineral can be hoisted in one lift. At the south shaft of the Randfontein Central Gold Mining Company the depth is 4,750 ft. In the past, at depths greater than this in metal mines, sub-inclines or sub-vertical shafts have been used.

Two separate shafts are compulsory in coal mines of Great Britain under the Mines and Quarries Act, 1954, Section 22 (1) which states:—

> "Subject to the provisions of this section, it shall not be lawful for any persons to be employed below ground in a mine of coal, stratified ironstone, shale or fireclay unless there are available, for affording to them alternative, and ready, means of ingress and egress, two shafts or outlets (whether belonging exclusively to that mine or not) which, except where they were sunk before January 1, 1865, are at no point separated from each other by less than 45 feet or (where the sinking thereof began before January 1, 1888) 10 feet."

The area of coal which is won from any pair of shafts will depend largely on the depths and number of seams to be worked. Where they are at shallow depth the outlay involved in the sinking of shafts is comparatively small and it therefore becomes less costly to sink new shafts than to haul coal over long distances underground. Deep shafts, however, involve considerable time and cost to sink and equip, consequently underground haulage over longer distances is justified.

SITING OF SHAFTS

The correct siting of the shafts in relation to the area to be developed is highly important, as upon this factor might depend the future success or failure of a mine. The capital outlay in shaft sinking might constitute over half of the total expenditure required, thus it is imperative that there should be no mistake in siting, otherwise, to rectify it might entail further heavy capital expenditure. Mistakes in siting are usually associated with unforeseen underground conditions, therefore a comprehensive investigation and study of the configuration of the underlying seams by prospecting and boring is essential for the detailed planning of the mining developments.

The position of the shafts is dependent upon both underground and surface factors.

Surface Factors.—(1) An ample supply of fresh water is needed for the colliery power plant, washeries, etc.

(2) The cost of laying railways and sidings is high, therefore short routes to the main line railways are desirable.

(3) The site should be level, or nearly so, and of some acres in extent. The actual size will bear a relation to the capacity of the colliery.

(4) It is an advantage, in European countries, to house labour near existing towns and villages, an asset of considerable importance if the site can be within their proximity.

(5) The disposal of spoil is a matter for careful consideration. It is unlikely that collieries, however highly modernised, will completely re-absorb all the debris produced, except where conditions are exceptionally favourable. Thus it is desirable to choose a site suited for debris disposal.

(6) A large electrical power supply is needed and, unless the colliery is to generate its own, the availability of power from the National Grid is desirable.

(7) Surface water should drain away from the site, which should not be within a possible flood area, and the surface plant and sidings should preferably be situated on firm ground.

(8) Access to main roads should be short.

Underground Factors.—(1) The site must be considered having regard to the shape and size of the colliery boundary, the presence of geological disturbances and the prevailing amount and direction of dip of the seams.

(2) The nature of the overlying strata needs careful study and examination to avoid, if possible, sinking through strata which would present considerable technical difficulties.

(3) If the seams are highly inclined and the horizon system of mining is to be practised, then the centre of the area might appear to be the best position for the location of the shafts, thereby reducing the lengths of the stone haulage roads to a minimum.

In general, if the seams are level, or nearly so, the centre of the area is the most suitable, particularly if the area is relatively undisturbed, but simple cases such as this rarely occur. In modern mining the natural surface features do not weigh as heavily as the underground factors and, assuming that a

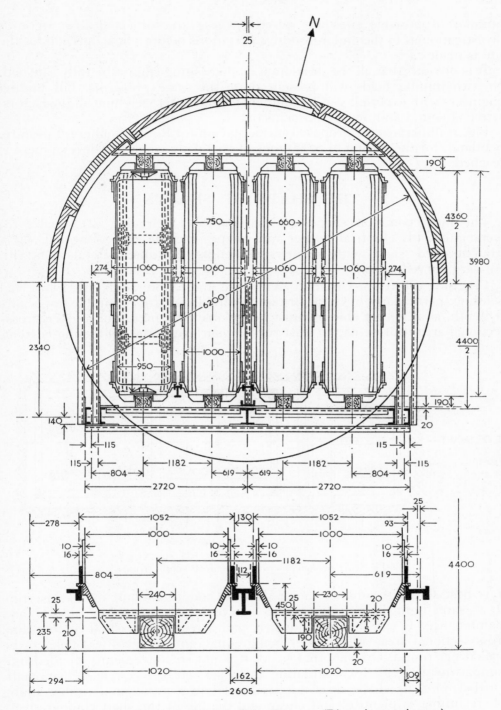

Fig. 2.—Circular compound shaft, Ruhr, Germany. (Dimensions are in mm.)

167

number of possible sites are selected, these are subjected to a rigorous investigation as to the underground implications before a final decision for the site is made.

It is obvious that all the desiderata in shaft siting cannot be fully satisfied. No two mining fields will present quite the same problems, but mining engineers with experience and judgment should, after weighing all the factors, arrive at sound and decisive conclusions.

Fig. 1[1] illustrates the proposed surface layout for Rothes Colliery, Fifeshire, Scotland, for the raising of 5,000 tons of coal daily when full development is reached.

THE SHAPE OF SHAFTS

The most common shapes of shafts are: (1) circular, (2) square, (3) rectangular, (4) elliptical. Other rare shapes include—(1) octagonal, (2) a straight-sided shaft with semicircular ends, (3) quadrilateral but with outward curved sides.

Circular Shafts.—Circular shafts are most commonly used for coal winding, particularly in Great Britain. A circular shaft is desirable, especially at depth, as it is best able to resist heavy side pressures. For a given cross-sectional area it presents the least rubbing surface to the ventilating current.

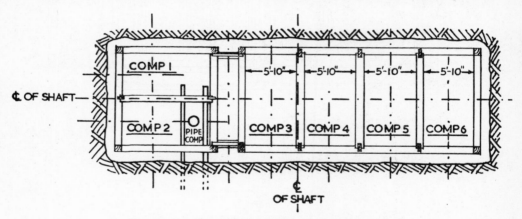

Fig. 3.—Rectangular shaft, Vlakfontein, South Africa.

It is best suited to sinking under difficult conditions and to the insertion of a water-tight lining, being also comparatively cheap in upkeep and maintenance. It can be sunk quicker than a rectangular shaft of the same cross-sectional area, other things being equal, and requires less holes to be drilled per round. On the other hand, it is not so conveniently divided into compartments (e.g., for ventilation purposes, etc.) as a rectangular shaft. Furthermore, its shape does not lend itself to a permanent timber lining where timber is plentiful and cheap and the life of the shaft comparatively short. Fig. 2 illustrates a layout for a circular compound shaft in the Ruhr.

The minimum size of a circular shaft is about 5 ft. and the largest shaft in Great Britain is 25 ft. diameter in the clear. The modern tendency in Great Britain is to sink shafts of large diameter. Recent examples are at Manton Colliery, Nottinghamshire, and Rothes, Fifeshire, where the shafts recently sunk are 24 ft. in diameter.

Rectangular Shafts.—Rectangular shafts are used extensively in metalliferous mining practice and were formerly used at coal mines in Wales and Scotland. They lend themselves to the use of a timber lining and can be divided readily into compartments with great economy in space. In practice the number of compartments varies up to a maximum of eight. South African mining practice indicates that for a given cross-sectional area, a rectangular shaft will cost more to sink than a circular shaft, although it is not possible to correlate properly sinking costs in South Africa with similar costs in Great Britain because it is usual in South Africa to consider *speed* in sinking as a prime factor, which adds to the sinking costs. The smallest size rectangular shaft is about $4\frac{1}{2}$ ft. $\times$ 6 ft., this being a minimum size which would allow sinkers to drill and load debris without undue restriction of working. Large section rectangular shafts are in operation at metal mines. Examples are the Vlakfontein No. 1 Shaft, South Africa, which is 43 ft. $\times$ 14·5 ft., in six compartments, and the Wolluter Shaft, South Africa, which is 46 ft. $\times$ 9 ft., in seven compartments. Fig. 3 shows the layout for the Vlakfontein No. 1 shaft.

Elliptical Shafts.— Elliptical shafts aim at combining the advan-

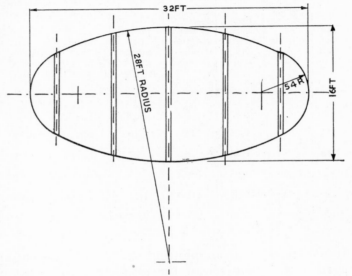

Fig. 4.—Elliptical shaft.

tages of both rectangular and circular shafts, namely, to obtain a strong, durable and economical section and, at the same time, to make maximum use of the available space. The shape of the so-called elliptical shaft may not be elliptical in the geometrical sense of the word but more simply composed of four circular arcs, as shown in Fig. 4. An elliptical shaft can be designed to have a concrete lining, when the shuttering plates would need to be specially designed for a particular section. In recent South African experience it is considered that the over-all cost of sinking and equipping an elliptical shaft might be intermediate between circular and rectangular shafts, and about 80 per cent. of the cost of a rectangular shaft of the same cross-sectional area.

Size of Shafts.—The size of the shafts will depend largely on the desired output from the mine and the type of winding. By the adoption of skips it is possible to draw a larger output than would be possible with cage winding for a given shaft section, whereupon the question of the maximum amount of ventilating air which is to pass through the shaft, and the need to reduce the ventilating power losses in the shaft to a minimum, would have to be considered. It is possible to weigh the annual costs of the ventilating power losses in the shaft in the design of the shaft section. Professor Statham gave (1939) the following table for the determination of the optimum size of a circular shaft when certain estimates were made. These estimates would not be strictly applicable at the present day, but the figures serve to illustrate, very clearly, the principles involved. (See also Vol. 3, Chap. 6.)

TABLE I

1	2	3	4	5	6	7	8	9	10
Dia. of shaft	Air velocity in shaft	Pressure absorbed in shaft	H.P. absorbed in shaft, assuming efficiency of 70%	Cost of power per annum $\frac{3}{8}d.$ per unit	Estimated capital cost of sinking and lining shaft	Annual charge for interest and redemption of capital at 10%	Total annual charge, assuming 10% for interest and redemption	Annual charge for interest and redemption of capital at 7½%	Total annual charge, assuming 7½% for interest and redemption
ft.	ft./min.	W.G. in.	H.P.	£	£	£	£	£	£
20	700	0·18	8·7	89	27,700	2,770	2,859	2,078	2,167
18	865	0·31	15·5	158	26,600	2,660	2,518	1,770	1,928
16	1,094	0·54	26·7	273	19,800	1,980	2,253	1,485	1,758
14	1,429	1·05	52·1	532	16,200	1,620	2,152	1,215	1,747
12	1,945	2·27	112·3	1,147	13,000	1,300	2,447	975	2,122
10	2,801	5·65	279·8	2,856	10,200	1,020	3,876	765	3,621

It will be seen from plotting the values in columns 9 and 10 of Table I against the diameter of the shaft that the most economical size of shaft would be:—

14 ft. with interest and redemption charges at 10 per cent.
15 ft. 　　 ,, 　　 ,, 　　 ,, 　　 ,, 　　 7½ 　　 ,,

Professor Statham stated further: ". . . these sizes are based purely on economic considerations of capital cost and annual charges for power and, in practice, other factors must be taken into consideration. Thus, with a 14 ft. diameter shaft, the air velocity of 1,429 ft. per minute is high . . . furthermore, the calculation does not include allowances for the resistance of the cages and shaft fittings. . . ."

Assuming that the ventilating power losses and the air velocity in the shaft are not too high, as in the case of larger diameter shafts, it can be regarded that the size of the shaft is related to the annual output of the mine. This output, knowing the reserves and the estimated life of the mine, can readily be calculated. From the annual output it is possible to calculate the daily and hourly output and having regard to the depth and speed of winding the output per wind can be determined.

This governs the size of cages or skips and the size of the shaft must be such as to accommodate these with due allowance for guides, etc.

It might be stated here that a commonly regarded disadvantage of circular shafts, namely, the lack of economy in space for the shaft equipment, might be an advantage where the shaft has to carry a large ventilating current of air.

PRELIMINARY OPERATIONS

Since it is the practice in coal mining in Great Britain to sink circular shafts, the preliminary operations described will refer to a circular shaft sunk through Coal Measure strata.

It is usually necessary to consolidate around the site of the proposed shaft and a certain amount of levelling the ground may be necessary prior to the erection of the surface plant.

The centre of the shaft is located and fixed and permanent marks are set in the ground from which the centre of the shaft may be checked at any time. Four concrete blocks, carrying centre marks, are usually used (Fig. 5) and the centre is obtained by cross-stringing from the blocks.

The perimeter of the area to be excavated is pegged out, using a radius rod, the actual diameter of this will depend upon the finished

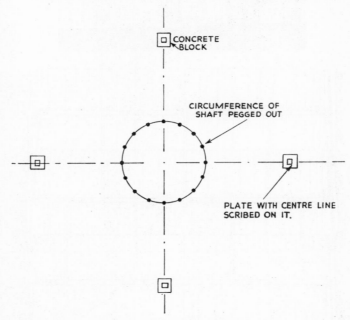

Fig. 5.—Centre mark of sinking shaft.

diameter of the shaft, the permanent lining and the nature of the ground. The purpose of the first excavation is to reach a strong bedrock. If a large thickness of unconsolidated ground such as sands or gravels overlies the rockhead, special methods of sinking may have to be adopted. Present practice in Great Britain for the preliminary operations is to raise the hoppit containing the debris by means of a crane fitted with a long jib, or a grab may be used in lieu of the hoppit, the crane being sited not less than 10 ft. from the edge of the excavation. This crane can be used down to a depth of about 100 ft.

Temporary Lining. —Temporary lining is inserted as excavation proceeds. This consists of skeleton rings, hangers, backing deals and tightening wedges. The skeleton rings are usually made in segments of from 6 to 10 ft. long, depending on the diameter, their section being about 4 in. by $\frac{5}{8}$ in. to 1 in. They are fish-plated together with 1-in. square-necked bolts, the skeleton rings carrying square holes and the fishplates round ones. Long fishplates are used if the diameter has to be increased beyond the standard diameter, due to minor collapses of the ground. The backing deals are made in standard sizes, commonly 6 in. $\times$ 1$\frac{1}{2}$ in. $\times$ 4$\frac{1}{2}$ ft. The hangers may be in two sizes, the shorter size being used when the skeleton rings have to be brought closer together. The wedges are driven between the skeleton rings and backing deals to secure the lining. Fig. 6a and b illustrate temporary lining in position.

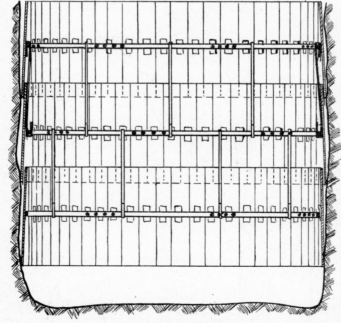

Fig. 6a and b.—Temporary lining.

The first skeleton ring to be inserted is usually suspended by chains from rolled-steel joists or wooden baulks which are arranged over the mouth of the shaft. Some of the subsequent skeleton rings are also lashed directly to the surface supports to reduce the load on the first skeleton ring as much as possible. The ground around the shaft is disturbed as little as possible during these preliminary operations and, if blasting has to be done, only light charges are used. Most of the trimming is done with pneumatic picks.

When a good strong bedrock has been reached, preparations are made for the insertion of the permanent lining. It is essential that the first length of lining should be thoroughly watertight, otherwise there is a probability of scaling and weathering due to ice action in cold weather. Modern practice,

Fig. 7.—Shuttering used whilst lining with concrete.

even when a permanent lining in brick is specified, is to line at least the first section in monolithic concrete.

Assuming that concrete is to be used, a curb at the bottom of the shaft is prepared and levelled in readiness for the first ring of shuttering or falsework (Fig. 7). This is prefabricated in sections about $2\frac{1}{2}$ ft. deep, made of $\frac{1}{4}$-in. plate, and one complete ring will consist of a number of equal segments which, when bolted together, will have an outside diameter equal to the finished diameter of the shaft. Each segment has a $2\frac{1}{2}$ in. $\times$ $2\frac{1}{2}$ in. angle iron riveted round the edge. On the bottom and one side the angle iron overlaps the plate and on the other two sides the plate overlaps the angle irons. This overlap prevents leakage of liquid cement but it necessitates the use of a special vertical joint to complete a ring of shuttering and also to facilitate removal of the shuttering when the concrete has set. One plain overlapping vertical joint

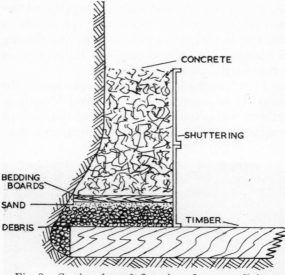

Fig. 8.—Section through first ring of concrete lining.

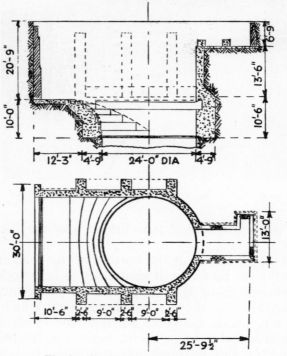

Fig. 9.—Shaft collar, Manton Colliery.

without angle irons is usually used for this purpose and the first segment of shuttering is removed by means of pinch bars.

The segments are bolted together at 6-in. centres for the vertical joints and 12-in. centres for the horizontal joints; a strengthening rib is riveted horizontally on to each segment.

The first ring of shuttering is set on timbers arranged radially around the curb and the ring is levelled with a "straight-edge". The shaft centre line is suspended and the ring is adjusted until it is central by measurement with a radius arm from the centre line. The two operations are repeated until there is no detectable error in level or in symmetry. The vertical joints are buttressed and the space between the ring and the back wall prepared for concrete. A thickness of about 6-in. of debris is laid and on top of this a thin layer of sand. Bedding boards are laid over the sand and the base completed with a brattice cloth bed. Concrete is then poured almost to the top of the first ring. It is essential that the concrete be rammed with a punning tool. This prevents honeycombing of the concrete and brings cement milk against the face of the shuttering to give a smooth finish to the lining. Fig. 8 shows diagrammatically the section through the first ring. The second ring is fixed and the lining built up towards the surface. A temporary scaffold may be used at this stage of the sinking or, if the first length of walling is not too deep, a timber or tubular steel scaffolding may be built up inside the falsework.

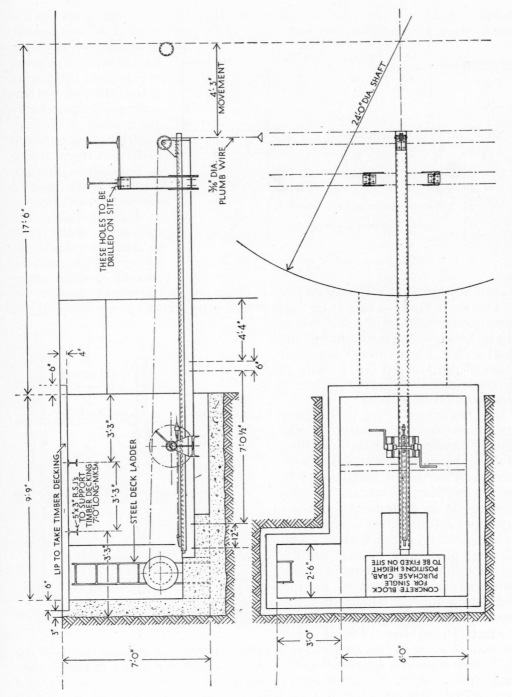

Fig. 10.—Centre line apparatus for circular shaft.

Bunton boxes are provided by fixing wooden boxes in the shaft at the approximate places within the shuttering. The ground around the boxes must be opened out to maintain an equal thickness of concrete at all points within the lining when walling in water-bearing ground. The temporary lining is removed as the permanent lining is built up, although, where corrugated sheets are used instead of backing deals, the temporary lining is left in and the space between the lining and the ground grouted afterwards. This process is described later in dealing with watertight linings.

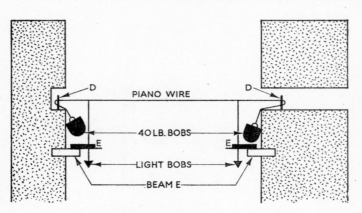

Fig. 11.—Plumbing apparatus for rectangular shaft.

The shaft lining ceases at an appropriate depth from the surface and the construction work of the shaft top is put in hand for the formation of the shaft collar. Fig. 9 shows the shaft collar of the Manton No. 4 Shaft. It is constructed to serve either a Koepe or Drum winder.

The last stages in the preliminary operations are the erection of the sinking headgear and the installing of the sinking equipment. All the surface plant needed is installed while the preliminary operations are proceeding. It is customary in large-capacity shafts to erect a temporary winding headgear for sinking. The winding plant may or may not be permanent, depending largely on the estimated time allotted to sinking and equipping the shafts and the capacity of the plant.

Shaft Plumbing.—Plumb lines

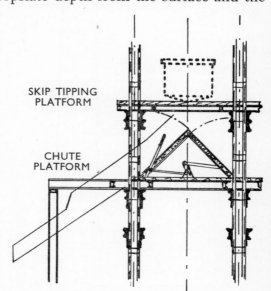

Fig. 12.—Folding doors in headgear to facilitate disposal of debris.

are used to assist in checking and maintaining the verticality and radius of the shaft during sinking operations. One central plumb line or centre line is used for a circular shaft. Fig. 10 illustrates one type of centre-line apparatus for a circular shaft. It is assembled in a specially built trench at the mouth of the shaft and consists of a 6 in. × 3 in. channel which runs on an 8 in. × 5 in. rolled-steel joist. The rolled-steel joist is concreted firmly and horizontally into the floor of the trench and its axis of prolongation lies along a diameter of the shaft section. The 6 in. × 3 in. channel, which has a racking bar welded along its longitudinal axis, rests on, and is a sliding fit over, the upper flange of the rolled-steel joist. Two stop blocks are concreted into the floor and another two are bolted to the sides of the channel. A spur wheel, engaging with the racking bar, is turned by a manually-operated winding handle and thus the channel can be racked along a diameter of the shaft. The plummet or centering wire is taken from a reel and wound up or down the shaft over a pulley at the end of the channel.

For plumbing rectangular shafts it is necessary to use at least four plumb lines. Usually four pockets are made in the shaft collar under which beams are concreted into the shaft side (Fig. 11), and to these beams four plumbing brackets (D and E) are attached. These plumbing brackets are fitted with adjustable centre tapped plugs which, when set, are not disturbed during sinking. The plumb wires are threaded through the brackets and form a rectangle, having dimensions a convenient amount less than the finished size of the shaft. Measurements taken from these plumb wires give the correct size, shape and orientation of the shaft section.

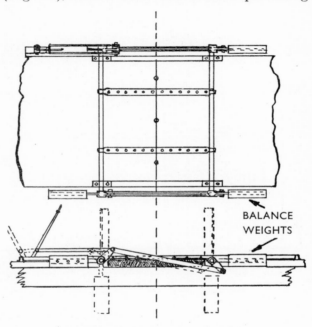

Fig. 13.—Safety doors at ground level.

SINKING EQUIPMENT

The major items of plant for an ordinary sinking, where no exceptional difficulties are expected, will include the following:—

The Headgear.—This is ordinarily constructed of standard "I" girders suitably braced. The height of the framework will vary from 50 to 80 ft. The walling-scaffold pulleys and the winding-rope pulleys are usually seated along the same horizontal axis. The pulleys for pumps, electrical power, lighting, shot-firing, cables, etc., are normally suspended at a lower position in the headgear, with the pulleys so arranged that the cables hang near the wall of the shaft. At about 15 to 20 ft. above ground level folding doors are built into the headgear for facilitating the disposal of spoil from the sinking bucket. The doors are lever operated (Fig. 12) by the banksman. The sinking bucket is tipped over the crown of the closed doors and the debris gravitates through a chute into a wagon or a dumping car. At ground level a pair of safety doors are fitted which, when closed, cover the mouth of the shaft (Fig. 13). These doors are also lever-operated by the banksman, and notches are cut in the edges through which the winding rope and the two scaffold ropes thread when the doors are closed. Fig. 14 illustrates a temporary headgear used at the sinking of one of the Rothes (Fife)[2] Colliery Shafts.

The ropes for both the hoppit and the walling scaffold should be of the

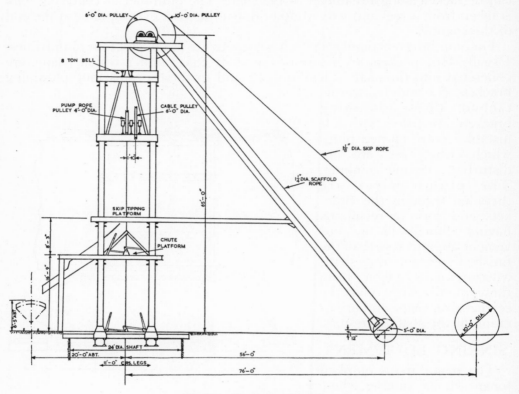

Fig. 14.—Temporary headgear.

locked-coil type. This is desirable for the suspension of the sinking bucket because of its non-spin qualities.

The Winding Engine.—This might be steam or electrically driven. The modern tendency is to install an electrically-driven winder. At Manton Colliery No. 4 Shaft sinking a steam winder was used with two 26-in. cylinders. The stroke was 5 ft. and steam pressure 150 lb. per sq. in. The diameter of the winding drum was 8 ft. It is compulsory by law to provide visual indicators whereby the winding engineman can, at all times, see the position of the sinking bucket. The indicators must also show the position of the walling scaffold, since the rider has to be brought to rest slowly over the walling scaffold rope capels.

The accessories at the end of the winding rope are illustrated in Fig. 15 and consist of:—

CLIVVY HOOK.—The clivvy hook is fitted with a safety drop tongue and balance lever. It is constructed of mild steel. The purpose of the balance lever is to allow the hoppit to be detached from the hook quickly and yet provide a safe link while raising and lowering.

LIFTING CONE.—A lifting cone is attached in an intermediate position between the chains connecting the clivvy and the detaching hook.

DETACHING HOOK.—The detaching hook is of standard type. (Vol. 2, Chap. 3.)

CAPEL.—The capel is usually of the waved-groove type and specially designed for heavy loads.

RIDER.—The rider runs on the ropes supporting the walling scaffold. Its action is to guide the hoppit and prevent it from swinging during its ascent and descent. The rider is fitted with renewable brasses to save wear on the walling scaffold ropes. When the sinking bucket has been lowered past the walling scaffold stage the rider rests on the capels of the scaffold ropes. The bell mouth at the centre of the rider is so constructed that the detaching hook and capel is allowed to pass through it. The action of the rider in steadying the sinking bucket is not opera-

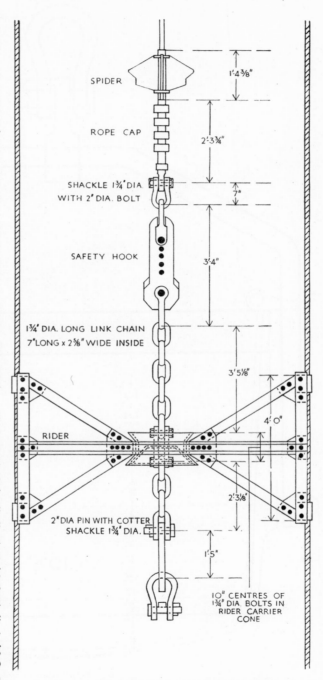

Fig. 15.—Safety attachments and accessories at end of winding rope for sinking.

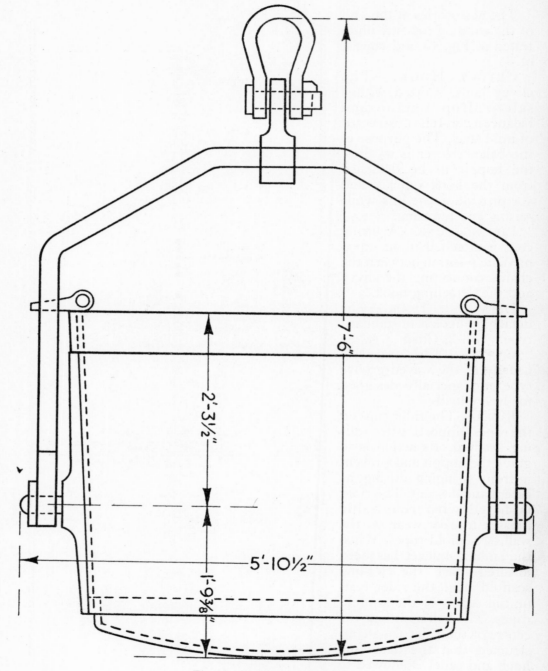

Fig. 16.—Hoppit used in sinking.

7'-6"

2'-3½"

5'-10½"

1'-9⅜"

tive for the whole depth of the shaft, depending on the height of the walling scaffold from the shaft floor. A brass guide sleeve or spider which rides on the winding rope is also necessary. Its purpose is to guide the winding rope after the bucket has passed the walling stage and it is shaped to fit the bell mouth of the rider. The effective diameter of the spider is greater than the diameter of the mouth of the headgear safety-catch plate. If the load is overwound the spider arms collapse against the catch plate, allowing the capel to pass through and the detaching hook to function.

THE HOPPIT.—The hoppit, bowk, or sinking bucket, of which a typical example is illustrated in Fig. 16, is used to raise debris and water as well as to transport men and materials. The capacity of the hoppit should be ample and it must be so secured to the bridle when in transit that there is no danger of debris or material falling out. It should be easily emptied and returned from the tipped to the upright position. For this purpose the centre of gravity of a hoppit should be slightly below the trunnions when it is empty and above when full.

Safety catches lock the bridle and prevent the hoppit from accidentally overturning. The hoppit shown in Fig. 16 has a capacity of about 64 cu. ft. and weighs approximately a ton. With such a hoppit the total load on the end of the winding rope when the hoppit is full of debris is roughly as follows:—

		lb.	
Hoppit	.. ..	2,300	
Debris	.. ..	6,400	(approximately)
Water in voids of debris..	.. .. ..	1,500	,,
Rope capel	.. ..	125	
Chains and shackles	.. .. ..	140	
Rider, etc.	.. ..	2,000	
Clivvy	.. ..	180	
Detaching hook	.. ..	240	
	TOTAL ..	12,885 lb. or 5·75 tons (approx.)	

The actual size of the rope for this load will depend on the depth of the winding. For a total sinking depth of, say, 3,000 ft. a $1\frac{1}{8}$-in. diameter locked-coil rope, with a breaking strain of 75 tons, would give a minimum static factor of safety of approximately 9.

THE WALLING SCAFFOLD.—This is a circular platform with a central trap-door to allow the hoppit to pass through. It also acts as a protective cover for the sinkers and to store light sinking equipment such as small pumps, electric lighting clusters, safety ladder, etc., during blasting. It consists of a framework of rolled-steel joists to which the wood floor is fixed. (Fig. 17.) Its diameter is approximately 6 in. less than the finished diameter of the shaft and it is supported by two ropes from four bull chains, two to each rope, with top and bottom shackles for connecting to the scaffold and rope-capel ring. The walling-scaffold ropes are usually of the locked-coil type and their diameter is about the same as that of the winding rope. Walling scaffolds have been

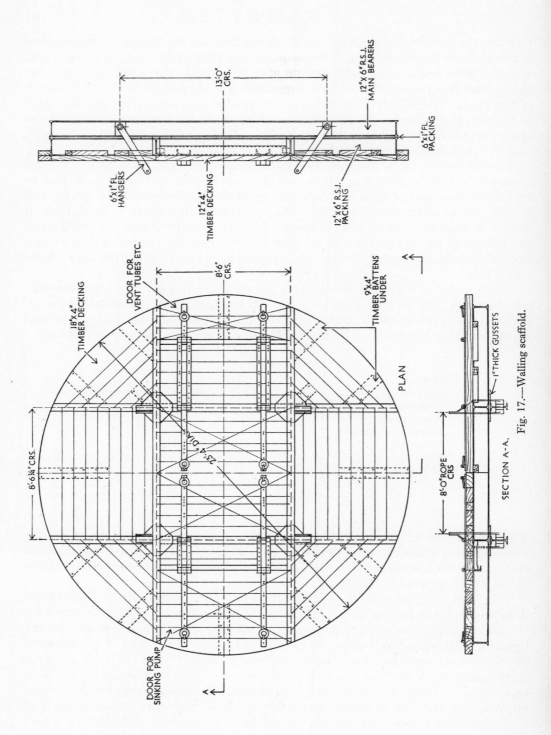

13'-0" CRS.

12"x 6"R.S.I. MAIN BEARERS

6"x1"FL PACKING

6"x1"FL. HANGERS

12"x4" TIMBER DECKING

12"x 6"R.S.I. PACKING

DOOR FOR VENT TUBES ETC.

8'-6" CRS.

18"x4" TIMBER DECKING

9"x4" TIMBER BATTENS UNDER

PLAN

8'-6¼" CRS.

23'-4" DIA.

DOOR FOR SINKING PUMP

1"THICK GUSSETS

8'-0"ROPE CRS

SECTION A-A.

Fig. 17.—Walling scaffold.

designed to allow sinking and walling operations to be performed simultaneously, but the system has not been practised to any great extent in Great Britain.

THE WALLING-SCAFFOLD CAPSTAN ENGINE.—The scaffold ropes are taken over the headgear pulleys to the drums of the capstan engine which for a $1\frac{1}{8}$-in. diameter rope, would normally be 4 to 6 ft. in diameter, with a separate drum for each rope. The drums are driven through worm gearing by a twin-cylinder steam engine and each drum has a separate band brake. The drums can be disengaged to allow each scaffold rope to be adjusted separately.

The maximum weight taken by the walling scaffold ropes, when a concrete lining is being inserted, would be, approximately:—

	lb.	
Walling scaffold	12,200	
Bull chains	3,360	*Note.*—For a short
64 cu. ft. hoppit (empty)	2,300	period the walling scaf-
Ditto (full of concrete)	10,620	fold might have to
12 men	2,240	support the weight of
Shuttering or falsework plates ..	4,480	two hoppits and their
64 cu. ft. concrete	8,320	contents.

43,520 lb. = say, 20 tons

Layout.—A typical sinking layout showing the equipment used is illustrated in Figs. 18*a* and *b*. The cementation plant is only necessary when applying this particular method where the strata needs special treatment to reduce the amount of water in the shaft.

Lighting.—Although carbide lamps may still, in exceptional circumstances, be used, the majority of shaft-lighting equipment consists of a combination of hand-battery lamps and hanging electric light clusters, the latter being supported by the shaft cable and energised from a surface power supply.

Fig. 19 illustrates a hand-battery lamp designed to meet the arduous conditions in the Kent coalfield during sinkings there. The very large quantities of water encountered demanded that the lamps should be constructed as watertight as possible. The lamp is carried by a steel bridle running on trunnions with leather packing, and locked by wing nuts, enabling the light to be directed accurately to any position. A strong aluminium casting carries four standard type interchangeable batteries, which are of the unspillable type. These are connected in series automatically by a contact plate on the lid. The lamp will give about 15 c.p. over a period of 8 hours from a Krypton-filled bulb.

HANGING-LIGHT CLUSTERS.—The bulbs of the mains-fed clusters usually have a rating of 60 W at 110 v., and there may be four or six lamps per cluster. A cluster is connected to the power cable which is suspended from the surface and is sufficiently strengthened by armoured braid to support its own weight

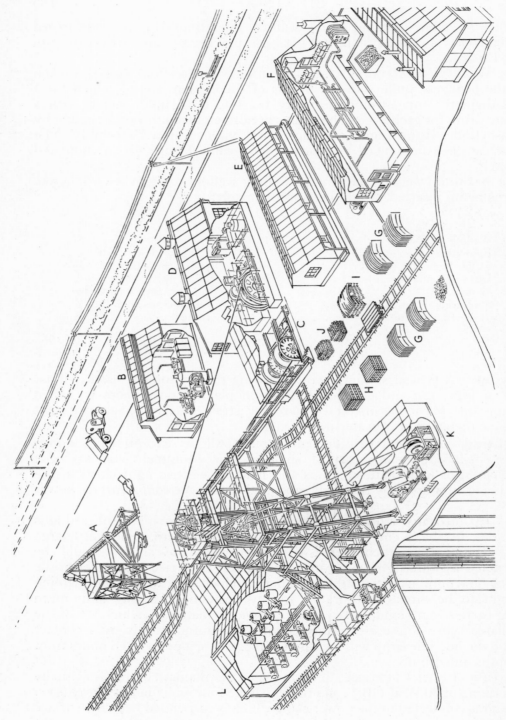

Fig. 18a.—Layout and surface equipment for sinking.

A—Batching plant.
B—Compressor house.
C—Scaffold capstan.
D—Winding engine.
E—Offices.
F—Drying shed.
G—Falsework segments.
H—Backing deals.
I—Skeleton rings.
J—Hangers.
K—Pump capstan and cable drum.
L—Cementation shed.

184

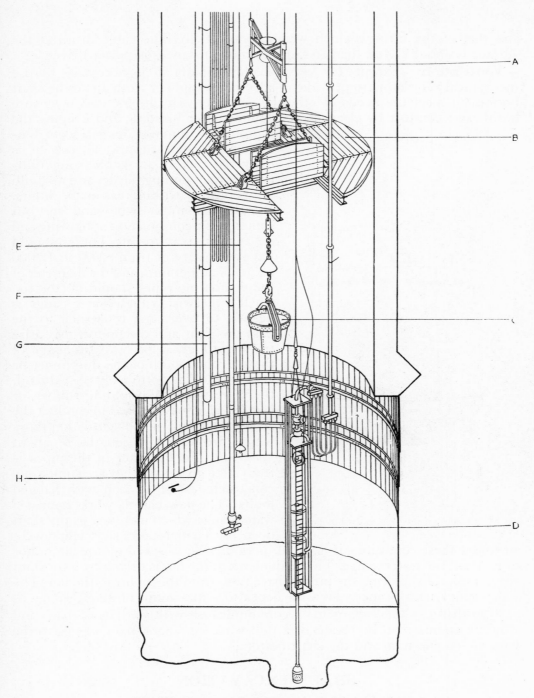

Fig. 18*b*.—Layout and equipment in shaft being sunk.

A—Rider.
B—Walling scaffold.
C—Sinking bucket or hoppit.
D—Sinking pump.
E—Lighting cable.
F—Compressed-air main.
G—Ventilating duct.
H—Signalling wire.

and that of the fittings which weigh about 20 lb. The cable drum at the surface is about 2–3 ft. diameter and in most instances is power driven.

Ventilation.—Except for very shallow shafts it is necessary to use mechanical ventilators to provide an adequate supply of fresh air to the shaft bottom to meet the needs of officials, workmen and others, and to ensure health and comfort by clearing away fumes after blasting, and keeping the bottom free from noxious gases, etc. Unless an adequate supply of fresh air is delivered there may also be some difficulty in maintaining the dry and wet bulb temperatures within reasonable limits. It is the custom to use blowing fans, but sometimes a combination of blowing and exhaust fans may operate. The fan should have a capacity of from 5,000 to 12,000 cu. ft. of air per min. and the diameter of the ventilating pipes should not be too small, otherwise a high water gauge is needed to overcome resistance to the passage of air and discomfort may arise from the high velocity of discharge of the air. The mouth of the duct must be kept close to the bottom of the shaft and, therefore, a length of folding-rubber, or canvas, tube may be used to conduct the air from the end of the ventilation pipes which are added in lengths of about 10–25 ft. The diameter of the pipes is from 20 to 36 in. and they are commonly constructed of sheet iron with flanged joints. The fan has to work against a water gauge which increases as the shaft deepens. To maintain a sufficient flow of air under these conditions it is usual, periodically, to speed up the fan motor to increase the water gauge. This is done when the fan is driven by a constant speed motor, by altering the pulley drive ratio from the motor to the fan. The water gauge usually increases with depth to a maximum of about 12 in.

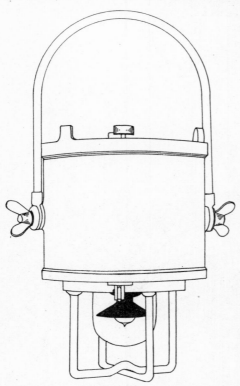

Fig. 19.—Electric hand-lamp as used in sinking.

Signalling.—The chargeman communicates with the banksman and winding engine-man by means of a pull wire. The banksman signals to the winding engine-man and the shaft bottom.

SHAFT EXCAVATION

The cycle of operations consists of three phases:—Drilling, blasting, and loading out the debris. At times, however, there may be cases when the ground does not require the use of explosives. (See also Chapters 8 and 9.)

Drilling.—The pattern of drilling will depend upon many factors such as the shape and size of the shaft, the nature of the rock and the type of explosive used. The depth of the holes may vary from 3 to 10 ft. A set pattern of holes will be formulated for any one shaft section but some flexibility may be allowed for any changes in the hardness of the rock and to take advantage of natural features in the strata which may increase the efficiency of blasting. It should be remembered that the purpose of blasting is not merely to free the rock from the space to be excavated but also to break it up to a size which can be most expeditiously handled and loaded into the hoppit. In addition the

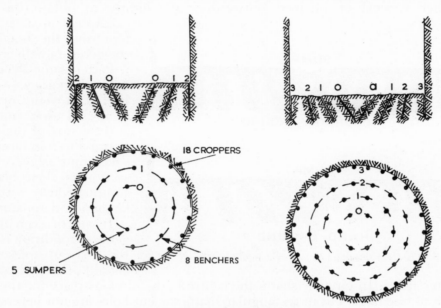

Fig. 20.—Blasting holes for circular shaft.

blasting must be arranged so that the side walls are disturbed as little as possible.

There are two methods which are commonly used to excavate a shaft section:—

    (i) To drill and blast a sump and then, while the sump debris is being loaded, to drill the remainder of the shaft and subsequently blast these holes with or without the use of delay-action detonators.

    (ii) To drill out the section completely and blast the round with the use of delay-action detonators.

The first method is sometimes practised for shaft sinking in Great Britain, while the second is commonly applied in South Africa. The advantage of the first is that it is possible to examine the free faces formed by the blowing of a sump and to place extra holes, if necessary, to facilitate the breaking of the ground, with less chance of blown-out shots. On the other hand, the first method is more time-consuming than the second, since the time taken to clear the shaft bottom of fumes and the delay in raising and lowering men and materials, is duplicated.

The use of delay-action detonators greatly reduces the risk of blown-out shots. The number of holes per round varies up to 120 in large rectangular shafts. Fig. 20 shows two typical patterns of holes for a circular shaft 20 ft. in diameter, in limestone and coal measures. The depths of the bencher holes are 6 ft. with the sumpers about $6\frac{1}{2}$ ft. The sumpers and the inner ring (i.e., the benchers) are inclined towards the centre of the shaft, the inner ring to a lesser degree than the sumpers. The outer ring of holes (i.e., the croppers) is either vertical or inclined outwards very slightly to obtain the full excavated area at the base and the holes are staggered radially.

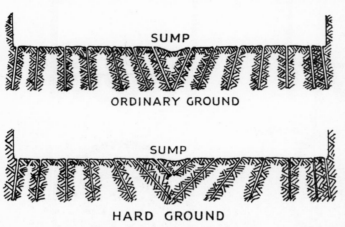

Fig. 21.—Blasting holes for rectangular shaft.

Patterns for a rectangular shaft are shown in Fig. 21. A wedge of rock is blasted away initially at the centre of the shaft to provide free faces for succeeding shots. This section is then blasted simultaneously with delay-action detonators.

It will be seen that a general condition is that the first-cut holes fired should provide faces for the later holes. In circular shafts the centre is the obvious place for the formation of free faces, but in rectangular shafts the cut holes are not necessarily in the centre of the shaft and are commonly near and parallel to one of the short sides.

Delay-action Detonators.—These are fired electrically and were introduced in 1910. They were of the safety-fuse type. Modern gasless delay detonators (Chap. 9) are much more compact and certain in use, and are manufactured in ranges of 0–10 with one second and half second delay; thus No. 7 in the one-second series would detonate 7 seconds after initiation of the fusehead and No. 7 in the half-second series would detonate $3\frac{1}{2}$ seconds afterwards. A tag attached to the leads gives the number of the delay. The "O" detonators are instantaneous and should always be used for the cut holes because all O detonators explode simultaneously. This is not strictly true of other detonators fitted with the same delay elements, although the time difference in detonation is very small.

It is the practice in South Africa to wire up the holes from busbars in a number of parallel connections. In Britain, under the Mines and Quarries Act, all shots must be connected in series. The primer cartridge must also be placed at the bottom of the hole; thus if one hole is partly cut off by another, the primer cartridge will initiate in the hole. The maximum permitted delay time in British sinkings is four seconds, although a longer period might be granted by H.M. Inspector of Mines. Furthermore, delay detonators cannot be used within 5 yd. of a known coal seam. A longer time is allowed in South African mining practice. Fig. 22 shows the arrangements for the use of delay action detonators for a rectangular shaft. The number indicates the delay period in each case.

Explosives.—Gelignite is very largely used except where conditions do not permit, such as in strata from which firedamp may issue, when permitted explosives have to be used. The gelignite is usually 40 to 60 per cent. nitroglycerine strength, although exceptionally a 93 per cent. nitroglycerine explosive or dynamite is used in very hard rock. The contents of two explosive types used for any normal sinking are as follows:—

Polar Ajax[3] (permitted explosive)		%	50% Gelignite[4] (non-permitted)		%
Nitroglycerine	.. ..	27	Nitroglycerine	.. ..	27·2
Nitro body	..	1·8	Nitro cotton	.. ..	0·8
Nitro cotton	.. ..	0·75	Sodium nitrate	.. ..	12·5
Ammonia nitrate	.. ..	40·45	Ammonia nitrate	.. ..	50·0
Sodium chloride	.. ..	24·0	Wheat flour	.. ..	4·0
Oat husk meal	.. ..	3·5	Oat husk flour	.. ..	5·0
Chemical clay	.. ..	2·5	Moisture	.. ..	0·5

Drilling Machines.—Shot-holes are normally drilled with compressed-air operated percussive hand-drilling machines. These machines weigh about 40 to 50 lb. and consume 80 to 140 cu. ft. of free air per minute at a working pressure of from 70 to 90 lb. per sq. in. The diameter of the drill steel is from $\frac{7}{8}$ in. to $1\frac{1}{4}$ in. A cross bit is usually used unless the ground is medium hard to soft, when a fish-tail bit might be used. The bit size and drill steel lengths for holes drilled to 8 ft. would be:—

Size	Maximum length ft.	Bit size in.
1	3	2
2	5	$1\frac{3}{8}$
3	$6\frac{1}{2}$	$1\frac{3}{4}$
4	$7\frac{1}{2}$	$1\frac{5}{8}$
5	$8\frac{1}{2}$	$1\frac{1}{2}$

The compressed air for the machines passes down the shaft through a 2 in. to 4 in. pipe range supported at intervals to the shaft side, by band brackets and chains. The joints may be either the flanged type or positive victaulic type. A manifold is attached to the bottom of the pipe range. If a large number of machines is in use then additional manifolds might be used, but a 2-in. manifold, from which 1-in. hose pipes about 25 ft. long are taken to the machines, is generally sufficient. The drilling time, as a percentage of the total working time, will vary considerably, depending on the nature of the ground, but it usually takes from 12 to 24 per cent. of the total sinking cycle.

The life of the drilling bits is considerably increased by the use of tungsten carbide tipped bits, although the first cost is rather high. The following figures relate to the sinking of South Shaft, West Rand Consolidated Mines Ltd.,[5] which is rectangular with an excavated area 31½ ft. by 13½ ft. approximately. Although it refers to metalliferous mining practice it is of general interest. The data is for sinking a total depth of 3,825 ft. The ground sunk through consisted largely of quartzite and a round of holes was drilled, blasted and loaded out in 8 hours. The number of misfires was noticeably large:—

Average number of drilling machines	10
Total machine shifts	10,780
Number of holes drilled	86,124
Total footage drilled	342,977 ft.
Footage drilled per ft. sunk	89·4 ft.
Number of rounds blasted	1,034
Average number of holes per round	83
Average footage drilled per round	331·7 ft.
Quantity of explosives used, 50% and 60% gelignite	86,265 lb.
Footage per 100 lb. of gelignite	4·45 ft.
No. of misfired holes	879
Average number of misfires per round	·85
Percentage of misfires on total blasted	1·02

The following figures[6] relate to circular shafts and show the volume of rock excavated per lb. of explosive:—

Type of rock	Excavated size of shaft ft. in.	Cubic ft. excavated per lb. of explosive
New Red Sandstone	25 2	60·5 (gelignite)
Permian Limestone	24 6	22·7 ,,
Coal Measure Sandstone	26 6	37·8
Hard fissured pennant	23 4	28·57 (58% gelignite)
Clift (Bind)	22 4	32·85 ,, ,,
Coals, Binds, fireclay	22 4	44·89 ,, ,,
Frozen sands and marls	17 5	150·8 (Favier explosive)
Frozen bunter sandstone	23 0	14·8 (Astralite)
Quartzite	22 6	14·8 (65% gelignite)
Hard Limestone	240 sq. ft. rect.	12·0 (40% ,,)

Exploders.—It has been the practice in Great Britain to use a rack-bar type exploder to initiate the detonators, while abroad power mains are often used. Permission for blasting from the power mains in Great Britain must be obtained from H.M. Inspector of Mines. The advantage of power mains would appear to be problematical since high percentages of misfires are reported, although this may be due, to some extent, to the use of parallel circuits, which are not used in this country. A type of exploder introduced recently is capable of firing 200 shots at a time, using low-tension detonators connected in series. The instrument weighs 10 lb. A hand-driven generator supplies an a.c. voltage which, in conjunction with a step-up transformer and metal rectifiers, charges a 6 microfarad condenser to a potential of not less than 1,200 volts. A neon lamp indicates when the condenser is charged and a button switch applies this voltage from the condenser to the terminals. Removal of the charging handle discharges the condenser as a safety precaution. It takes 3 seconds to charge the condenser fully. The exploder will fire 200 detonators of 1·4 ohms resistance each, connected in series through 440 yd. of cable.

Blasting from power mains was applied in the sinking of Vlakfontein No. 1

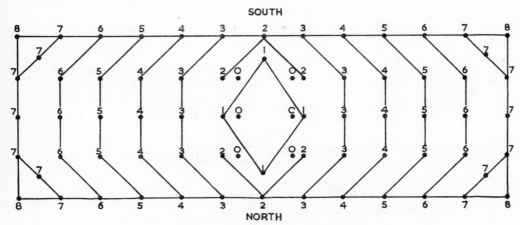

Fig. 22.—Blasting holes, South African practice.

Shaft.[7] Delay-action detonators were used and the safety precautions practised are of interest. After charging the shot holes the main busbar wires, to which about 100 charges were connected, were coupled to two cables suspended from a manifold platform. These cables were attached to a switch by thumb screws C (Fig. 23), the switch being of the two-pole, 60-ampere, knife type, totally enclosed. The shaft cable to this switch was 7 core and was taken via reeling drums to the main blasting switch which was situated in a separate brick house on the surface, fitted with locks, the keys of which were not issued except to those authorised to use them. The blasting cable for the shaft was plugged into an earth socket E, painted green. Before blasting, the plug was pulled out and inserted into a blasting socket F, painted red, which was connected to a main switch. The blasting switch was of the two-pole, spring limit type, and a lever had to be maintained against a spring in the ON position. Thus at all other times the lever was automatically in the OFF position. The red and green lamps H, H were visible from outside the building as an additional safety precaution and indicated the position of the plug attached to the blasting cable, which would normally be plugged into the earth socket. An ammeter A was included in the switch circuit. To eliminate the possibility of induced currents in the blasting cable the headgear and steel structures in its vicinity were effectively earthed.

Loading out the Debris.—Because of the restricted space at the bottom of a sinking shaft, the debris is commonly hand filled. A single hoppit is wound in British sinkings. When two hoppits are used they are filled

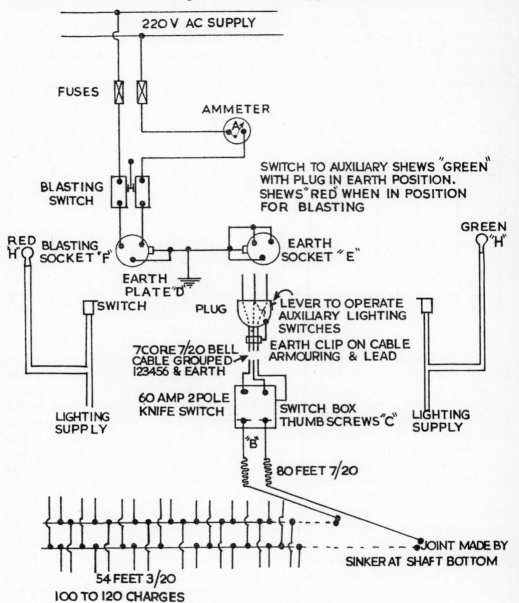

Fig. 23.—Shaft switch, mains firing, Vlakfontein No. 1 shaft.

alternately by the loading party. Sometimes, however, three or more hoppits may be in use. The hoppit, on descending, must be stopped some 18 ft. above the bottom of the shaft. It is then lowered to the bottom of the shaft after receipt of the signal of the chargeman. The hoppit is similarly stopped some 4 ft. above the floor on raising. The number of men employed on loading out debris is controlled by the available space. It is possible, in a rectangular shaft divided into compartments, to employ as many as four of these for loading out, and thus, with native labour, large parties are enabled to perform an

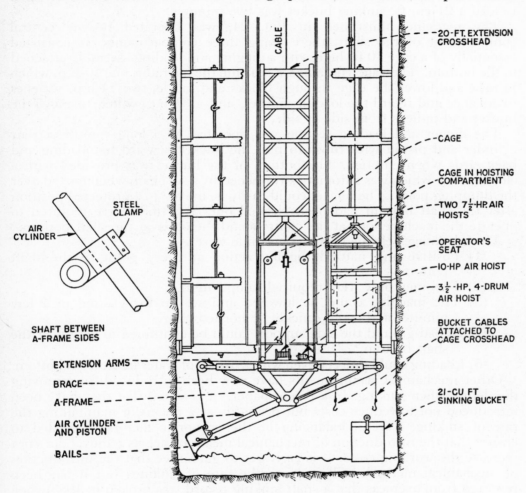

Fig. 24.—Loading machine, American sinking.

8-hour filling, drilling and blasting cycle. In Great Britain a 16-hour or 24-hour cycle is common, with rather larger depths per round of holes. Mechanical loading machines and appliances have been developed for use in both rectangular and circular shafts.

An interesting development of the power-shovel principle for the loading of debris in shafts was in the Mayflower Shaft of the New Park Mining Co., Keltley, Utah.[8] The shaft, rectangular in shape, 17 ft. × 7 ft., was being deepened from the 1,470 ft. level to the 1,850 ft. level. A considerable quantity of water was encountered during the sinking and it required, by hand loading, $9\frac{1}{2}$ shifts of $5\frac{1}{2}$ hours per shift, to complete a 5-ft. advance, of which loading out took six shifts. After the installation of a loading machine, four $5\frac{1}{2}$-hour shifts were required, of which loading occupied only 2 shifts. The time taken to load a 21-cu. ft. sinking bucket was two minutes.

The machine, illustrated in Fig. 24, was operated in the central compartment of the shaft, there being three compartments. It consisted essentially of a cage 10 ft. high with a digging and loading assembly attached to the bottom. The cage contained a seat for the operator, one 10-h.p. winch to raise and lower the cage through blocks and tackle, two $7\frac{1}{2}$-h.p. winches to advance and retard the loading bucket, and a $3\frac{1}{2}$-h.p. winch to move the bucket and pulleys from side to side.

The digger and loading section was operated by a long compressed-air cylinder and piston with ropes to pull the bucket forward for loading and backwards when emptied. The bottom of the bucket was provided with a closure plate which was automatically opened by a set chain when moved over the dumping point. The bucket could easily be moved to a protected position after the shaft bottom had been cleaned out. Two men were required to operate the machine, one at the controls and the other at the shaft bottom.

The advantages claimed for the machine were:—

    (1) Positive and natural digging action at every point in the shaft bottom.

    (2) Two men only were required to operate it.

    (3) The machine could be lowered and set up for loading in a few minutes and could quickly be hoisted clear.

    (4) In bad ground the side support could be continued to very near the shaft bottom.

    (5) Loading could proceed even with 2 to 3 ft. of water in the shaft bottom.

Other mechanical arrangements have now been introduced for removing the debris when sinking. In a recent paper,[9] it is stated that they have been introduced not to reduce costs but primarily as a means of maintaining the rate of sinking. Careful balancing of the economic factors is needed to ensure that the introduction of mechanical means of debris removal does not increase the working costs. It is early yet to guarantee that the introduction of mechanical methods will increase the rate of sinking; but it has been reported from overseas that a shaft-sinking record was broken in 1953 when a pneumatic cactus grab, operating in a shaft of approximately 26 ft. 6 in. diameter, excavated a depth of more than 560 ft. in one month. It is also reported that this type of grab has been recognised in South Africa as the most efficient and economical method of removing the debris in shaft sinking.

In this country, the first mechanical units were slung from the surface, because winches and headgear pulleys, previously used for sinking pumps, were available. The arrangement was, however, uneconomic owing to the high cost of surface winches and headgear arrangements, the cost of the

(*Priestman Bros. Ltd.*)

PNEUMATIC CACTUS GRAB IN OPEN AND CLOSED POSITIONS

The grab is used for loading debris in shaft sinking.

(*Left*) The Worden gravimeter at a road station.

(*Right*) Direct current resistivity apparatus in field use.

(*Left*) The Hilger and Watts vertical-force variometer.

(*Right*) Current and potential units of the resistivity apparatus.

RESEARCH IN APPLIED GEOPHYSICS
(*The Mining Department, Leeds University*)

ropes, and the need for manpower when the unit was raised or lowered. To overcome these difficulties a hoisting winch has been incorporated in subsequent units which are slung from buntons in the shaft wall.

Two general types of pneumatic cactus grab are available, both similar in principle; the features common to both types being an inverted pneumatic cylinder with a tine beam attached to the piston rod. "Orange-peel" tines hinged to the side of the cylinder are closed by links attached to the tine beam when the piston is withdrawn into the cylinder. Reversal of the piston opens the grab for discharge (see Plate facing p. 194). The two types of grab differ in the method of suspension. In the first, the grab is suspended from the top of the cylinder so that the tines swing sensibly in one plane when opening or closing. In the second, the grab is suspended from the tine beam so that, as the piston is withdrawn for closing, the grab drops and thereby exerts a crowding and digging action on the dirt pile. This design has been found the more satisfactory in sinking shafts.

PERMANENT SHAFT LININGS

A permanent shaft lining is necessary for at least one of the following reasons:—

(a) To seal off the country rock from the weathering effects of water and air, thereby preventing slabbing or flaking of the sides, and to support jointed and broken rock.

(b) To seal off water and to resist its static pressure.

(c) To resist the static pressure of running ground such as sands, alluvium and gravels. The pressures in these cases are usually determined by multiplying the hydrostatic pressure by a constant. Thus constants[10] of 1·8 for sand, 1·5 for sand clays and clays, 1·25 for marls and 1 for tufa, limestone and compact marls have been given.

(d) To resist, at great depths (i) the bursting of rocks from the sides, and (ii) the natural tendency, due to overlying pressure, to close up slowly and damage or cause collapse of the shaft section.

The choice of lining will depend on the degree of incidence of each or a combination of the factors aforementioned. Where two or more types of lining are equally applicable, the cost, availability of labour and materials, and the intended life of the lining, are taken into consideration before any final choice of lining is made.

TIMBERED SHAFTS.—These are rarely, if ever, used in the coal mines of Great Britain; but in metal mines timber is widely used although it has been replaced, to some extent in recent years, by steel and concrete lining. Timber will, no doubt, continue to be used at metal mines where it is cheap (even though the cost of maintaining the shafts is high) and the life of the shafts comparatively short.

BRICKED SHAFTS.—This is a standard type lining in circular shafts where the ground is strong and fairly dry. The thickness of the wall depends largely on the size of the shaft, a common thickness is 14 in. The brickwork is inserted in lengths of approximately 100 ft. or more and is built up from a specially prepared walling or bricking curb. This curb might be made of wood, or cast iron (Fig. 25a) but modern practice is to prepare a curb in reinforced or mass concrete.

Assuming that the required length of shaft has been excavated, preparations are made for the insertion of the bricking curb slightly above the level to which the shaft has been excavated.

Fig. 25b shows a section of a cast-iron curb in position with the wall

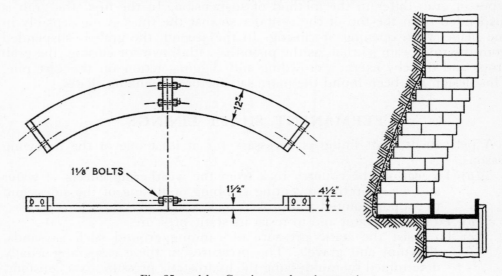

Fig. 25a and b.—Cast-iron curb and water ring.

dressed back to form a water ring or garland. The curb must be carefully levelled before bricking commences.

If a concrete curb is to be used, the side wall may or may not be trimmed back to form a wedge, depending on the nature of the lining and the ground through which the shaft is being sunk. A ring of shuttering is placed in position and carefully levelled and centred. The shuttering usually rests on a ledge of levelled debris, and boards covered with brattice cloth are laid to form a base for the concrete. Concrete is then poured behind the shuttering to the required height and left to set. The shuttering or falsework is removed when the concrete has set and the work of building the wall up to the previous bricking curb is commenced. The advantages of a concrete curb are that it gives strength to the wall, is self-supporting, and is less liable to damage or displacement than a wood or cast-iron curb.

The space between the side wall and the inner lining of brick might be filled with screening material such as cinders or loose brick, or rammed tight with concrete, depending on the specification. Where small quantities of water are issuing from the rock the screening material should be such that it will allow the water to run down and thereby prevent the hydrostatic pressure building up behind the walling. The water is then collected in water garlands at the curb (Fig. 25b), through "weep" holes set in the brickwork at curb level and is piped down the shaft from garland to garland. To key the wall to the previous bricking curb the bricks are cut and shaped by hand. For a 100-ft. length of walling in a shaft 20 ft. finished diameter, thickness 14 in., the number of bricks required would be 85,000 approximately, which would require about 130 bricklayer-shifts of 8 hours per shift to lay. Alternate header and stretcher courses make a strong lining. Two types of bonding used in shaft linings are illustrated in Fig. 26.

MONOLITHIC CONCRETE LINING.—In recent years this type of lining has, to a considerable extent, replaced other linings for both dry and wet shafts. In dry shafts mass concrete might be used whereas reinforced concrete is used where high pressures have to be resisted, the amount and type of reinforcement depending on the pressure. Monolithic concrete is stronger than

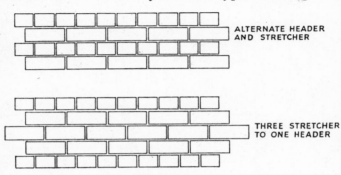

ALTERNATE HEADER AND STRETCHER

THREE STRETCHER TO ONE HEADER

Fig. 26.—Brick shaft lining.

brickwork and has a lower frictional resistance to air currents. On the other hand, it might be more difficult to repair and its essential rigidity might be a disadvantage where slight earth movements are liable to occur. Where the ground tends to break away from the shaft sides the consumption of concrete over the estimated consumption might be large.

In order to insert a length of lining of this type a bed is prepared at the bottom of the shaft to take the first ring of shuttering, which is carefully centred and levelled. The base is prepared to give a stepped joint when the shuttering is removed. Concrete is poured behind the first ring and rammed home. Further rings are added and the wall is taken up to the base of the previous length of walling. The temporary lining is removed as the successive rings of shuttering are inserted. Special matching segments of shuttering are kept with depths of 2 ft., 1 ft. and 6 in., respectively. With the use of these rings the lining is brought to within a few inches of the base of the previous lining and a "grouter ring" is then attached. The grouter ring consists of a $2\frac{1}{2}$ in. $\times$ $2\frac{1}{2}$ in. angle iron which, when fixed in place (Fig. 27), admits an open annulus about $2\frac{1}{2}$ in. wide all round the shaft, and a plate, about 12 in. high, fixed to the angle iron to form an apron behind which a fine sand and cement mixture is poured until its level is some inches above the base of the previous lining. When the grout has set the plates are removed and the wall is dressed back at the joint until it is flush with the lining.

By using additional shuttering in an inclined position behind the normal type of shuttering, the shape of the finished lining may be altered and a horizontal ledge about 6 in. wide provided, on which a cast-iron or steel water-garland can be secured (Fig. 28).

The falsework segments are removed after the concrete has set and are sent to the surface to be cleaned and greased on the inner side in readiness for further use. Concrete for shaft lining usually consists of four parts of aggregate, two of sand and one of cement, although, exceptionally, a 3 : 2 : 1

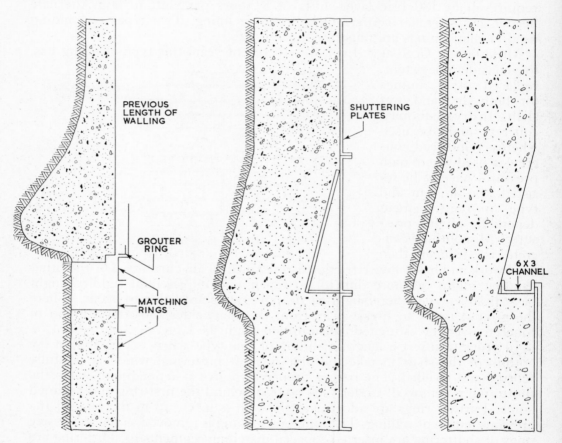

PREVIOUS LENGTH OF WALLING

GROUTER RING

MATCHING RINGS

SHUTTERING PLATES

6 X 3 CHANNEL

Fig. 27.—Grouter ring used when concreting.

Fig. 28.—Cast-iron or steel water garland.

or 2 : 1 : 1 mixture is used. The concrete is sent down the shaft in a specially constructed hoppit which has a bottom door for emptying the concrete on to a chute fixed over the walling scaffold, whence it gravitates into place behind the shuttering. Three hoppits are used at one time, while one is being filled at the mixer with concrete, the other is awaiting descent at the shaft mouth, and the third is in transit in the shaft.

A recent development in South Africa is to convey the concrete down the shaft in steel pipes 6–8 in. diameter to within a few feet of the shuttering. Here a manifold is inserted and rubber pipes are used to discharge the concrete behind the shuttering. In this way hoppits are left free for loading debris, and the speed of inserting the lining is considerably increased. With this procedure as much as 30 ft. of walling has been inserted within the normal blasting interval.

REINFORCED CONCRETE.— This is used where the sides of the shaft are subject to water pressure, ground pressure, or both. The type of reinforcement will be related to the amount and distribution of the pressure and the nature of the tensile stresses to which the lining might be subjected. As it is not easy to foresee the nature or calculate the magnitude of these stresses, it is usual to allow a considerable factor of safety in the design of the reinforced concrete.

Examples of the use of reinforced concrete linings in recent sinkings are:—

(a) In the sinking of the Comrie Colliery Shaft [11] in Fifeshire, the concrete was reinforced with horizontal mild-steel rods $\frac{1}{2}$ in. diameter and spaced vertically at 9-in. intervals. Nine flat iron

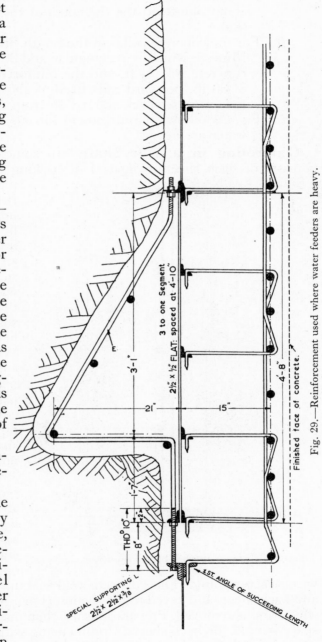

Fig. 29.—Reinforcement used where water feeders are heavy.

hangers were used around the perimeter to support the $\frac{1}{2}$-in. reinforcing rings. The thickness of walling in this case increased with depth, being 9 in. at 133 ft., 12 in. from 133 ft. to 400 ft. and 15 in.

from 400 ft. to 497 ft. The reinforcement was placed at a distance of about one-third the thickness of the concrete behind the surface skin.

(b) For the concrete collar of the South Shaft, West Rand Consolidated Mines,[12] which is rectangular and 30 ft. by 12 ft., the thickness of concrete was $2\frac{1}{2}$ ft. and the reinforcement consisted of rectangles of 30 lb. per yard rails fixed at about 6 ft. vertical centres. The rails were set back about 1 ft. from the surface skin.

(c) Fig. 29[13] shows reinforcement for use in strata where the feeders of water are heavy.

Concreting in a Wet Shaft.—In some cases the temporary lining consists of back sheeting instead of backing deals. This back sheeting is placed behind the usual skeleton rings and forms part of the reinforcement for the permanent lining. This type of temporary lining serves two purposes, (a) as an immediate support for the sidewalls, and (b) to retain the water between the side walls and the sheeting in its descent to the shaft sump, whence it is either baled or pumped to the surface. When it is decided to concrete a length of the shaft a garland is fixed above the site of a specially-prepared wedge or form of curb (Fig. 30) and the water is piped from this garland to the shaft sump; thus the water does not flow freely over or through any part of the shaft which is to receive concrete. A relief pipe about $1\frac{1}{2}$ in. diameter is screwed behind the shuttering segments as indicated in Fig. 30. The pipe end against the back sheeting is open and the other end is fitted

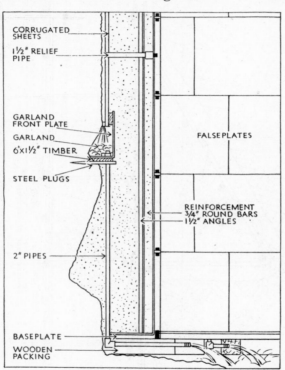

CORRUGATED SHEETS

$1\frac{1}{2}"$ RELIEF PIPE

GARLAND FRONT PLATE

GARLAND

$6'\times1\frac{1}{2}"$ TIMBER

STEEL PLUGS

FALSE PLATES

REINFORCEMENT $\frac{3}{4}"$ ROUND BARS $1\frac{1}{2}"$ ANGLES

$2"$ PIPES

BASEPLATE

WOODEN PACKING

Fig. 30.—Relief pipe attached behind shuttering segment.

with a screw plug. The concrete wall is built up between the shuttering and back sheets and keyed to the section above. When the concrete has set the shuttering is removed. Preparations are then made to seal and consolidate the space behind the back sheets. Commencing with the first ring of relief pipes around the shaft, holes are punched in the back sheeting by the use of an iron bar inserted through the relief pipes. Cement milk is then injected through the pipes which run from the temporary garland. The grout is continuously injected until it reaches and overflows at the first ring of relief pipes. Holes are punched in the second ring of relief pipes and the injection is continued through the first ring until the cement overflows at the second ring. The process is repeated until the entire length of new lining has been sealed.

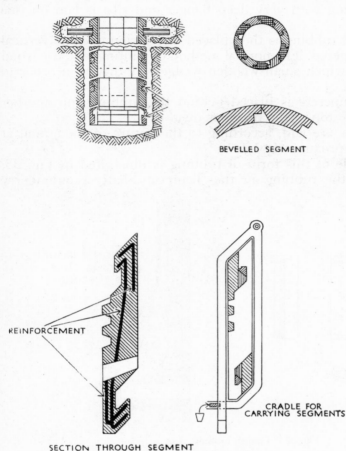

BEVELLED SEGMENT

REINFORCEMENT

SECTION THROUGH SEGMENT

CRADLE FOR CARRYING SEGMENTS

Fig. 31.—Method of suspending precast concrete blocks.

Precast Concrete Blocks.—These have been used for permanent linings although monolithic concrete has now replaced this type of lining almost completely. The blocks may be built upwards from a prepared curb or, as at a Belgian colliery,[14] they may be suspended from a strong crown ring or curb at the top of the lining. Fig. 31 shows details of the latter type of reinforcement and method of suspension. Cement milk is poured behind the lining to make it firm and secure. One of the disadvantages of this type of lining is that the last block to be inserted to complete a ring has to be specially shaped for insertion, and it does not interlock along one of the vertical joints.

Cast-Iron Tubbing.—This type of lining has been used in the past where the ordinary types of linings, such as brickwork or a specially built type of watertight brickwork known as coffering, have been insufficiently strong to resist the inflow into the shaft of large volumes of water or running sands under high hydrostatic pressure. It is used, at the present time, expressly as a lining in running sands.

English Tubbing.—This is built in segments with overlapping rims along one side and the bottom, and with corresponding grooves along the edges of the other two sides. It is strengthened on the back face, which is adjacent to the strata, with flanges, ribs and webs. Fig. 32 illustrates this form of tubbing and a brief outline of the procedure adopted for its insertion is as follows:—

(1) A base for the curb is prepared in good, strong ground and a cast-iron wedging curb is carefully laid on soft pine wood and wedged into position after being carefully centred and levelled.

(2) A foundation ring with very deep flanges and ribs is laid on this curb.

(3) The first ring of tubbing is then placed in position and the vertical joints are staggered. The normal method of jointing is to use wood sheeting into which small wooden wedges are driven in order to seal the joints.

(4) Quick-setting concrete is placed behind the tubbing and another ring is built on top of the previous one.

(5) Additional curbs are laid, according to the nature of the strata, at intervals of approximately 150 ft.

An interesting example of this form of tubbing is illustrated in Fig. 33, which gives details of the tubbing in the Tempest Shaft, Londonderry

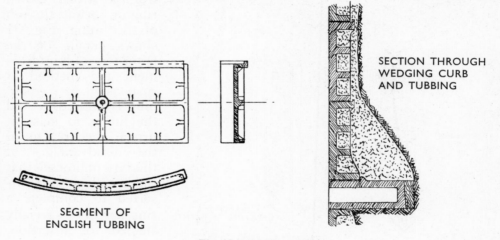

SECTION THROUGH WEDGING CURB AND TUBBING

SEGMENT OF ENGLISH TUBBING

Fig. 32.—English tubbing.

Collieries, sunk by the application of the freezing process. The tubbing commences at a depth of approximately 70 ft. and terminates at a little less than 600 ft. Each ring is composed of sixteen segments, each segment being 2 ft. high. The first twenty rings are $\frac{7}{8}$ in. thick, and this thickness is increased by $\frac{1}{8}$ in. for each succeeding twenty rings. The cribs are placed as shown in the diagram. The bottom crib was wedged but not the other four, as this was not deemed necessary. The space between the tubbing and the excavated shaft is backed with quick-setting concrete. Wood sheeting constituted the joints and a section of sinking 60 yards in length was tubbed at one time.

Continental or German and Suspended Tubbing.—This is cast in segments with flanges, strengthening ribs and webs on the inner side, facing the centre of the shaft. The flanges are machined and provided with

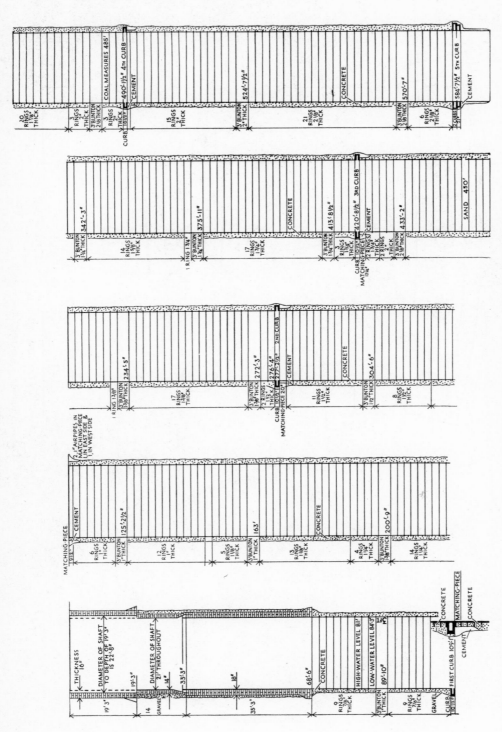

Fig. 33.—English tubbing, Tempest Shaft, Londonderry Colliery.

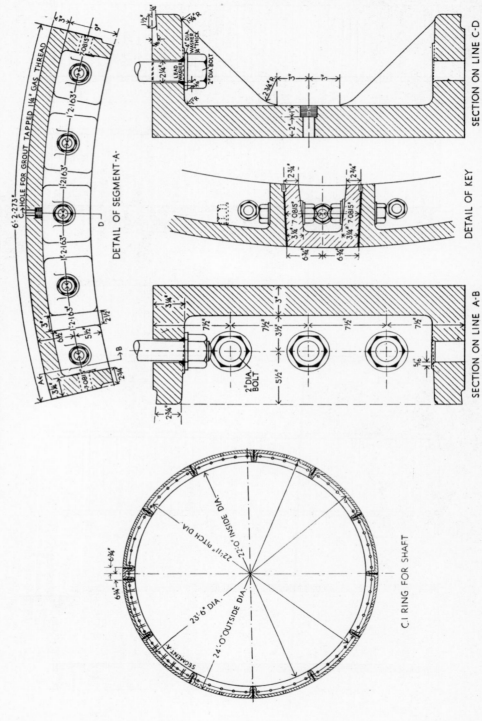

Fig. 34.—German tubbing, segments bolted together.

204

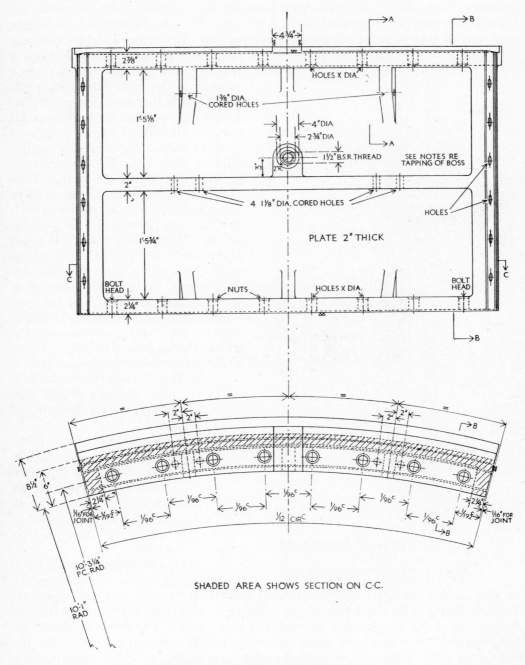

SHADED AREA SHOWS SECTION ON C·C.

Fig. 35*a*.—German tubbing, single segment.

grooves. Thin sheet lead is inserted between the joints and the segments are bolted together as illustrated in Fig. 34. Fig. 35a shows details of a single segment of this form of tubbing. It is easier to insert than English tubbing and can be built upwards from a prepared curb or suspended from a crown or anchor ring and built downwards as the sinking proceeds, to offer protection in weak ground for the sinkers. A short length of ground only is exposed during the sinking and Fig. 35b illustrates a section of suspended tubbing. This type of tubbing has been widely used, especially in conjunction with the freezing process. In the sinking of the Houthalen shafts, Belgian Campine,[15] 666 yd. of sand, clays, marls and chalk were successfully negotiated by a combination of freezing and tubbing. The tubbing was inserted in accordance with the nature and requirements of the ground being passed through. Three different methods were practised:—

(a) Big sections were used and the tubbing built upwards from bottom to top.

(b) Small sections were used. A tubbing section was first assembled and then lifted and secured to the one above it. Thus a small number of rings of tubbing were suspended by sections.

(c) One complete ring was built at a time and suspended.

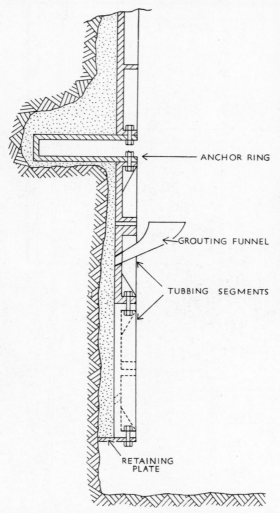

ANCHOR RING

GROUTING FUNNEL

TUBBING SEGMENTS

RETAINING PLATE

Fig. 35b.—German tubbing, single segment.

The useful diameter of the tubbing was 16 ft. 4½ in. and ten segments formed a ring. The thickness of the tubbing varied from 1·18 to 6·69 in. and the height of the rings was 5 ft. with the exception of the 6·69 in. segments, which were 3 ft. 9 in. Curbs were laid every 65½ ft. with an exception for the lining in clay, when they were located every 29½ ft. The tubbing was high-grade grey cast-iron and the bolts were made of steel having a tensile strength of 23·5 to 27·9 tons per sq. in. The total length of tubbing inserted was 642 metres.

It is essential to caulk all joints with lead and tighten the bolts periodically after a section of tubbing has been inserted. When using suspended tubbing concrete is run in behind through holes cast in the tubbing and plates are fixed around the base to support the weight of the concrete until it has set. Reinforced concrete[16] may be used behind the tubbing as in the case of the re-sinking of Augusta Victoria Shaft, where the tubbing was suspended. Fig. 36 shows the section through a curb with one ring of tubbing below it.

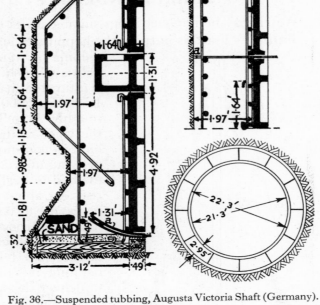

Fig. 36.—Suspended tubbing, Augusta Victoria Shaft (Germany).

Thickness of Tubbing. —Several formulae[17] are available for the calculation of the thickness of tubbing required at different static pressures. Treating the shaft lining as a thin cylinder subject to a uniform external pressure all around the cylinder, the following formula applies:—

$$t = \frac{Pd}{24f}$$

where t is the required thickness of tubbing in in.
P is the external pressure in lb. per sq. ft.
f is the safe compressive load in lb. per sq. in.
d is the diameter in ft.

A factor of safety must be incorporated in this formula and $\frac{1}{2}$ in. is usually added to the calculated thickness to give security against defects in casting and to allow for corrosion. A common value for f is between 10,000 and 15,000 lb. per sq. in. Taking a shaft 16 ft. diameter with a pressure of 250 lb. per sq. in. and $f = 12,000$ lb. per sq. in., the thickness of tubbing is calculated as follows:—

$$t = \frac{250 \times 12 \times 12 \times 16}{24 \times 12,000} = 2 \text{ in.}$$

Allowing a further $\frac{1}{2}$ in. for corrosion and casting defects the required thickness of cast iron would be $2\frac{1}{2}$ in.

SINKING UNDER WET CONDITIONS

Water may be removed from sinking shafts by baling or pumping.

Baling.—For this purpose the hoppit or a water-barrel is used. A certain volume of water will be removed with the debris when it is loaded into the hoppit. It is estimated that in a 64-cu. ft. hoppit about 1,500 to 2,000 lb. of water, equivalent to roughly 24 to 32 cu. ft., can be contained in the voids of the debris. Over a period of 24 hours a continuous feed of about 7 to 8 gals. per minute does not require any special method to deal with it but where the feeder rises to about 20 gals. per minute, it is necessary to bale. The hoppit may be used for this purpose and it is filled from buckets or by a small pump. Where the feed of water to the shaft bottom exceeds about 25 gals. per min., it is more economical to use a pump to deliver the water directly to the surface.

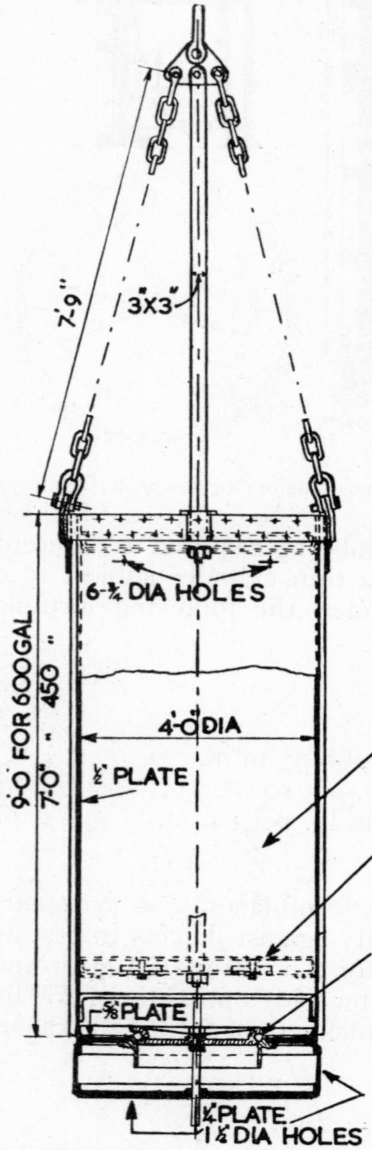

A water-barrel is commonly used to clear the shaft bottom of water after week-end breaks in the sinking operations. A suction-type of barrel for this purpose (Fig. 37) operates, as its name implies, on the suction-pump principle. The barrel descends into the sump and, on being brought to rest, the piston C gravitates to the bottom of the cylinder B. On the upward lift of the barrel the piston C rises, the valve A opens and water is drawn into the barrel. The amount of water which a water-barrel can deal with will depend largely on the depth of the sinking and the capacity of the barrel. Barrels of 1,000 gals. capacity can deal with large quantities of water at shallow depths but, as the depth and thus the winding time increases, the over-all baling time might be too long and thus seriously handicap the rate of sinking. It might, however, be less costly to use a barrel where a fairly heavy feed of water is expected in a small section of the shaft only, rather than suspend a pump in the shaft,

Fig. 37.—Suction-type water-barrel.

which requires extra fittings and some considerable preparation before installation.

Sinking Pumps.—Reciprocating pumps working on the bucket or ram

principle, and pulsometer pumps, driven by steam, have
been used for varying quantities of water under different
static pressures. These have, however, been superseded
by the electrically driven centrifugal pump which has been
widely used for sinkings in recent years. This type of
pump is compact, quiet in operation, but has to be primed
initially and does not work on snore. It is particularly
suitable for use in conjunction with the cementation process applied to sinking, where large quantities of water
have to be sealed off, since by balancing the cost and time
in cementation against the cost of pumping, it is possible to
formulate a scheme involving cementation and pumping
for any particular sinking which will be less costly and
quicker than (*a*) attempting to seal off effectively almost
all the water by cementation or (*b*) the use of pumps, without cementation.

The Sulzer multi-stage centrifugal sinking pump (Fig.
38) is specially designed to deal with large quantities of
water in sinking shafts. At the beginning of a sinking
only one or two stages are used and further stages are
added as the depth increases. If the water being pumped
contains a lot of sand in suspension, as when passing
through New Red Sandstone, there may be excessive wear
on the shaft and impellers. Rubber-necked bushes are used
to reduce this wear. A sinking pump of large capacity is
usually suspended in double-purchase, as illustrated in
Fig. 39, one end of the rope being firmly clamped in the
headgear and the other end passed over a headgear pulley
to the pump capstan engine. Cleats are used at intervals
and are firmly clamped to the rising main. The supporting
rope and pump cable thread through these cleats. When
the pump has to be raised the rising main may be removed
in sections at the surface.

An adequate sump must be provided for the foot valve
of the pump.

SINKING UNDER DIFFICULT CONDITIONS

The conditions that usually militate against straightfor-
ward sinking are water and unstable ground, such as running sands, gravels, marls and strata which are highly disturbed. The history of sinking reveals a continual struggle
to overcome the difficulties presented by these factors,
which may give rise to inundations or cause the shaft to
collapse. The difficulties invariably increase with depth
due particularly to the higher pressure encountered.

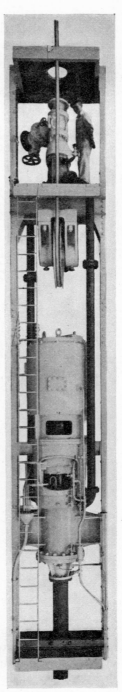

Fig. 38.—Sulzer cen-
trifugal pump.

Some notable sinkings were carried out in Great Britain in the 19th century, although the sinkers were greatly handicapped by plant that was crude and unwieldy compared with modern standards. A good example is that of the three Murton shafts[18] in Co. Durham, where sinking commenced in 1837 and was successfully completed in 1842. The shafts passed through some 400 ft. of fissured magnesium limestone and at the base of the limestone

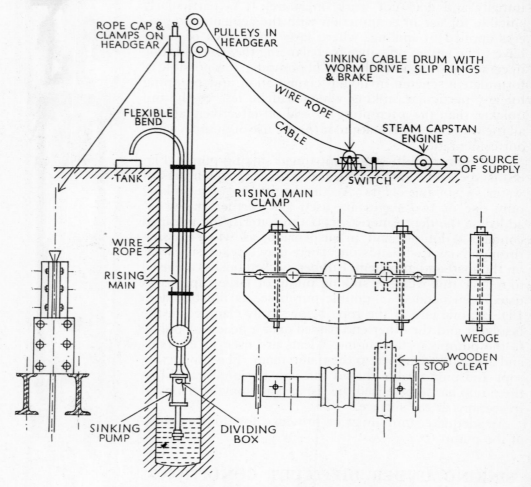

Fig. 39.—Large-capacity pump, showing method of suspension.

30 ft. of running sands were encountered. At one time over 9,000 gals. of water per min. were being pumped from 27 sets of lifting bucket pumps. Another example is that of two Marsden shafts, Co. Durham, which were successfully sunk between 1877 and 1884. These made over 11,000 gals. of water per min. at one stage in the sinking and it was impossible to continue sinking by normal methods because the pumps could not cope with the

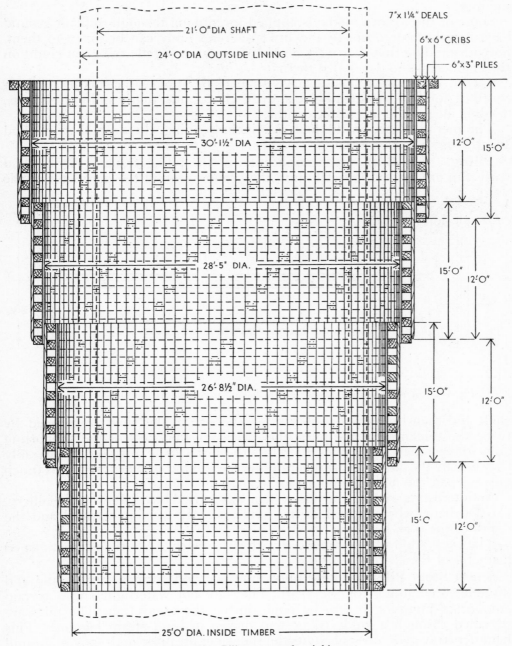

21'-0" DIA SHAFT

24'-0" DIA OUTSIDE LINING

7" x 1¼" DEALS

6" x 6" CRIBS

6" x 3" PILES

30'-1½" DIA

28'-5" DIA.

26'-8½" DIA.

25'-0" DIA. INSIDE TIMBER

12'-0"

15'-0"

15'-0"

12'-0"

15'-0"

12'-0"

15'-0"

12'-0"

Fig. 40.—Piling system for sinking.

influx. The Kind Chauldron system of boring was used to complete the sinkings.

Some of the former methods applied for sinking through difficult ground have now become obsolete and brief reference only can be given to them, notwithstanding that they were highly ingenious and reflected great credit on the engineers who developed them.

Special methods of sinking have often to be applied for sinking through (*a*) thick surface deposits of glacial drift, clay, sands, marls and gravels, etc., (*b*) difficult ground at greater depths.

The methods used in the first case include piling, the drop-shaft method and the use of compressed-air caissons.

Piling.—Fig. 40 shows an application of the piling system. Planks shod with iron are driven vertically into the ground around the perimeter of the

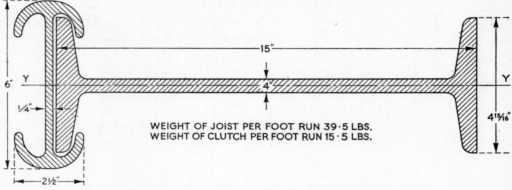

WEIGHT OF JOIST PER FOOT RUN 39·5 LBS.
WEIGHT OF CLUTCH PER FOOT RUN 15·5 LBS.

Fig. 41.—Interlocking steel piles as used in sinking at Hatfield Main Colliery, Doncaster.

shaft and then braced by timber sets. The size of the shaft is reduced by twice the thickness of the piles plus twice the thickness of the supporting cribs for each new set of piles, therefore the surface size must be considerably larger than the finished diameter. Thus the ground to be excavated is much greater than the normal amount for a shaft sinking.

An interesting example of this system was carried out at Bowburn Colliery, Co. Durham, where glacial drifts, sand and clay were penetrated and the depth to the rock head was 157 ft.

The excavation was commenced with a diameter of 25 ft. and the finished diameter of the shaft was 19 ft.

Sheet Steel Piles.—These piles interlock and form a very sound and durable inner lining for the shaft. They are not watertight and a certain amount of pumping has to be done during the excavation. The piles are threaded through a guide frame and driven in by a steam hammer. This hammer traverses on rails outside the ring of piles and moves around alternately clockwise and anti-clockwise, to prevent the piles twisting in the ground.

These piles might also be used at depth, when hydraulic jacks are used to force them down. Fig. 41 shows details of the interlocking steel piles used at Hatfield Main Colliery, Doncaster. The piles so interlocked that very little water seeped through the joints during the subsequent excavation.

Figs. 42 and 43 show a method of piling adopted by The Cementation Co., Ltd., in sinking of a shaft at Fallin, Scotland. A ring of steel tubes of 1 ft. or more in diameter was driven through the ground to the rock-head and the material within the tubes was then removed by sludging. Reinforced concrete was filled into the tubes which were then slowly withdrawn in stages leaving

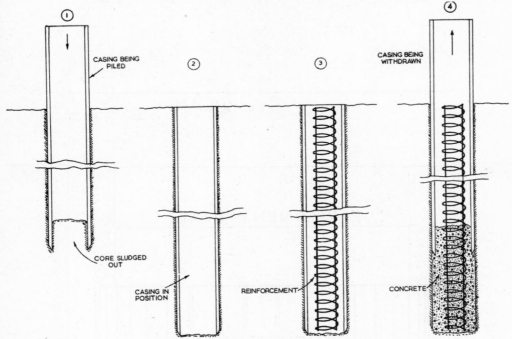

Fig. 42.—Insertion and reinforcing of piles.

concrete piles which, when set, formed a closed cylinder inside which the shaft was excavated.

Drop-Shafts.—The drop-shaft method consists in building up the permanent lining or shaft walling at the surface over a special cutting shoe (Fig. 44). The shoe and superimposed lining penetrates the ground under its own weight as the excavation proceeds inside the lining. Drop shafts are usually sunk from the bottom of a preliminary shallow excavation and great care must be taken to ensure that the lining sinks vertically downwards. It is essential for the ground to be excavated uniformly around the cutting shoe, otherwise there is a tendency for the lining to tilt.

The lining for a drop-shaft may consist of either brickwork and steel or cast-iron rings, but more recent practice has been to construct the lining of reinforced concrete with steel cutting shoes.

One of the difficulties experienced in the sinking of drop shafts is the effect

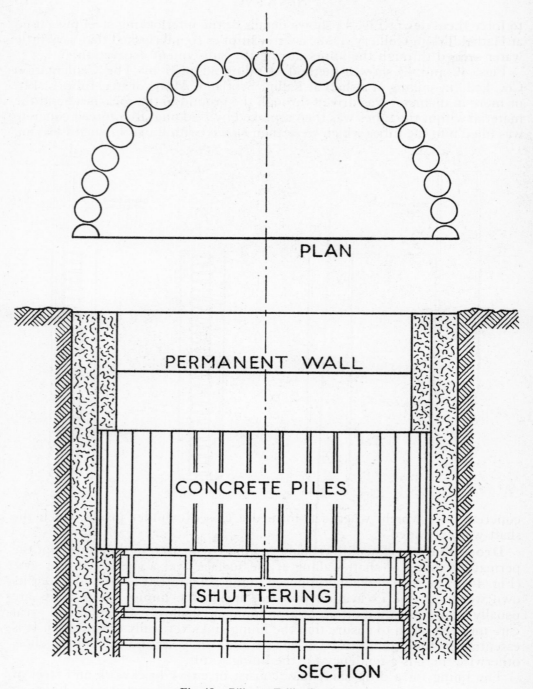

PLAN

PERMANENT WALL

CONCRETE PILES

SHUTTERING

SECTION

Fig. 43.—Piling at Fallin, Scotland.

of friction between the outside of the lining and the ground through which it is passing. This friction may vary from 100 to 1,000 lb. per sq. ft. but the actual amount is difficult to estimate. It might become necessary to overcome the friction by forcing the shoe and lining down by hydraulic jacks from a specially prepared crown ring. Jets may also be inserted in the shaft wall through which compressed-air or water is pumped to reduce the frictional forces. Some notable drop shafts have been sunk in Great Britain and include the north shaft, Chislet Colliery, which was sunk with a finished diameter of 16 ft. and the Astley Green Shaft, which was sunk with the aid of hydraulic jacks to a depth of 111 ft. with a finished diameter of 21 ft.

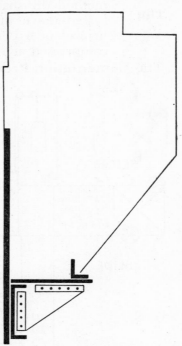

Fig. 44.—Drop shaft sinking and lining.

Compressed-Air Caissons.—This method is applied where there is a danger of the ground filling up the shaft or where there is a considerable make of water under a small head which is difficult or impossible to seal. The method resembles that of the drop shaft, but in this case air-lock stages are placed at intervals and the lower chamber filled with compressed air. The pressure of air inside the chamber neutralises the static pressure of the water or the water-bearing ground. There is a limit to the pressure of air beyond which it is impossible for men to work. This limit corresponds to about a 120 ft. head of water (52 lb. per sq. in.). Under this pressure men can work for only very short periods and long before this depth is reached progress is impeded by the effect of pressure. This system was applied in the sinking of a shaft at Ardeer,[19] Scotland (Fig. 45), which was sunk to $91\frac{1}{2}$ ft. with a finished diameter of 14 ft., the maximum air pressure in the shaft being 23 lb. per sq. in. An 18-ft. finished diameter shaft was also sunk by this system at Terre Haute, Indiana, U.S.A., through 157 ft. of wet gravel and sand. The maximum pressure of compressed air in this case was 51 lb. sq. in.

METHODS OF SINKING THROUGH WATER-BEARING STRATA OF CONSIDERABLE THICKNESS

Methods which have been used to sink through water-bearing strata under high static pressures fall into two categories:—
  (a) Where the water is completely sealed off to allow ordinary sinking, as in the freezing process, or partially sealed off as in the cementation process.
  (b) Where the shaft is bored out under water, as in the Kind Chauldron,

the Pattberg and the Honigmann systems. These methods were very slow and expensive and have now been mostly replaced by the freezing or the cementation process. They consisted in boring out the shafts with the aid of a large trepan or borer. In the Kind Chauldron method a preliminary hole was bored with a small percussive trepan, followed by a large one, while the Pattberg system used a single trepan to bore the full diameter. In the latter method the shaft was lined as it was deepened and the tubbing forced down under pressure. Honigmann used a rotary trepan instead of a percussive one and the cuttings were removed by compressed air.

The Cementation Process.—Of the special methods of sinking through thick deposits of water-bearing strata it may be said that cementation and freezing are the only two methods which have so far been developed and perfected to have a permanent place in their application to shaft sinking. Cementation is applicable to all types of strata with the exception of "running" sands and certain impure gravels.

M. François introduced the process into England in 1911, when he applied it successfully to the sinking of the two shafts at Hatfield Main Colliery, Yorkshire.

Cementation consists essentially in the injection through boreholes, of a cement and

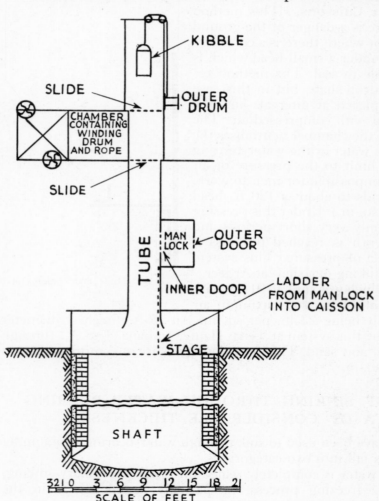

Fig. 45.—Compressed-air Caisson system, Ardeer, Scotland.

water mixture under pressure, into the water-bearing strata. The object of the injection is to fill up the cavities, joints, fissures and pores of the rock with cement which, when it hardens, renders the rock impervious to water. The character of the rock has a considerable influence on the mode of application of the system. For example, the strength of the cement mixture injected into non-porous rocks, will depend on the nature of the fissures or joints. Where these take the form of a fine network, a very weak mixture of cement milk (sometimes as low as 1 part cement to 100 parts water) is injected to enable the mixture to flow to a suitable distance from the point of injection. If the cavities are very large a more concentrated mixture of cement and water is used and the injecting pressure carefully regulated to avoid pumping the mixture beyond the required zone of the borehole. Rocks with large cavities have usually to be injected several times with mixtures in which the amount of cement is progressively decreased as the voids are gradually sealed. Large cavities might consume a prohibitive amount of cement but the use of diluting solids to reduce the consumption of cement might seriously weaken the resistance of the closed cavities to pressure. Tests were carried out in South Africa[20] on the dilution of cement with milling slimes, which had about the same degree of fineness, and the following results were obtained:—

Materials					Tensile strength lb.
Neat cement ..	..	..	..	..	670
1 cement 1 slime	..	..	..	..	100
1 „ 2 „	.	..	..	..	55
1 „ 3 „	.	..	..	..	Nil

It was concluded that the grains of cement were separated by such dilution to an extent which interfered with their adhesion.

It is necessary, when applying cementation to certain types of rocks which are porous, to prepare the rocks prior to the injection of the cement. This consists in reducing the resistance of the rock to the passage of a cement mixture by the use of chemical reagents which act as a lubricant for the passage of cement through the pores of the rock and also as a sealing agent in a manner similar to the cement. A solution of sodium silicate and aluminium sulphate are used alternately and the reaction between the two chemicals is:—

$$3Na_2SiO_3 + Al_2(SO_4)_3 = 3Na_2SO_4 + Al_2(SiO_3)_3$$

The precipitate is colloidal in character, which probably explains why it serves to lubricate the pores for the passage of cement. This treatment is necessary, otherwise the porous rock may act as a filter and take the cement particles out of suspension, causing the pores near the point of injection to be choked, thereby preventing penetration. The injection of chemicals is sometimes repeated after the cement mixture has been injected. The general term given to this special process is "silicatisation". The New Red Sandstone

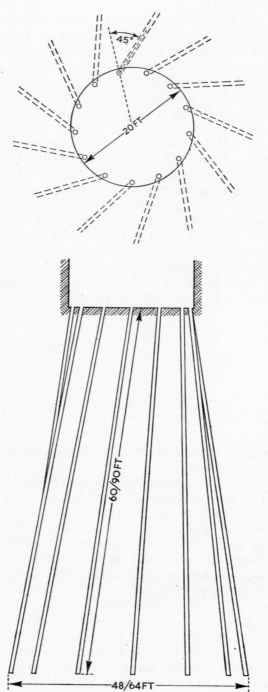

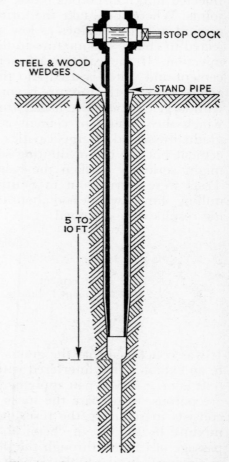

45°

20 FT

STOP COCK

STEEL & WOOD
WEDGES

STAND PIPE

5 TO
10 FT

Fig. 47.—Standpipe used in cementation
system.

60/90 FT

48/64 FT

Fig. 46.—Cementation holes, non-porous ground.

in the South Yorkshire coalfield is a classic example of a rock which requires silicatisation before the injection of the cement mixture.

CEMENTATION IN SHAFT SINKING.—The modern practice is to inject the surrounding strata in stages from the bottom of the shaft with the object of sealing the body of the rock down to 60 or 90 ft. below the shaft bottom. The number of boreholes drilled for this purpose depends on the shape and size of the shaft and whether the strata requires silicatisation prior to the injection.

Considering a shaft being sunk with a diameter of 20 ft. through non-porous strata, the holes are drilled around the periphery at approximately 5 ft. intervals; thus a 20 ft. diameter shaft would require about 13 holes. The water-bearing fissures might be inclined at any angle within the body of rock, and to ensure that a fissure is intersected by at least one borehole, the holes are drilled at 45 degrees to the tangent of the circle of the shaft and inclined outwards from the vertical at an angle of about 15 degrees (Fig. 46). Operating with boreholes 60 ft. long, their extremities lie on a circle which has a diameter of about 28 ft. greater than the diameter of the shaft.

The holes are drilled with ordinary sinking jack-hammers, and hollow boring rods, having flushed screwed joints, are used. It is essential to have under immediate control any water under high static head that may be tapped during drilling. A standpipe hole is first drilled over the site of each cementation hole. These are about 5 to 10 ft. long, depending on the nature of the ground and the anticipated pressure of water. A standpipe (Fig. 47) is inserted and grouted solidly into position and caulked with hemp rope and wedges. The standpipe projects about a foot from the mouth of the hole and is fitted with a stop cock. The standpipe is then bored through and tested at a pressure approximately equal to twice that of the anticipated water pressure. The holes are numbered, and using alternate standpipes, e.g., those with odd numbers, holes are drilled through for a distance of about 10 ft. to 15 ft. or until water is tapped. A suitable cement mixture is then injected and allowed to set. The holes are cleaned out and further injections made if the water has not been sufficiently sealed off. When the portion of ground under treatment has been effectively sealed the holes are deepened for about another 10 ft. to 15 ft. and the injections repeated. The remainder of the holes, e.g., those having even numbers, are drilled and treated at about two stages above the leading holes. Sinking recommences when it is considered that the ground has been effectively sealed to a predetermined standard. It is not possible to seal off the water completely from the shaft. A plug of cemented ground is always left at the base of the shaft about 15 to 20 ft. in depth to prevent an inrush of water and to allow for the insertion of another set of standpipes.

CEMENTING POROUS FISSURED GROUND.—Where the silicatisation process has to be applied, special boreholes called product holes are drilled (Fig. 48). The chemical reagents are injected through these holes. The usual ratio of product to cementation holes is about 3 to 1. The diagram illustrates a scheme for a 22-ft. diameter shaft. Thirty product holes are drilled on a circle $23\frac{1}{2}$ ft.

diameter and 10 cementing holes are inclined radially from the shaft. The efficacy of chemical treatment is quite apparent from the following operation.[21] Before treatment only 20 lb. of cement could be injected at a

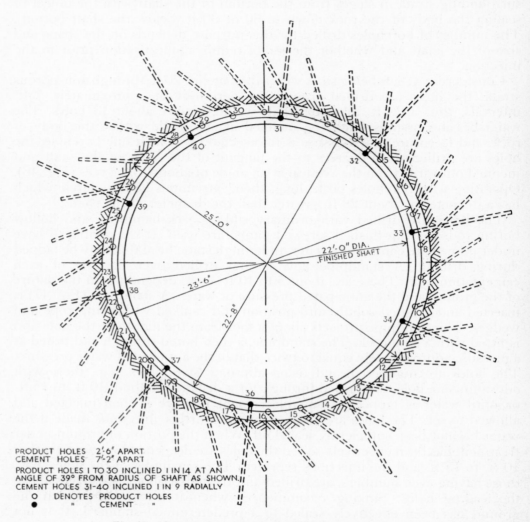

PRODUCT HOLES 2′-6″ APART
CEMENT HOLES 7′-2″ APART
PRODUCT HOLES I TO 30 INCLINED I IN 14 AT AN
ANGLE OF 39° FROM RADIUS OF SHAFT AS SHOWN.
CEMENT HOLES 31-40 INCLINED I IN 9 RADIALLY
O   DENOTES PRODUCT HOLES
●   "   CEMENT   "

Fig. 48.—Cementation and silicatisation holes, porous ground.

pressure of 1,000 lb. per sq. in. After treatment 20 tons of cement were injected at a pressure of 250 lb. per sq. in.

Rectangular shafts may be treated similarly to circular shafts, but it is not possible to be as economical in the use of cementation holes because a larger area of ground is exposed for a given effective area of shaft. The diameter of the cementation holes is progressively decreased as the depths of the borings increase. The following bit sizes relate to a 40-ft. hole :—

0 ft.		$22\frac{1}{2}$ ft.	
	$3\frac{1}{2}$-in. bits (for stand pipe)		$2\frac{1}{8}$-in. bits
$7\frac{1}{2}$ ft.		25 ft.	
	$2\frac{7}{8}$-in. ,,		2-in. ,,
10 ft.		$27\frac{1}{2}$ ft.	
	$2\frac{3}{4}$-in. ,,		$1\frac{7}{8}$-in. ,,
$12\frac{1}{2}$ ft.		30 ft.	
	$2\frac{5}{8}$-in. ,,		$1\frac{3}{4}$-in. ,,
15 ft.		$32\frac{1}{2}$ ft.	
	$2\frac{1}{2}$-in. ,,		$1\frac{5}{8}$-in. ,,
$17\frac{1}{2}$ ft.		35 ft.	
	$2\frac{3}{8}$-in. ,,		$1\frac{1}{2}$ in. ,,
20 ft.		$37\frac{1}{2}$ ft.	
	$2\frac{1}{4}$-in. ,,		$1\frac{3}{8}$-in. ,,
$22\frac{1}{2}$ ft.		40 ft.	

The type of cement used will depend on the nature of the strata and the fissures. Quick-setting cement can be used for large fissures but not for small

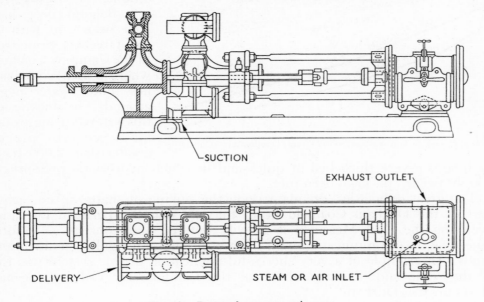

Fig. 49.—Pumps for cement mixtures.

fissures. The cement is mixed in tanks of about 80 gals. capacity each. These are provided with mechanical agitators to produce a uniform consistency in the mixture, which is run through a filter to the pump tank, also equipped with mechanical agitators, and delivered to the cementation pumps. The pumps (Fig. 49) are specially designed for dealing with cement mixtures and are of the high-pressure double-acting ram type. The motive power may be either steam or compressed air and the size of the ram varies from 2 in. for ordinary work to $\frac{3}{4}$ in. where small quantities of cement have to be pumped. Steel balls are used in the valve chamber and there are no sharp corners where the cement may settle out to build up and choke the pump.

The principle of cementation may also be applied to assist in the dewatering of flooded shafts and the sealing of existing shafts from the walls of which large quantities of water may be issuing. In the case of a flooded shaft the level of the water is artificially raised from an outside source and a cement mixture pumped to the bottom of the shaft through a range of cementation pipes. The excess artificial head of water created in the shaft forces the cement into the strata. Concrete plugs can also be formed at the bottom of flooded shafts prior to their dewatering.

The Freezing Process.—This method is specially applicable in fissured ground and where running sands, under great pressure of water, have to be passed through during sinking.

Within the last thirty years the process has been used with success at very considerable depths and under most difficult conditions.

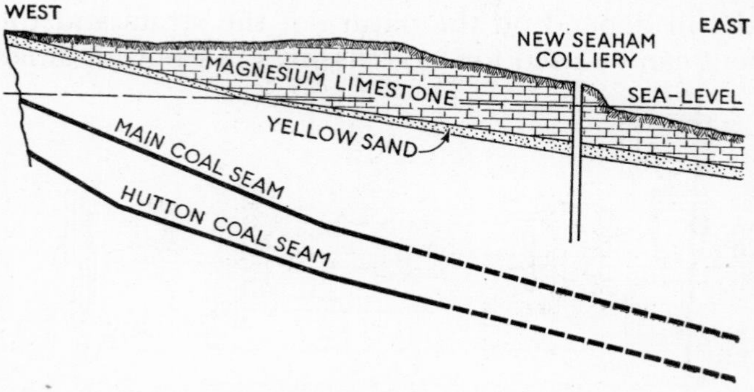

Fig. 50.—East and west section of strata, Londonderry Colliery.

In Belgium, deep shafts have been sunk with the aid of freezing, principally in the Campine Coalfield, where a rich coal basin lies under water-logged ground. The thickness of this water-bearing ground is, in certain places, greater than 2,000 ft. At its base is a very thick bed of quicksand in which hydrostatic pressures of 900 lb. per sq. in. have been met.

The great difficulties attendant upon the sinking of shafts in the eastern part of the Durham Coalfield lie in the fact that the Permian formation overlying the Coal Measures is heavily watered and consists of fissured limestone, in communication with the sea through large gullets and running sands. An example of a very successful application of this system was that of the Vane and Tempest shafts at the Londonderry Colliery, Seaham Harbour, Co. Durham.[22]

Fig. 50 is a geological section illustrating the disposition of the water-bearing strata in relation to the Coal Measures, while Fig. 51 shows a section of the water-bearing strata from the surface to the Coal Measures, as given by a test boring put down to prove the nature of the overlying strata. This hole was bored in such a position that it could also be utilised for the freezing operations.

Careful tests were made in this hole, and also in others, at a later date, in order to ascertain the water level. This was found to vary with the tide to an amount of 3 to 4 ft., and to follow the rise and fall of the sea by about two hours.

Samples of the water, when analysed, were found to be saline. It was therefore obvious that the water was in communication with the sea, and in movement. This fact, as well as the salinity of the water, complicated the problem of freezing. The strata through which it was required to sink the shafts also receive the water which flows naturally from inland to the sea, thus adding further difficulties to the freezing due to the heat constantly introduced in this way.

PRINCIPLE OF THE FREEZING PROCESS.—The freezing process consists in the formation, in the water-bearing strata, of a large block of frozen ground, in which it is possible to sink a shaft without danger of an influx of water, providing the ice-wall between the water outside and the shaft itself is strong enough to resist the hydrostatic pressure. This is effected by putting down a number of boreholes around, and at a short distance from, the outside circumference of the shaft which is about to be sunk. By passing a cold solution through the freezing tubes inserted in these boreholes, heat is slowly absorbed from the ground, so that the temperature of the water and ground is first gradually reduced to freezing point and afterwards far below that point, thereby making the ice-wall thicker and more resistant. Fig. 52 illustrates the principle of the process.

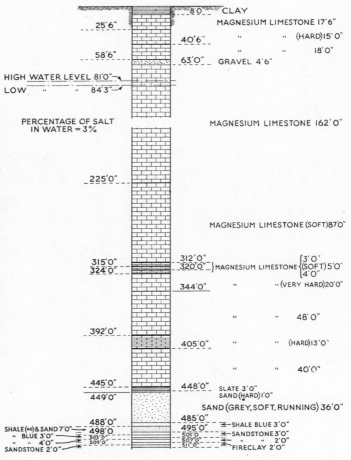

Fig. 51.—Section of strata in test borehole.

In each borehole a length of steel pipe, called a freezing-tube, is inserted, and this is sealed securely at the base. Down this freezing-tube a second column of piping is lowered, having a much smaller diameter, open at the end, and reaching nearly to the sealed end of the larger tube. These two tubes, as will be seen from the diagram, constitute a freezing circuit. The cold solution (brine) which enters by the small pipe A passes to the bottom of the borehole. After reaching the bottom of the inner tube, the brine ascends

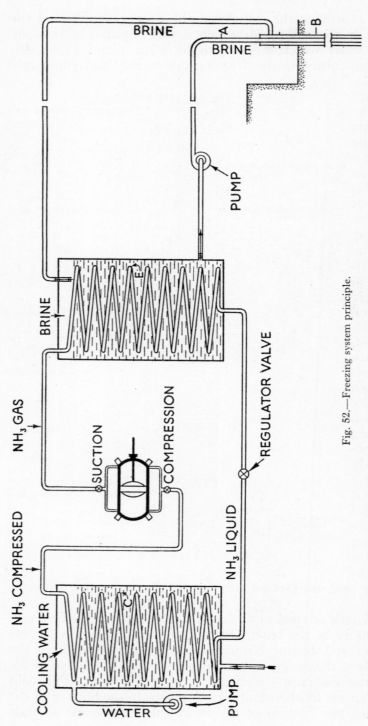

BRINE

BRINE

A

B

PUMP

BRINE

E

NH₃ GAS

SUCTION

COMPRESSION

REGULATOR VALVE

NH₃ COMPRESSED

NH₃ LIQUID

COOLING WATER

C

WATER

PUMP

Fig. 52.—Freezing system principle.

between the inner tubes A and the outer tubes B. During this ascent the brine effects an exchange of heat with the ground. Thus the ground becomes colder, and the brine arriving at the top of the freezing tubes has lost a certain amount of its coldness. The brine then comes into contact with the coils E of an evaporator. These evaporators contain a liquid—usually anhydrous ammonia (NH_3) or carbon dioxide (CO_2)—which vaporises at the low temperature at which it is worked. The latent heat of evaporation of this liquid is taken from the brine, which is thus cooled. The evaporation of the refrigerant contained in the coils is produced by a gas-pump, which afterwards compresses the gas into a condenser C, where, under the influence of the cooling-water, it liquefies, only to be expanded into a gas again in the coils E of the evaporator. These two distinct circuits, the refrigerant and the brine, are maintained for a greater or lesser period, according to the nature of the ground, the amount of water which the ground contains, the depth of the shaft, the hydrostatic pressure, etc.

In sinking a shaft by the freezing process, there are three distinct operations, namely: (1) the boring, (2) the freezing and (3) the sinking.

Fig. 53 is a plan of the boreholes at the Vane Shaft, Seaham Harbour, which were bored through approximately 500 ft. of heavily watered strata.

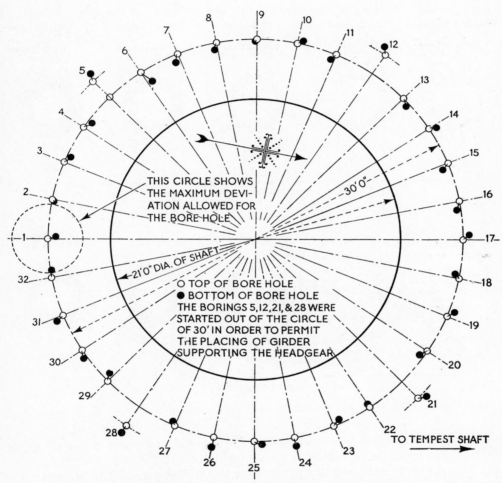

THIS CIRCLE SHOWS THE MAXIMUM DEVIATION ALLOWED FOR THE BORE HOLE

30' 0"

21' 0" DIA. OF SHAFT

O TOP OF BORE HOLE
● BOTTOM OF BORE HOLE
THE BORINGS 5, 12, 21, & 28 WERE STARTED OUT OF THE CIRCLE OF 30' IN ORDER TO PERMIT THE PLACING OF GIRDER SUPPORTING THE HEADGEAR

TO TEMPEST SHAFT

Fig. 53.—Plan of boreholes, Vane Shaft, Londonderry Colliery.

There were thirty-two boreholes around the shaft and one in the centre. The central borehole was for observation purposes. The holes were bored to a depth of 535 ft. in order to guard against any possibility of water percolating through from the water-bearing strata above. The boreholes were lined with 6-in. tubes throughout, and the freezing-tubes were inserted, every joint of these being tested to a pressure of 300 lb. per sq. in. The outer circulating-tubes consisted of internally-socketed pipes 5 in. in diameter, and the inner tubes consisted of externally-socketed pipes 2 in. in diameter. When the freezing tubes were in place, the lining tubes were withdrawn.

VERTICALITY OF THE FREEZING HOLES.—Special care had to be taken to keep the boreholes as vertical as possible, otherwise the distance over which the cold had to be transmitted may have been too great for the closing of the ice-wall between adjacent boreholes.

Fig. 53 also shows the deviation from the vertical at the Vane Shaft. It was less than 0·15 per cent., but a deviation of 1 per cent. was permissible.

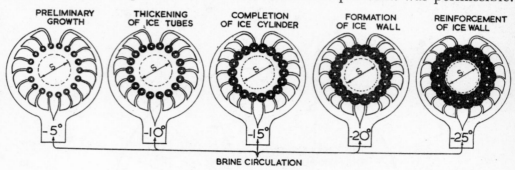

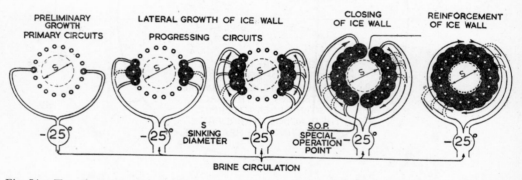

Fig. 54.—Top, formation of ice wall by ordinary method and the bottom, method used at Londonderry Colliery.

Calculations relating to the thickness of the ice-wall, to resist the hydrostatic pressure, are given in a technical paper published in 1926.[23]

As the pressure is naturally greater in the lower strata, the form of the ice-wall must be such as to give a greater thickness at the bottom than at the top.

Knowing the temperature of the brine entering and leaving the freezing tubes, as well as the quantity of brine circulating through them, it is possible to arrive at the quantity of heat given up by the ground.

THE FREEZING STATION.—The cold necessary for freezing at Seaham was produced in a freezing station, the plant having a refrigerating power of 540,000 negative calories per hour at − 20° C. Details of the plant are referred to in the publication by Henrard and Whetton, referred to previously.

From the freezing station to the shaft, and vice versa, the cold solution was carried in pipes.

When the brine arrived at the shaft, it was properly distributed to the borings by circular pipes, from which there were branch connections with valves and cocks. The connecting pipes were of lead, so as to allow for contraction produced by the cold. Meters were fitted to register the total quantity of brine passing through each engine and each circuit in different borings. Thermometers were placed at certain positions in the plant to ensure perfect control of the whole process.

The brine used was a solution of calcium chloride ($CaCl_2$) with a density of 1·25. Danger-signals were arranged, for safety, to indicate immediately any leakage of brine into the ground, thus enabling the trouble to be rectified at once.

METHOD OF FREEZING.—Owing to the peculiar conditions prevailing at Seaham, the contractors considerably modified the usual practice. Previous to the Seaham sinking, it had been usual to pass the cold solution through all the borings simultaneously from the commencement of the freezing. The ice-wall grew slowly around each freezing tube until the cylinders of ice joined together.

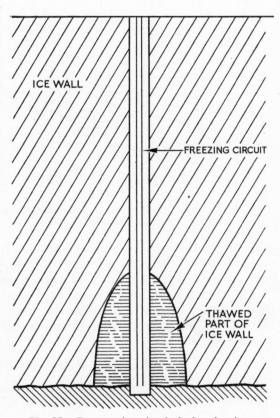

Fig. 55.—Re-warming circuit during thawing.

At Seaham Harbour, on the contrary, only two borings (Fig. 54, bottom) were put into circulation at the commencement, one on the western side of the shaft and one on the eastern side (sea-side). Only these two borings were in circulation until the temperature of the four adjacent holes was found to be sufficiently low. Then these four holes also received the cold solution, thus making a total of six. These six borings alone remained the only ones in circulation until the temperature of the next four became low enough to receive the cold solution, and so on, until the number of borings in circulation increased, the ice-wall meanwhile growing in four different directions until it finally joined in two places.

The sinking was proceeded with as soon as the ice-wall was completed, the work proceeding in a manner similar to that used for dry, hard ground; non-freezing explosives being used. The shaft was lined with cast-iron tubbing sufficiently strong to resist the water pressure at the various depths.

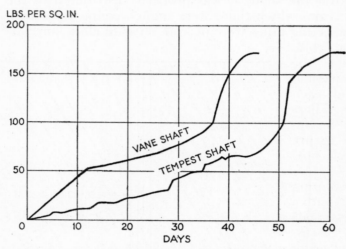

Fig. 56.—Pressure chart for thawing at the Vane and Tempest Shafts, Londonderry Colliery.

The thawing was done by passing warm brine through the freezing tubes.

To effect the thawing, the dispersion of the heat was so arranged that the thawing commenced at the foot of every freezing tube and progressed gradually towards the top, as shown in Fig. 55. The whole tubbing was thus subjected to a progressively increasing pressure; if any defect appeared, the difficulty of sealing was dealt with at a minimum of pressure and, in many cases, also without having any water trouble, because the ice-wall still in existence outside the thawed cavity resisted the pressure of the outside water.

The thawing at the Tempest and Vane shafts at Seaham was executed in this manner with the greatest success, as may be seen from the pressure chart (Fig. 56) as recorded by the pressure-gauge at the base of the water-bearing strata.

LABOUR, PROGRESS, COSTS, ETC.

Labour.—The labour complement will vary considerably in sinking a shaft, in accordance with many factors which are not necessarily common for all shafts. Drilling, blasting and filling cycles might consume from 60 to 85 per cent. of the total sinking time. Two main systems which may be applied are : (1) The employment of skilled sinkers who are expected to perform all the normal tasks entailed in a sinking programme, with the exception of filling-out, which is done by teams of hired unskilled labour, and (2) the employment of teams of sinkers who do the actual loading-out in addition to their other duties.

The first system might require careful supervision and organisation but, if successfully applied, is generally cheaper than the second method, where skilled men are engaged for considerable periods on common task work.

The cycle of excavation may be 8, 16 or 24 hours. It is usual to use an 8-hour cycle in South Africa, with 3 to 5 ft. blasting depths while, in Great

Britain, a longer cycle is used, with larger blasting depths. The ratio of actual sinkers to all employed may vary from between 40 to 60 per cent. A common practice in Great Britain is to engage a firm or company which specialises in this type of work. Such firms provide their own teams of skilled sinkers, and these are diluted by semi-skilled or unskilled labour from other sources.

Progress.—Charts are maintained which show the month-to-month advance of the sinking. Usually, each month's sinking is given a different colour on the chart, which also shows the exact location of all the permanent fixtures in the shaft, such as curbs, garlands, insets, buntons, etc. A complete section of the strata must be kept and the depths at which the strata change

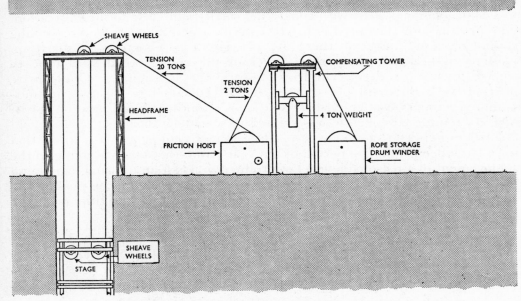

Fig. 57.—Simplified diagram showing the course of one of the two ropes in the Blair hoist.

are noted. Valuable data are thereby provided for correlation with strata encountered during the development and working of the mine and for comparison with borehole cores, rocks from cross-measure drifts, staple pits, and from the vicinity of faults. Samples of coal seams and other important rocks are retained for analysis. Further records include the quantities of explosive, detonators and other expendable items consumed from day to day. Usually a daily progress pro-forma is completed by the site engineer or by each master sinker, for these purposes.

The rate at which shafts can be sunk has increased in recent years, particularly in South Africa where, in the rectangular shaft sinkings, large native filling teams are used around as many as four debris skips. Some of the new shafts at the Orange Free State gold mines have been sunk at phenomenal speed. Approximately fifty shafts have been sunk over the past ten years. The shafts, circular in shape, vary in diameter from 20 ft. to 25 ft. and are lined with concrete. In general, they have the advantage of being in strong ground which does not require temporary supports. Multi-deck scaffolds were used so that sinking and walling could be carried out simultaneously. With the object of supporting large weights and increasing the number of buckets that can be used simultaneously in shaft-sinking, Mr. Blair, Consulting Mechanical Engineer to the Anglo-American Corporation of South Africa, designed an eight-rope stage (Fig. 57), which thus provides four sets of guides for buckets. Special Cactus grabs (see Plate facing this page) were used for mechanical dirt removal in some of the shafts. Average weekly rates of advance of over 100 ft. were common and on many occasions this was up to 130 or 140 ft. The record advance was 597 ft. in one month in a 21-ft. diameter shaft with concreting carried out close to the excavation. The practice now favoured is to erect permanent headgears before sinking commences and most of these are of reinforced-concrete construction. Designs of headgear vary from copies of the conventional steel type to square towers, or even cylindrical towers like lighthouses. One square tower, 103 ft. high, in pre-stressed reinforced concrete for two ground-mounted winders was erected in nine days. Another square tower, 144 ft. high, in reinforced concrete was erected in seventeen days.

TIME SCHEDULE FOR A NEW COLLIERY.—In a recent paper[24] it is stated that for a large deep sinking a period of ten years from the start of sinking to the achievement of a reasonable level of production is not an unusual happening in Great Britain, but the opinion is expressed that it should be possible by adopting new techniques to reduce, by at least one-half, the time normally taken as set out in the following table:—

COMPARISON OF NORMAL AND POSSIBLE TIME SCHEDULES FOR A NEW SINKING

Item	Approximate time period	
	Normal (months)	Possible (months)
Site preparation for sinking	12	9
Shaft collars, fan inset, etc.	12	6
Shaft sinking, say 1,000 yd.	50	18
Inset formation, say 3 levels	9	4
Equipping of shaft	9	3
Pit-bottom drivage	12	6
Drift drivage for development to production	24	8
Total	128	54
Say	10½ years	4½ years

BLAIR MECHANICAL GRAB FOR LOADING DEBRIS IN SHAFT SINKING
(*Optima*)

MECHANICAL "MUCKER" OR GRAB DISCHARGING INTO HOPPIT

Speed of Sinking Operations.—This is extremely important from the economic point of view. Speedy execution will save a large amount both in revenue and in capital costs.

Measures necessary to secure a good sinking rate include:—

(1) Careful planning of the different phases of the work, with regard to the technical aspects and time of execution.

(2) Planning should embody accurate phasing in ordering of plant and materials as delays due to shortage of materials or late arrival of plant will prove costly.

(3) Use of modern techniques based on research and experience. Various methods of carrying out an operation should be analysed and the decision reached should depend both on past experience and on any special features of the project under consideration.

(4) A separate organisation should be developed to ensure adequate supervision of the work at all levels. By this means, realistic time schedules may be observed and co-ordination of the various operations obtained.

The elimination of unnecessary delays is perhaps one of the most important factors in maintaining a good sinking rate and thereby ensuring maximum economy. In Great Britain at present the average monthly rate of progress varies between 100 and 150 ft. per month in an ordinary sinking.

Costs.—It is impossible to lay down any standard cost figures as these vary within considerable limits, depending on the difficulties encountered. Some specimen figures relating to a shaft at a metal mine are given as an illustration only:—

(1) West Rand Consolidated Mines Ltd.,[25] 1931 to 1933.
Excavated size of shaft 31½ ft. × 13½ ft. rectangular, timbered below the shaft collar, in five compartments, to a depth of 3,921 ft. The total cost of the sinking was £111,564 9s. 8d., or £28 9s. 1d. per foot sunk. Details were:—

	Total cost			Cost per ft.		
	£	s.	d.	£	s.	d.
Sinking	47,523	7	8	12	2	5
Timbering	37,913	19	2	9	13	5
Hoisting	12,847	2	3	3	5	6
De-watering	514	8	9		2	8
General charges ..	12,765	11	10	3	5	1
	111,564	9	8	28	9	1

(2) Rothes Colliery, Fifeshire, Scotland.[26]
Estimated cost of sinking two 24-ft. diameter shafts, 1947, onwards, to a depth of 800 yd.:—

	£	s.	d.
Preparation and temporary work ..	6,000	0	0
Sinking	560,000	0	0
	£ 566,000	0	0

which works out at an over-all cost of £236 per foot sunk.

INCLINED DRIFTS

For coal seams lying at comparatively shallow depths it might be cheaper and more profitable to develop and work the seams from inclined drifts instead of vertical shafts. Drifts are quite commonly used in the outcropping areas of a coal basin and normally follow the seam from an outcrop. The modern tendency, where conditions are suitable, is to drive cross-measure drifts from the surface to intersect the seams at shallow depths. This practice should result in a more durable road, less likely to be affected by ground movement.

There are advantages and disadvantages in the use of drifts as compared with vertical shafts, both in the driving and in the subsequent working of the seams.

Advantages Accruing During Driving.—(1) Loading-out of the debris takes a comparatively long time in vertical shafts, while mechanical loading devices can often be adapted to the driving of drifts.

(2) The permanent lining can be inserted as part of a continuous cycle of work instead of intermittently, to the temporary exclusion of sinking, as in vertical shafts.

(3) The blasting and shift changing times are shorter.

(4) The spoil may be more expeditiously transported to the surface.

(5) Drifts might be cheaper to sink than vertical shafts for the same capacity, although the inclination of the drift must be taken into account since this affects the length of the drift, and its cost compared with vertical shafts.

Disadvantages During Driving.—(1) It may, under certain conditions, be more difficult to negotiate weak ground, due to roof weighting.

(2) There is an economic limit to the length of a drift beyond which it is cheaper to sink and equip a vertical shaft. This limit is in the neighbourhood of 600 ft. vertical depth.

(3) When passing through water-bearing beds which have to be sealed by cementation, the volume of rock to be treated is necessarily greater with inclined shafts. Similarly, the area exposed in such beds is greater and this might result in a greater make of water.

(4) The necessary equipment, such as cables, pipes, ropes, etc., is a minimum length in a vertical shaft for a given depth.

(5) It is not so easy to maintain direction and gradient in a drift as it is to plumb a vertical shaft.

(6) The driving of a drift to a given vertical depth is slower than that of sinking a vertical shaft.

Equipping and Working Advantages of a Drift.—(1) Drifts are more flexible than shafts in regard to output and can be more easily adapted to carry larger outputs, if necessary.

(2) Under certain conditions of gradient it is possible to use conveyors to bring the coal directly to the surface as a continuous flow.

(3) Drifts do not require elaborate headgear and the transfer of coal can be dealt with expeditiously at the surface.

(4) Drifts do not require costly shaft equipment such as guide ropes and the effects of overwinds are not as serious as in vertical shafts. The drift equipment is also more accessible for maintenance and repair.

(5) In an emergency it is quicker to vacate the mine through a drift than through vertical shafts.

(6) With certain inclined seams the method of working may be more cheaply arranged from drifts.

Equipping and Working Disadvantages of a Drift.—(1) The haulage time from a given vertical depth is longer and there are greater frictional power losses.

(2) There is a greater ventilating power loss in drifts for a given depth.

(3) The cost of maintaining the drift is higher and the amount of coal left as pillars to protect the drift must be greater than would be afforded in a vertical shaft.

Drifts are not as a rule designed for such large outputs as are vertical shafts. This is because drifts are usually associated with shallow seams where the conditions do not, as a rule, point to any large-scale mining from a single outlet.

The driving of a drift entails a loading, drilling and blasting cycle, where the ground is strong enough to permit the use of explosives. Thus in an 8-hour cycle the blasting fumes are cleared during the change over. Assuming that the drift starts from the surface and is driven down to the seams, special methods of driving may have to be adopted until strong ground is reached. A common practice for driving through unconsolidated ground is to forepole by means of timber or by steel rails. Quite a considerable amount of water may have to be pumped away from the face of the drift in the initial stages.

On reaching good ground the permanent drifting equipment is inserted. Scraper-type loaders are commonly used for loading purposes, where the gradient is not too great. The advantages of mechanical loaders may be to speed up but not necessarily to reduce the cost of driving. Thus, where three different schemes of driving were used,[27] namely:—

(1) Drilling with hand-held jack-hammers, single shot firing, hand filling into tubs.

(2) Drilling with hand-held jack-hammers, firing two shots simultaneously and mechanical loading.

(3) Drilling with hand-held jack-hammers, multi-shot with delay-action detonators and mechanical loading, it was found that:—

    (a) The cost of driving remained appreciably the same when (2) replaced (1).

(*b*) The cost of driving rose by 16 per cent. when (3) replaced (2).
(*c*) The weekly advance rose by 53 per cent. when (2) replaced (1).
(*d*) The weekly advance rose by 200 per cent. (over (1)) when (3) replaced (2).

Loading out the Debris.—The debris is hauled from the sinking drift in mine cars. The capacity of these cars has an important bearing on the progress. They should be of large capacity, to reduce long waiting periods during loading, especially where it is not possible to lay a double track. Where the inclination is high they should have a low centre of gravity and adequate precautions should be taken to avoid the danger of cars running back. For the sinking of a drift mine in Scotland[28] it was decided to use, for loading purposes, a drop-bottom car of the pattern designed for hauling the coal from the mine. A single track was used of 42-in. gauge and 50 lb. per yd. rail. The capacity of the car was 2 tons (coal) and the dimensions were:—

Length of body	10 ft. 3½ in.
Over-all width of body..	4 ft. 3 in.
Depth of body	2 ft. 3 in.
Over-all length over buffers	11 ft.
Height over rail level	2 ft. 10 in.
Tare	21 cwt.
Carrying capacity	85 cu. ft.

Types of mechanical loaders which might be used for drifting are described in Chapter 9. The limitations of gradient preclude the use of many common types. Rocker type shovel loaders have been successfully used in driving inclined drifts which dip as steeply as 12 degrees, the cars in this case are controlled by a winch. The Joy loader has been adapted for use in stone drifts, although it requires a carefully organised system to keep it well supplied with tubs or cars. To supply pass byes for tubs or cars a number of devices have been developed. These include (1) the "cherry-picker", (2) complete assembly[29] of two switches and two parallel tracks which sit on top of the main track and which can be moved forward quickly towards the face when necessary. (3) Transfer carriages which take an empty tub and which can be rolled to one side to allow a full tub to pass.

The following details[30] refer to mechanical loaders of various types.

SHOVEL LOADERS.—These are at present limited to level or gently dipping drifts. The following data refer to three typical types:—

	A	B	C
Weight	5,700 lb.	—	8½ tons.
Over-all width	33 in.	41 in.	48 in.
Working length	81 in.	81 in.	22 ft.
Clean-up width	85 in.	84 in.	10 ft.
Working height	87–95 in.	91 in.	79 in.
Tramming height	56 in.	56 in.	67 in.
Range of track gauge.	18–36 in.	24–30 in.	18–56 in.
Capacity of bucket	9 cu. ft.	4–5 cu. ft.	5 cu. ft.
Loading capacity cu. ft. per min. ..	30–35	20–25	25

JOY LOADERS.—This machine has been specially adapted by the makers for stonework. It is very suitable for rapid loading, but where the gradient exceeds about 1 in 5 cannot be used successfully at the present time.

SCRAPER LOADERS.—This type of loader is very commonly used on steep gradients in metalliferous mining practice and it is possible that a scraper loader could be applied where other mechanical loaders would fail.

Drilling and Blasting.—The positions of the holes will, as for vertical shafts, depend on similar factors. A pyramid cut is commonly used in good ground. Fig. 58 shows a typical round of holes for an 8 ft. × 10 ft. drift. The holes are drilled by hand-held jack-hammers or from drilling frames or columns. Fig. 59 illustrates a drilling frame used in driving a drift at Lumphinnans Colliery, Fife. A highly flexible and speedy type of drilling chassis is the hydro-drill jib (see Chapter 9).

Permanent Lining of Drifts.—Steel arches are most commonly used for the permanent lining of drifts. The lining between the arches used at the Merrilees Drift[31] consists of precast concrete blocks which are inter-

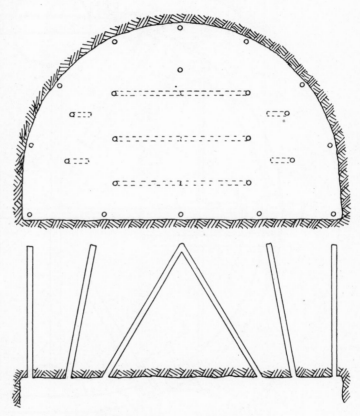

Fig. 58.—Round of holes for drift mine drivage.

locked and a special crown block is used to complete the ring (see Vol. 2, Chap. 2). No attempt is made, as a rule, to render drift linings completely water-tight as this would involve considerable expense. Water in such small quantities is usually dealt with by inserting a permanent water channel in the side of the drift to carry the water to an inset or to a lodgement below the water-bearing strata for pumping to the surface. Where large quantities of water issue from the strata the ground may have to be cemented.

COSTS AND PROGRESS.—The following details of costs are given for the driving of two drift mines in Scotland;[32] the figures show the yardage driven per week and details of the weekly cost:—

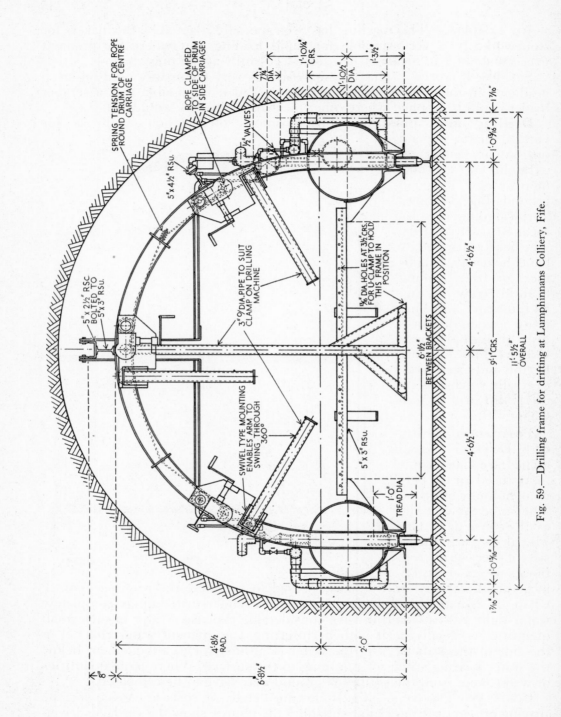

Fig. 59.—Drilling frame for drifting at Lumphinnans Colliery, Fife.

SPRING TENSION FOR ROPE
ROUND DRUM OF CENTRE
CARRIAGE

ROPE CLAMPED
TO SIDE OF DRUM
IN SIDE CARRIAGES

5" x 4½" RSJ.

½" VALVES

7¼"
DIA.

1'-10¼"
CRS.

1'-0½"
DIA.

1'-3½"

1'-0 ¹³⁄₁₆"

1 ¹⁄₁₆"

4'-6½"

9'-1" CRS.

11'-5½"
OVERALL

6'-1½"

BETWEEN BRACKETS

5" x 2½" RSC
BOLTED TO
5" x 3" RSJ.

3"∅ DIA. PIPE TO SUIT
CLAMP ON DRILLING
MACHINE

⅝" DIA. HOLES AT 3½" CRS.
FOR U-CLAMP TO HOLD
THIS FRAME IN
POSITION

SWIVEL TYPE MOUNTING
ENABLES ARM TO
SWING THROUGH
360°

5" x 3" RSJ.

4'-6½"

1'-0"
TREAD DIA.

1'-0 ¹³⁄₁₆"

1 ¹⁄₁₆"

4'-8½"
RAD.

8"

2'-0"

6'-8½"

I. COST OF MAKING DRIFTS AT FORDELL COLLIERY
HENDERSON MINE

Gradient 1 in 5

14 ft. × 10 ft. Circle Girders. Yardage 13 yd.
  Week ending 4th September, 1948

	Total Weekly Cost	Cost per yard	
	£ s. d.	£ s. d.	
Face	154 0 9	11 17 0	5 men working at
On cost	41 0 10	3 3 2	face per shift.
Surface	55 13 0	4 5 7	
Explosives ..	24 2 8	1 17 1	
	£274 17 3	£21 2 10	

14 ft. × 10 ft. Circle Girders. Yardage 14 yd.
  Week ending 11th September, 1948

	£ s. d.	£ s. d.	
Face	157 18 11	11 5 8	
On cost	48 6 0	3 9 0	5 men working at
Surface	54 18 9	3 18 6	face per shift.
Explosives ..	19 6 5	1 7 7	
	£280 10 1	£20 0 9	

13 ft. × 9 in. Circle Girders. Yardage 12 yd.
  Week ending 17th July, 1948

	£ s. d.	£ s. d.	
Face	132 11 7	11 0 11	
On cost	57 19 8	4 16 8	4 men working at
Surface	74 3 5	6 3 7	face per shift.
Explosives ..	15 5 6	1 5 6	
	£280 0 2	£23 6 8	

II. COST OF DRIVING SURFACE MINE AT LUMPHINNANS NOS. XI AND XII COLLIERIES

Gradient 1 in 3·8

14 ft. × 10 ft. *circle girders*

Week Ending 19th October, 1946—8 yd. cutting.

Shifts	£ s. d.	Wages Price per yd. £ s. d.
15—Face	130 7 6	16 5 11
6—On cost	49 18 7	6 4 10
13—Surface	70 11 11	8 16 6
Explosives	17 19 11	2 5 0
	£268 17 11	£33 12 3

Material cost for lining and temporary track. Price per yd., £5 2s 2d.
TOTAL COST PER YARD, £38 14s. 5d.

Week Ending 13*th September,* 1947—13 *yd. cutting.*

	Shifts			£	s.	d.	Wages Price per yd. £	s.	d.
15—Face	..	..		120	7	6	9	5	2
7—On cost	..			65	12	10	5	1	0
11—Surface	..			54	19	0	4	4	6
Explosives	..			41	5	9	3	3	6
				£282	5	1	£21	14	2

Material cost for lining and temporary track. Price per yd., £5 9s. 1d.

TOTAL COST PER YARD, £27 3s. 3d.

Drifting Speeds.—It is unlikely, because of differing conditions, that the rate of advance of drifts for British coal mines will ever be comparable with the spectacular tunnelling speeds which have been achieved in civil engineering and kindred schemes. However, there seems to be no reason to doubt that the progress of the drifting work could be considerably accelerated with substantial economic benefit accruing. The principal factors necessary to secure a good drifting rate are:—

(1) A high standard of planning, organisation and supervision;

(2) Suitable equipment and working methods.

The planning will include the careful siting of the drift to avoid bad ground. The organisation should be such as to obtain continuous work. Multi-shift working, combined with adequate supervision, will ensure a steady rate of advance.

The selection of equipment will depend on the conditions under which it will have to work. For example, the important factors in the selection of machinery for the power-loading of debris will be the gradient of the drift, the system of transport and the nature and quantity of debris.

An important part of the working methods is the system of drilling and blasting used. Skilled drilling and blasting will ensure as large a pull as is possible, consistent with safety and correct fragmentation (See Chapter 9).

Thus it will be seen that consistent application of sound principles and methods should render it possible to increase substantially the rates of advance normally achieved in some British mines.

REFERENCES

[1] Reid and King, Planning a new Colliery in 1947. *Trans. Inst. Min. Eng.*, Vol. 106, Plate 12.

[2] Reid and King, Planning a new Colliery in 1947. *Trans. Inst. Min. Eng.*, Vol. 106, Plate 15.

[3] Imperial Chemical Industries Limited.

[4] Jeppe, *Gold Mining on the Witwatersrand*, Vol. 1, p. 263.

[5] C. S. McLean, Sinking the South Shaft, West Rand Mines Consolidated Ltd. *Transactions, of Association of Mine Managers of the Transvaal*, 1931–6, p. 33.

[6] Forster Brown, *Vertical Shaft Sinking*, Table VII.

[7] Vail. Some Notes on Sinking Vlakfontein No. 1 Shaft. *Transactions, Association of Mine Managers of the Transvaal*, 1931–6, pp. 53, 55.

[8] J. B. Huttl, *Engineering and Mining Journal*, Vol. 149, No. 6, p. 83.

[9] W. A. Pickersgill, Mechanical Mucking in a Sinking Pit, *Trans. Inst. Min. Eng.*, 1956–7, Vol. 116, Part C3, December, 1956.

[10] Sinking Shafts by the Freezing Method in Belgium, *Colliery Guardian*, 9th April, 1936, p. 687.

[11] Shaft Sinking at Comrie, *Colliery Engineering*, June, 1937, p. 195.

[12] McLean, Sinking the South Shaft, West Rand Mines, Consolidated Ltd. *Transactions, Association of Mine Managers of the Transvaal*, 1931–6, Fig. 7, facing p. 16.

[13] The Cementation Company Ltd.

[14] Gillieaux, Lining Shafts with Concrete Z Blocks, *Trans. Inst. Min. Eng.*, Vol. 50, p. 51.

[15] Sinking Shafts by the Freezing Method in Belgium, *Colliery Guardian*, 9th April, 1936, p. 287.

[16] Reconstructing a Fallen-in Shaft, *Colliery Guardian*, 3rd April, 1936, p. 628.

[17] Forster Brown, *Vertical Shaft Sinking*, pp. 252–7; Statham, *Winning and Working*, p. 104.

[18] Forster Brown, *Historical Review of Coal Mining*, p. 30.

[19] Mottram, Description of the sinking of shafts through Sand at Ardeer, Ayrshire by the Pneumatic Process, etc., *Trans., Inst. Min. Eng.*, Vol. 30, p. 205.

[20] Allen and Crawhall, Shaft Sinking in Dolomite at Venterspost, *Transactions, Association of Mine Managers of the Transvaal*, 1937–8, p. 15.

[21] Atherton, *Leeds University Mining Society Journal*, 1947, p. 107.

[22] The Sinking of Londonderry Colliery, Seaham Harbour, Co. Durham, by the Freezing Process. Henrard and Whetton, *Trans., Inst. Min. Eng.*, Vol. 75, pp. 358–9 and Vol. 76, pp. 63–6.

[23] The Sinking of Two Shafts by the Freezing Process, Henrard and Whetton, *The Journal of Armstrong College Mining Society*, Vol. 2, 1925.

[24] H. R. King, The Construction of New Collieries in Scotland, *Trans., Inst. Min. Eng.*, Vol. 115, Part 8, 1956, p. 597.

[25] McLean, Sinking the South Shaft, West Rand Consolidated Mines Ltd., *Transactions, Association of Mine Managers of the Transvaal*, 1931–6, p. 34.

[26] Reid and King, Planning a new Colliery in 1947, *Trans., Inst. Min. Eng.*, Vol. 106, p. 728.

[27] Noble, Reorganisation of Hatfield Main Colliery, *Trans., Ins. Min. Eng.*, Vol. 107, p. 127.

[28] Central Fife Sub-area, Scottish Division, National Coal Board.

[29] *Bulletin of the Institution of Mining and Metallurgy*, No. 502, p. 26.

[30] H. R. King, Planning, Development and Re-organisation of Collieries, Heriot Watt College Paper.

[31] Driving Merrilees Drift, Butterley and Mitchell, Vol. 104, 1944–5, p. 703.

[32] Central Fife Sub-area, Scottish Division, National Coal Board.

CHAPTER 6

PLANNING, LAYOUT AND DEVELOPMENT OF MINE WORKINGS

The Necessity for Mine Planning.—The science and art of mine planning as practised today evolved gradually from the earliest days of mining. To the early miners the necessity to work the coal in such a manner that the next day's output could be obtained with certainty and minimum hindrance and trouble must have been a lesson gradually and painfully learned by employer and employee alike. From the results of trial and error, often accompanied by failure and loss of life, the procedure of planning in advance developed and the results obtained stimulated incentive and progress towards increased safety and larger output.

The earliest coal workings consisted simply of digging the exposed coal from the surface, where the seams outcropped, followed by the sinking of bell pits or the driving of drifts or adits where the seam was shallow (see also Chapter 1). Such mining was primitive in character and limited in extent. With the growth of knowledge and experience, aided by improvements in roof support, ventilation and haulage, shafts were sunk to deeper seams and larger areas of coal had of necessity to be won from these shafts to make the project economic.

As the depth and size of the mines increased, planning ahead became more and more essential to success. Although the need for such planning was long recognised, it was not until the early days of the present century, when large collieries were laid out to provide output of 3,000 tons per day or even more, that its importance was fully realised and advantage taken of its benefits.

The sinking equipment of pits for even larger outputs from large areas of coal lying at depths of 1,000 yd. or more and the impact of mechanisation render planning more and more important today, as evidenced by the fact that the National Coal Board now employ large numbers of specialists in the various planning departments.

Probably the greatest influence upon the conceptions of colliery layout and development within the last 50 years has been the change of the whole field of mining operations brought about by the introduction of mechanical methods of winning coal at the coalface, and the introduction of electric power underground.

LAYOUT OF MINES

Shafts.—The Mines and Quarries Act, 1954, Sec. 22 (1), stipulates that, subject to certain provisos, "it shall not be lawful for any persons to be employed below ground in a mine of coal, stratified ironstone, shale or fire-clay unless there are available, for affording to them alternative, and ready, means of ingress or egress, two shafts or outlets . . . which, except where they were sunk before 1st January, 1865, are at no point separated from each other by less than 45 ft. or (where the sinking thereof began before 1st January, 1888) 10 ft."

The two shafts provide also means for the circulation of the ventilating air of the mine, one of which is the downcast, or intake, and the other is the upcast or return, and each have to be fitted with "proper and separate

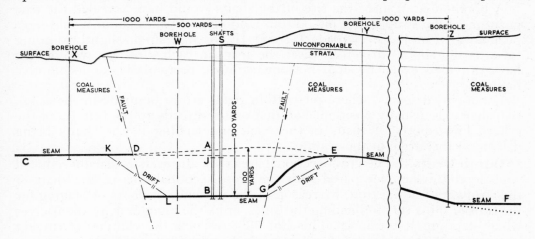

Fig. 1.—Sketch illustrating the effect of sinking shafts with incomplete information owing to displacement of seams by faults.

apparatus for raising and lowering persons". According to the output desired and the shaft equipment provided, one or both of the shafts may be used for the extraction of mineral, the lowering of materials used in the working of the mine, including goaf-stowing material, for the pumping of water and for the transmission of power—usually compressed-air and/or electricity—to the underground workings.

It is usual nowadays to sink shafts at a greater distance apart than the statutory minimum, and surface as well as underground considerations often influence the distance. Prior to shaft sinking, adequate information as to the thickness and rate of dip of the seam, and the depth of the seam from the surface should have been obtained by a series of boreholes as explained in Chapter 4, as otherwise much operating efficiency can be lost by an unsuitable pit-bottom layout. In this respect it is not sufficient to rely solely upon geological maps as the necessary information may not be sufficiently accurate for the purpose. Fig. 1 shows how the presence of unsuspected faults and dipping strata may lead to an expensively-operated pit-bottom arrangement which would impose an extra burden of cost upon each ton of coal wrought throughout the life of the mine. In this case boreholes X, Y and Z were put down at 1,000-yd. intervals, and from these, and from geological data obtained from surrounding collieries it was anticipated that shafts sunk at S would intercept the seam at A, about 400 yd. from the surface, thus allowing a pit bottom to be constructed in the seam itself, as shown by the line CDE. But on sinking the shafts, the seam was reached at B, some 500 yd. below the surface, roughly 100 yd. below the anticipated position. Only after exploratory headings had been driven, and working commenced, was it found that a trough fault system had displaced the strata downwards in the region of the shafts. Cross-measure drifts at GE and at LK were thus necessary, involving considerable expense.

A borehole at W near the site of the shafts would have revealed the true position of the seam and a pit-bottom landing and water sump would have been formed at J. Level roads JD and JE (or if desired, slightly dipping towards the shafts) driven to meet the seam in each direction would then have provided excellent shaft-bottom facilities, particularly for locomotive haulage.

For inclined seams, where pit-bottom roads are to be made in the seam, two shafts are usually positioned so that one is directly to the full dip of the other. This allows of roads in the seam and leading to the shafts being driven on the strike of the seam.

Dumb Drifts.—The cross-sectional area of shaft insets is usually reduced considerably, when compared with the cross-sectional area of the shaft or the roadways leading to it, by reason of the presence of decks or staging for the tubs or mine cars for loading the cages, or by the cages or skips themselves when standing at the inset. This not only restricts the ventilation current but increases the velocity of the air, which in turn raises dust and causes discomfort and inconvenience to the personnel. To avoid this, "dumb drifts", as they are called, are sometimes driven to connect the airways and the shaft directly and thus to by-pass the inset where cages or skips are loaded.

Shaft Pillars.—Support for surface buildings and plant and for the shafts themselves must be left in the form of a pillar of coal around the shafts, to ensure that no movement of the surface or of the shafts takes place due to subsidence. Without such a pillar, or with an inadequate one, shafts may be "pulled" from the vertical causing inconvenience and the need for costly repairs. It is always wise, in the case of a colliery where there is a large area of coal to be worked over a number of years, to err on the generous side in fixing the size of the pillar.

For a full explanation and discussion of the factors affecting the size, shape and position of shaft pillars, reference should be made to Vol. 2, Chap. 2.

Shaft pillars in seams liable to spontaneous combustion also present special difficulty and two methods have been employed in the past to over-come this. First, by sinking the shaft through the spontaneously combustible seam to be worked, to a seam or to an artificial horizon, say 50 yards or so below the seam. Short drifts are then driven up from the shaft-bottom roads to points on the edge of the shaft pillar left in the seam to be worked and working then proceeds normally. Outbreaks of fire at the shaft pillar-edge are, however, not always prevented by this means.

In the second system, roads are driven from the shaft bottom for some considerable distance beyond the shaft pillar. Faces are then opened out advancing from, and retreating towards, the shaft pillar. Crushing of the shaft pillar by the first weighting—a potential source of spontaneous combustion—is thus reduced, and it is also possible to study the effects of subsidence, although some considerable time elapses before settlement is finally completed.

Pit-Bottom Roadways and Main Roadways.—The direction, gradient, and cross-sectional area of pit-bottom roadways through the shaft pillar and beyond as main roadways depend upon the following factors, although some of these relate to special circumstances as specified:—

(1) The size and shape of the area of the coal to be worked.
(2) The position of the shafts in the royalty.
(3) The general dip of the seam.
(4) The presence of faults, washouts, rolls, anticlines, synclines, dykes, steeply-dipping ground and other geological abnormalities.
(5) The nature of the roof and floor, and hence the type of roadway support required.
(6) The liability of the seam to spontaneous combustion.
(7) The presence of workings in other seams in the same area and their proximity to the seam to be worked.
(8) The type of haulage to be adopted.
(9) The position and extent of areas of coal to be left unworked due to:—
   (a) Support to be left for towns, buildings, works, bridges, railways, rivers, canals, locks and reservoirs and areas of low-lying ground at surface.
   (b) The presence of underground or surface water levels for drainage and for preventing water from rise workings reaching those to the dip.
   (c) Areas too much disturbed geologically to be worked economically.
   (d) Barriers against waterlogged workings (see Mines and Quarries Act, 1954, Sec. 77).
   (e) Barriers to be left against areas sealed off due to spontaneous combustion, fires or other causes.
   (f) Barriers to be left to protect against large faults due to possible ground movement, or their water-conducting properties.
   (g) Barriers to be left against old workings where disturbance of the barrier would lead to conditions liable to cause bumps or crumps, or excessive floor lift.

(10) The presence of water, possibly making the mine naturally wet throughout and calling for special provision for drainage.

(11) The emission of noxious gases occluded in the seam and neighbouring strata. This will determine the quantity of ventilation required for the working of the coal which the roads serve.

(12) The possibility of large pieces of machinery and plant having to be transported along the underground roadways.

(13) The necessity for the roads to be routes for the distribution of power, e.g., large air mains.

(14) The layout and method of working the districts of the mine and their interdependence upon the main roads.

(15) The relative size and percentage contribution to the output of the mine of a district.

The above factors may or may not be fully known to the mining engineer at the time when he considers the layout of the main roads from the shafts to serve the future workings on the projection plan. It is evident that as complete information as possible should be obtained from all available sources, and then the majority of items mentioned above can be assessed and a decision arrived at. But when one considers the working history of the average British colliery, it is significant that very few indeed are working at the present time in the method and manner which was originally intended and forecast by the first operators who sank its shafts. The same will doubtless occur in future at collieries now being sunk and developed, for circumstances force us to be ready to accept the challenges of cheaper coal, and an increased output of coal per man per annum, with a reduction of personnel. New machinery for winning, transporting, handling and cleaning coal now engage attention, and plant and equipment not yet conceived will transform colliery operations as in the past. Greater safety to the miner, improved working conditions, altered money values and taxation burdens, are only some of the many problems which are constantly before the mining engineer.

1. THE SIZE AND SHAPE OF THE AREA OF WORKABLE COAL AVAILABLE.—This, in the past, was dependent upon whether the prospective colliery proprietor could conclude satisfactory bargains with landowners and mineral owners. Some collieries were severely burdened with high minimum rents and royalty charges for every ton worked: often the mineral owner would recognise that he was to be lessor of a parcel of coal which would prevent the lessee from developing an otherwise valuable field of coal, unless he had the right to work it, and the owner would raise his price accordingly. Or, alternatively, the lessor would recognise that unless his parcel of coal were leased to the colliery concern the output of the colliery would be jeopardised, or even stopped. Such instances were fortunately the exception rather than the rule, although in some coalfields lessees were liable by prevailing local custom to have to pay higher royalty dues than in others. In Great Britain the passing of the Coal Act of 1938, of which the vesting date was 1st July, 1942, meant that individual royalty owners no longer existed,

and all royalties, present and future, were vested in the Coal Commission, and later, on 1st January, 1947, in the National Coal Board.

Under the present ownership of minerals by the State, through the National Coal Board, considerable simplification in equalising boundaries between colliery takes has been rendered possible. Awkwardly placed and awkwardly shaped areas of coal have largely disappeared, and since the operation of all the coal mines is now the responsibility of a unified State body, advantage accrues from the fixing of boundaries between colliery workings to allow the most efficient working. This is a step towards the elimination of uneconomic collieries. In the past it was not uncommon for the shaft pillar of one colliery to be the boundary of a neighbouring colliery, and the writer is aware of an example where three sides of a colliery's shaft pillar within some 300 to 400 yd. of the shafts formed the boundaries of neighbouring collieries with shafts some three miles away. Again, one colliery would be working an upper seam directly below which the lessor allowed another colliery owner to work a lower seam without the official knowledge or consent of the upper seam lessee. In such a case damage to roadways and working installations was inevitable, unless there was a high degree of planning, co-operation and co-ordination between the parties concerned. With the leases of all seams in the same ownership it is possible to plan workings in such a way that those in one seam will not disturb those in other seams.

As the result of unified ownership it is now possible for the layout of workings to determine the size and shape of the area of coal to be worked from a particular shaft or shafts. In the past this was possible only to those groups of collieries under the same ownership, whose royalties were situated adjacent to one another.

Fig. 2 shows the layout of a parcel of coal, the boundaries of which were determined by the conveying plant to be used—in this case a troughed rubber belt conveyor 30 in. wide, transporting the coal to a pit-bottom loading point, whose length of 1,100 yd. was considered appropriate for the duty to be performed. Gate conveyors running at right-angles to the trunk conveyor fed this with coal from double-unit faces, and the length of the gate conveyors was such that the plant was not overloaded at any time. Since the ground to the south-east of the main trunk road dipped away steeply, the gate conveyors on this side were of less length than those on the north-west side of the main road. All the coal in this parcel was loaded at one point, without shifting of the main trunk-conveyor loading station, and thus a permanent installation of good design could be provided. The gate conveyor lengths were arranged to give economic working, taking into consideration the amount of coal yielded from each working face and the capital cost and depreciation of the plant employed. In laying out a similar area nowadays the only modification necessory would be to arrange for two intake airways (p. 254).

The ideally shaped area for a horizontal seam would, other things being equal, be one whose boundaries are equidistant from the shaft, but local

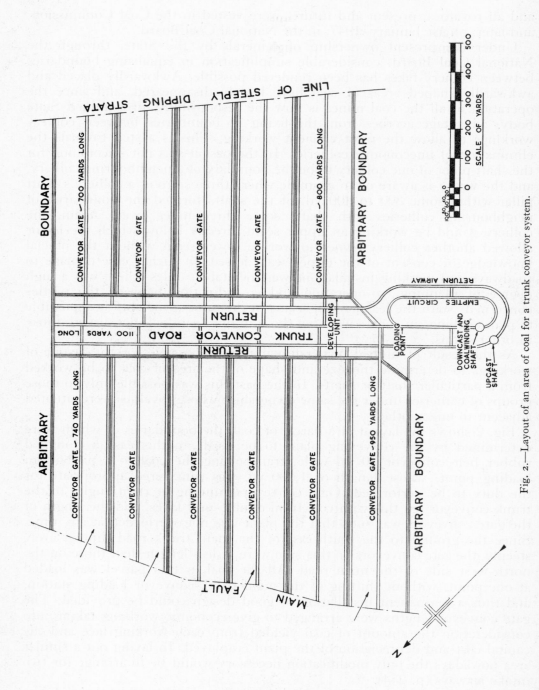

Fig. 2.—Layout of an area of coal for a trunk conveyor system.

SCALE OF YARDS

0   100   200   300   400   500

246

conditions may or may not be wholly favourable for such a shape. As to size—the ideal royalty varies, *inter alia*, according to depth of the seams, as the deeper the shafts the more expensive they are to sink and equip, so that for deep shafts a larger area of coal, within limits of ventilation and haulage efficiency, is required to achieve profitable working over a period of years. No rule can be given relating depth of shaft and area of coal to be worked: factors such as thickness of seam, nature of roof and floor, quality of coal wrought and working efficiency all play a part in the solution of the problem, but the tendency is to work larger and larger areas from a pair of shafts.

2. THE POSITION OF THE SHAFTS IN THE TAKE.—Surface considerations have a large bearing upon the position of colliery shafts. Thus contours of the surrounding country, proximity to means of transport by rail, road and canal, availability of bulk supply of electricity, water supply, surface land ownership and rents, housing and transport of workers, and foundations for plant and buildings, all demand consideration. Underground the shafts should be in as central a position as possible for seams of normal inclination. Maximum use can thus be assured for the shafts in the area they serve.

3. THE GENERAL DIP OF THE SEAM.—The notion held many years ago that there should be as much "rise side" coal as possible was mainly due to the use of self-acting haulages, but whilst it is of some advantage to have the gradient (not exceeding 1 in 10 or so) in favour of the load, it is not considered today a serious disadvantage to have to haul coal to the rise. Braking of loaded mine tubs or cars down inclines may be a greater problem than hauling them uphill, and of the two, whatever the type of haulage, with the exception of locomotives which are inapplicable on steep gradients, modern haulage plant is suitable and effective for the latter.

The use of locomotives involves careful grading of roads, and unless the seam is horizontal or nearly so, it is advisable to drive stone drifts to form such roads between the shafts and the point where the seam is met. Alternatively, in certain cases, locomotive roads may be carried on the strike or level line of the seam.

4. THE PRESENCE OF GEOLOGICAL DISTURBANCES AND ABNORMALITIES.—Although usually regarded as having nuisance value only, much can be done to mitigate the disadvantages of these features when deciding layout of roads and workings. They fall into two main categories—those which can be found before planning takes place by boring, geological deduction or other methods—for example by geophysical prospecting—and those which cannot be so found to exist, and are discovered only as working proceeds. The success and feasibility of the original plan for a mine depends largely upon how well these abnormalities have been determined, and in a virgin area, it may be desirable that exploratory headings, narrow workings or even panels should be set out to prove a given area of coal before full reliance for large and continuous daily outputs is placed upon it.

Planning the layout of a mine should allow an element of flexibility, and the major policy of working must be sufficiently wide to embrace change and be adaptable to the conditions met underground.

In seams where locomotive haulage following the seam is employed, such abnormalities can seriously upset layout; faults, anticlines, synclines, steeply dipping ground and the like can be negotiated only by long and expensive gradings of roadways or drifts. In some cases the locomotive run may be terminated, and another locomotive run commenced at the far side of the disturbance, or it may be possible to arrange for the locomotive to be assisted for a short distance, say, by means of a main-rope haulage gear.

It will be seen that the ideal conditions from the point of view of planning of workings is where another seam, reasonably near, has been extracted previously, since full information as to geological disturbances and phenomena is then available with fair accuracy. An interval of 250 yd. between seams was found by the writer to be most useful, and amenable to good planning purposes. In this particular case the upper seam had been worked first, and in the lower seam, whose roof was a massive sandstone some sixty yards thick, faults were of less throw, although in the same relative position as in the upper seam.

Washouts, rolls and clod (Vol. 2, Chap. 1) occurring in the working section (more especially clod which lies between the coal and the normal roof) cannot usually be proved prior to the actual working of the coal, and their irregular shape and erratic occurrence, following no rule, is a hazard which the planner must be prepared to counteract, by having spare coalfaces developed ready to replace output capacity thus lost or delayed. Main roads therefore must be so arranged to allow for such a contingency. It should be noted that headings, or narrow workings are not sufficient for exploratory purposes in all cases, as if washouts, rolls or clod-areas, etc., are or are not encountered by the narrow work, no proof is available of their absence since they may exist alongside the exploratory workings. A network or "grill" of such workings would greatly hinder longwall working in good coal areas, but could no doubt be turned to advantage if bord and pillar methods were pursued, as described in Chapter 7.

5. THE NATURE OF THE ROOF AND FLOOR.—These may so affect the strata in the vicinity of the pit bottom that the construction of roadways of large cross-sectional area is difficult. In many cases it is necessary to remake completely the pit-bottom roads at considerable expense, apart from possible delay in, or cessation of, coal output. The behaviour of the roof or floor in a longwall working is little if any guide to their behaviour in a narrow working such as a road through a pillar, and *vice versa*. A strong roof and floor are of great assistance where it is necessary to construct large roadways, while friable strata mean that roadways will tend to crush badly, and under such conditions it is not always a simple matter to devise supports for roof and sides which will stand permanently. A pit-bottom roadway with a sectional area of 150 square feet, at a depth of 750 yd., in the writer's knowledge, was supported by brick walls 4 ft. 6 in. thick, 10 ft. high and 15 ft. apart, supporting rolled steel joists 19 ft. long by 12 in. by 8 in. section, resting on wood crushing timber, and having 2 ft. of seating on each wall. A 3-ft. cavity was left between the walls and the side of the excavation and some lengths

of the walls had wood crushing courses, whilst the foundations were of concrete, 6 ft. in depth, laid on a clunch floor—which was the hardest available. These walls failed due to side pressure and the roof girders were crushed and bent. Steel arches 5 in. × 4½ in. section were next tried, 15 ft. wide across the base, 14 ft. wide at the spring and 11 ft. 6 in. under the central fishplates. They were spaced at 2 ft. 3 in. centres and were well strutted, and although they tended to twist and buckle, they kept the roadway open for the purpose for which it was driven.

On the other hand, some pit-bottom and main roadways in strong ground stand without artificial support.

6. THE LIABILITY OF THE SEAM TO SPONTANEOUS COMBUSTION.—This presents special problems, and in such cases it is desirable to drive as few pit-bottom roads as practicable, and if possible to use one of the methods described previously under the heading of "shaft pillars".

The usual precautionary measures must be taken against spontaneous combustion, and, in addition, footings made and the sides and roof prepared for two brick stoppings, 20 yd. apart, to be quickly built in each roadway of importance.

7. THE PRESENCE OF WORKINGS IN OTHER SEAMS IN THE AREA, AND THEIR PROXIMITY TO THE SEAM TO BE WORKED.—This is a matter in which the experience of the mining engineer is best relied upon, in order to prevent damage to roadways under which faces are to be worked. As far as possible, the layout should be so planned as to avoid working areas in any seam until an upper seam has been exhausted from the area, unless a specially adequate type of lining is installed. Alternatively it may be possible to arrange that work is carried on in the upper seam in areas reached by roads which pass over the settled goafs of workings in the lower seam. In assessing the disturbed area the angle of draw from the workings of the lower seam should be ascertained and allowed for.

8. THE TYPE OF HAULAGE TO BE ADOPTED.—This may be by rope, conveyor, or locomotive (see Vol. 2, Chaps 6 and 7). Rope haulage may be main-rope, main-and-tail rope, or endless rope, and in an up-to-date pit the cross-sectional area of roadway required for these systems does not usually exceed that required for ventilation purposes.

The conveyor is gaining favour on account of its ability to handle coal directly from the coalface to the shaft bottom, or to the cleaning plant in the case of a drift mine, with the minimum of labour.

The locomotive is very sensitive to gradient in that its tractive effort, and hence its useful load, diminishes rapidly as the gradient increases. Although gradients up to 1 in 15 or more can be negotiated, the nearer to level line the better.

According to the dip of the seam, therefore, the direction of the roadways in the seam for coal handling and man-riding is influenced by the type of haulage to be adopted; alternatively the type of haulage may influence the direction and gradient of the roadways, when they are driven in the seam. Horizon mining, apart from other considerations, is a product of locomotive haulage, and is particularly suitable where seams occur close together and lie at high inclination, as in certain European coalfields (p. 275).

9. THE POSITION AND EXTENT OF AREAS OF COAL TO BE LEFT UNWORKED.—Knowledge of these enables the layout of the area to be won to be delineated to the best advantage. Details of (*a*) and (*b*) under item (9) (p. 242) are generally available from the leases and from easily obtainable information, but items (*c*) to (*h*) inclusive are matters with which the mining engineer should be familiar from a study of the area concerned.

10. THE PRESENCE OF WATER.—The presence of water has its effect upon the layout of the mine in dipping seams since roads may be arranged not only to leave barriers for water which would otherwise drain to the dip, but also as channels along which the water may flow to a central sump and pumping station. For such a purpose roads in German coal mines are often driven through the strata or in the seam with a gradient, varying from 1 in 100 to 1 in 200, and on these locomotive haulage is employed.

At certain collieries water occurs in quantities sufficient to render working troublesome when longwall faces are advanced. In such cases attempts are made to arrange the direction of advance of the faces so that the roads leading to the face rise slightly, thus allowing the water to drain down the road to a sump and pump.

11. THE EMISSION OF LARGE VOLUMES OF NOXIOUS GASES FROM THE SEAM AND NEIGHBOURING STRATA.—This affects the ventilation problem which can be solved only when it is known what quantity of such gases, usually methane, are given off per ton of coal wrought. From this may be calculated the size of roadways required to pass the quantity of ventilation needed to dilute and render harmless the gas given off by the daily output. The quantity of ventilation required represents one of the most vitally important matters in the planning of the roads between the shafts and the working faces.

For details the reader is referred to Vol. 3, Chap. 5, Ventilation.

12. TRANSPORT OF MACHINERY AND PLANT ALONG THE ROADWAYS.—This is particularly likely to arise in a mechanised mine. The cross-sectional area of the roadways must be such as to enable quick transport to be effected, as it is usually at week-ends, or on the night shift, when time is limited, that this work is done. Ventilation requirements as to cross-sectional area, and the introduction of large-capacity mine cars ensure, in almost all cases, that machinery and plant may be easily handled, but coalface machinery is still in its infancy, and a reasonable forecast of future requirements in this respect should be made in designing layouts.

It should also be borne in mind that trolley-wire locomotives may, at some future date, be more largely used in British coal mines. They require headroom to accommodate the overhead live wire.

13. THE DISTRIBUTION OF POWER.—This again raises the question of the cross-sectional area of the roadway. Electric cables are easily accommodated in roadways, but compressed-air mains, which may be up to 16 inches internal diameter, require careful grading and support, usually upon brick or concrete pillars on the floor at the side of the road. This substantially

reduces the width of the road available for haulage tracks and the area available for ventilation as well as increasing the resistance. Care should be thus exercised to allow for this contingency.

14. THE LAYOUT AND METHOD OF WORKING THE DISTRICTS OF THE MINE, AND THEIR INTERDEPENDENCE UPON THE MAIN ROADS.—This mainly affects the direction of the roads, but so far as the cross-sectional area is concerned, the distance the roads have to be driven and their ventilation duty are relevant. Working of coal seams in Great Britain and certain other countries, unlike the general practice adopted in the United States of America, often makes use of the direction of the cleat of the coal (p. 261), and this may have a bearing upon the direction of the main roadways. When rope haulage is used, the straightness of main roads and the absence of turns are of importance; yet if these conditions were not satisfied this type of haulage would not be entirely ruled out, as turns can be negotiated provided curves of suitable radii are employed.

With locomotive haulage it is gradient rather than straightness that is important for successful and economical operation. Nevertheless it is essential that the layout of the coal-producing districts should in all cases, as far as practicable, provide straight roads, to as far inbye as possible, with the minimum number of bends, and with reasonable grades. The problem becomes more difficult nearer to the coalface, but facility is afforded by methods of transport such as conveyors, shuttle cars, and subsidiary rope haulages. The major point is that the main haulage may have to be extended as the faces advance, and the layout should allow of continuing favourable conditions of straightness, and even gradient.

Making of main roads.—Main roads to serve working districts may be constructed in the following ways.

(i) By driving the roads in the coal, to the required height and width, and leaving coal pillars on either side to protect the roads as subsequent faces advance to left and right. Ripping or brushing will be necessary in the thinner seams, and may be necessary in thicker ones, according to circumstances. The ripping dirt from the roadways may either be taken elsewhere, or it may be packed in the roadsides after taking out sufficient coal for the purpose. This method has been developed to the extent of taking out the coal by means of a short face, of some 20 or 30 or more yards in length, served by coal-cutting machines and conveyors. Fig. 3 shows an arrangement which may be adopted in such a case. This method is particularly suitable where large roadways are required and where no ripping dirt is sent from the district, since the face length is so arranged for a given thickness of seam to allow all the ripping dirt to be stowed. Temporary local ventilation may be arranged as shown. Speed of advance depends upon intensity of working, and for rapid advance the length of cut taken is usually arranged so that a complete cycle of cutting, blasting, filling, supporting, moving conveyors forward, ripping and packing are all completed in one working shift. A "tunnel" or protecting cover for the gate conveyor is provided under the ripping lip. With good packing material excellent roadway conditions are attained, sufficiently good in the majority of cases not to require further repair at a later date. Where conditions allow or require, dinting, or taking up the floor of the roadway, may be substituted for ripping.

(ii) Another method which has been successfully employed for forming roadways through pillars of coal is to make first a pilot coal-heading, either by hand driving or using a shortwall or arcwall coal cutter (Chapter 9), in

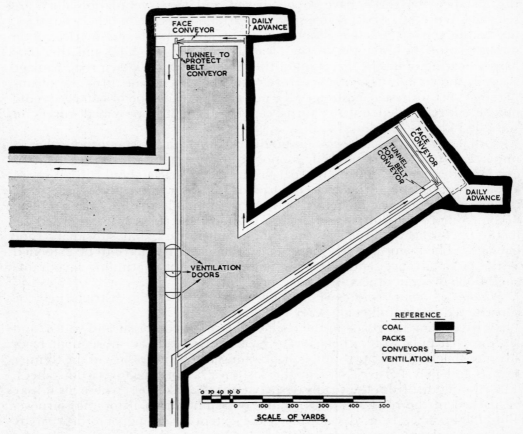

Fig. 3.—A method of making main roads using short faces. The dirt excavated for enlargements of the roadway is packed as shown. The "tunnel" protects the conveyor during ripping operations.

conjunction with a conveyor. When, say, 100 yd., or other distance as may be found to be suitable, has been driven, a longwall coal cutter makes a cut first at one side of the road and then at the other, which facilitates the removal of the coal to a width decided by the amount of ripping dirt to be disposed of, by packing this in the place of the coal extracted. If the pilot heading is not as wide as the finished road, this may be widened before packing commences. Fig. 4 indicates the application of this method.

The above methods, by which pillars of coal are left to support main roads, depend for their success upon the ability of the excavation to stand without

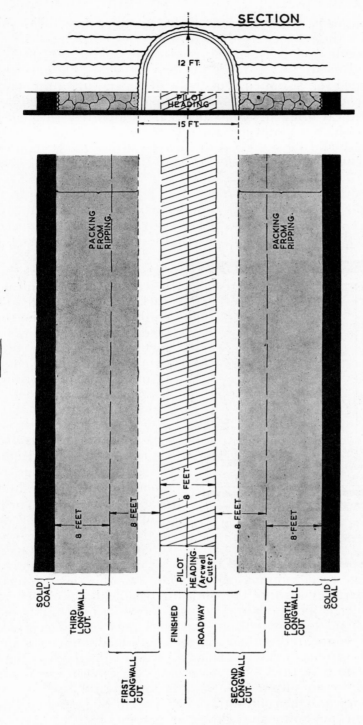

SECTION

12 FT.

PILOT HEADING

15 FT.

PLAN

PACKING FROM RIPPING.

PACKING FROM RIPPING.

8 FEET

8 FEET

8 FEET

8 FEET

8 FEET

SOLID COAL.

THIRD LONGWALL CUT.

FIRST LONGWALL CUT.

PILOT HEADING (Arcwall Cutter).

FINISHED ROADWAY

SECOND LONGWALL CUT.

FOURTH LONGWALL CUT.

SOLID COAL.

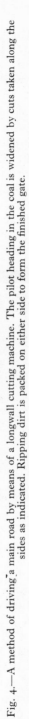

10 5 0 10 20 30

SCALE OF FEET

Fig. 4.—A method of driving a main road by means of a longwall cutting machine. The pilot heading in the coal is widened by cuts taken along the sides as indicated. Ripping dirt is packed on either side to form the finished gate.

253

further repairs. In many collieries roads so driven suffer floor lift to such an extent as to render the pillars very difficult to extract.

(iii) Another method of constructing roads is by taking out the coal by longwall faces and making main roads through the goaf. These roads may have to be re-ripped (or re-dinted) but this will depend upon the nature of the roof and floor, the quality and quantity of packing used at the face, and the size of the roadway originally constructed and supported. In the original layout of the face which is to develop the area to be worked and to form the main roads, care should be exercised to include all the roads required, as otherwise expensive scourings, roads driven through the goaf, will be necessary.

Fig. 5 shows an arrangement of roads for developing a large area of a 3-ft. seam, but the principle applies to any thickness of seam, up to, say, 7 ft. The secret of success of the system is the provision of sound packing to take, as far as possible, the place of the coal extracted, and the ideal is to pack the goafs solid. This is easily achieved in the thinner seams, but in the thicker ones involves importing stone or debris. Some mining engineers favour the use of cavity or strip packing for this reason.

PLAN

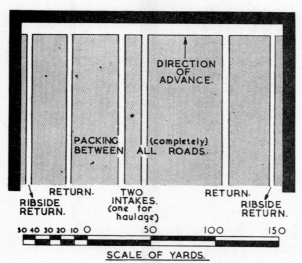

Fig. 5.—Arrangement of roadways for developing unit of large area of coal seam.

15. THE RELATIVE SIZE AND PERCENTAGE CONTRIBUTION OF THE DISTRICT TO THE OUTPUT OF THE MINE.—This is important, particularly in a large mine when the output per shift will, of itself, dictate the type of the haulage system. If the road is in the seam, we have seen that dip of seam will affect its direction for certain types of haulage, and the density of traffic may be such as to require two haulage roads running parallel to one another, as in some cases in the very rich Barnsley seam of the Yorkshire coalfield and elsewhere.

In planning haulage operations the aim is to obtain a high traffic density for a given road, and for this reason, workings must be concentrated in various areas of the mine, rather than scattered and thus requiring a number of haulage ways in various directions. Handgot working methods at the coalface, even in a seam 6 ft. thick, may necessitate six or even more endless-rope haulage roads for an output of 4,000 tons per day and over; in favourable conditions a much higher output may be wrought by mechanical means and brought to the pit bottom on three, or perhaps two, haulage roads.

Thus it will be seen that the traffic density and the number of ton-miles of a haulage route is dependent upon the type of mining pursued and on the length of haul. Today's scarcity of labour and low over-all productivity have focused attention upon the number of tons of coal handled per person employed upon haulage operation and maintenance, as a pointer to the efficiency of the system. By and large, this is a useful figure, but its limitations will occur to the reader, chief among which is the fact that haulage roads require a certain minimum number of workers in order to move almost any quantity of coal on a continuous system; and whether those persons are employed fully or not rests with the mining engineer responsible for the planning of the road and its equipment, and the method of working at the face.

The Number, Uses and Sizes of Main Roadways.—Secs. 42 and 45 of the Coal Mines Act 1911 set out certain minimum requirements regarding the provision and sizes of travelling roads. Thus Sec. 42 required that for every seam in a mine newly opened after the commencement of the Act, there should be provided (except within such distance from the shaft as may be fixed by Regulations) two main intake airways of such size and so maintained as to afford ready means of ingress to and egress from the workings and one of which should not be used for the haulage of coal. Sec. 45 required that every travelling road should be of adequate height.

Sec. 45 was intended to ensure means of escape for workmen in case of fire, etc., but was somewhat ambiguous and has not been re-enacted in the Mines and Quarries Act 1954 which deals with the fire risk along different lines (see Sec. 70 and Vol. 4, Chap. 8.).

It is, however, recognised that wherever practicable two main intake airways should be provided for all major ventilation districts in new mines or in new developments in existing mines.

The need for two main intakes was brought home forcibly by a disaster at Cresswell Colliery on 26th September, 1950, when 80 men lost their lives as the result of a fire on a single main intake airway.

Following this disaster the National Coal Board issued a directive[1] to the effect that, with certain specified exceptions, for each part of the mine having a main transport system serving more than one ventilating district, two main trunk intake airways (which shall be of such size and shall be maintained in such condition as to afford a ready means of ingress and egress) shall be provided from the entrance to the seam (except within the distances from the shaft or outlet fixed in General Regulations) to the point where the last split is taken to ventilate any district of the mine.

The provision of two main trunk airways shall not be required in the following cases: (i) where the number of persons employed below ground on any one shift in that part of the mine does not exceed 100; (ii) where the seam is entered by a cross-measures drift from the surface or from the shaft bottom or from another seam, in which case the "entrance" to the seam shall be the point where the cross-measures drift strikes the seam; (iii) in the case of drainage through old workings or goaf existing at the date of the directive (1st January, 1952).

In the case of each ventilating district where any working face is more than 1,000 yd. from the main transport system, and where an inflammable belt conveyor exceeding 250 yd. in length (other than a coalface conveyor) is installed, the two main intake airways shall be extended to the working face except (i) where the number of persons employed below ground in that district on any shift does not exceed 50, or (ii) in the case of drivage through old workings or goafs existing at the date of the directive.

Where part of the workings in a seam is connected to the workings in another part of the same seam by cross-measures drifts, owing to faults or other natural disturbances in the strata, two main intakes need not be provided through or beyond the cross-measures drifts if they are not justified by the anticipated length of life of that part of the mine or the number of men to be employed does not justify the provision of two main intake airways.

It is accepted by most mining engineers that it is good practice in general to haul coal in one of the intake airways and to provide man-riding facilities in the second intake, and present-day layout usually includes provision for this procedure.

Provisions against fire risks in the Mines and Quarries Act are made in Sec. 70 by eliminating the possibility of fire as far as practicable or by limiting the number of men at risk, and these requirements call for careful study.

Secs. 34 and 35 of this Act contain provisions regarding the construction, maintenance, height and width of travelling roads (see Vol. 4, Chap. 8, Legislation).

A Classification of the Coal Haulage Roads.—For the purpose of reference, it is convenient to classify coal haulage roads in a mine as follows:—

(*a*) PRIMARY OR MAIN HAULAGE.—From some point or points near the shaft bottom to a district station.

(*b*) SECONDARY HAULAGE.—From the district station to the loading point for the coal, or passbye in the case of handgot work.

(*c*) TERTIARY HAULAGE.—From the coal-loading point or passbye to the coalface.

Between the primary haulage and the coal-winding shaft, locomotives, creepers, retarders, gravity, or subsidiary rope-haulages may be used to afford manoeuvrability and control of tubs or cars in the neighbourhood of the pit bottom.

Pit-Bottom Arrangement of Roads.—Whether cage-and-tub or skip winding is employed at the shaft there should be ample siding accommodation for both full and empty tubs, or mine cars, near to the shaft bottom. Alternatively, if belt conveyors are used to deliver coal to the shaft bottom, ample hopper or storage accommodation should be provided.

The amount of siding accommodation required for full tubs varies according to the cycle of operations in the workings and at the shaft or shafts used for coal winding. When the coal is filled into tubs for one shift per day, it is necessary to have sufficient coal left in stock at the end of the winding shift to keep the shafts working on the next winding shift, at full capacity, until coal wrought on that shift actually reaches the shaft. The quantity so required depends upon the speed and length of the haulage system. If the period is, say, two hours, and the shaft capacity is 200 tons per hour, there should be left, in sidings for contingencies and ready to be wound, about 400 tons plus 50 tons of coal, which, if the tubs each contain 15 cwt. of coal, means 600 tubs. Such a pit tub would measure about 5 ft. in length, hence between 1,000 and 1,200 yd. of track would be required for this purpose, allowing for points, crossings, turns, non-parking lengths in front of junctions and the like. In the case of the empty sidings, the length of track needed is not so great as for the full sidings. The majority of the empty tubs will be situated inbye and will be standing near to the loading points in the districts, and the standage room required for empties in the pit bottom would be for the number of necessary empties to keep the haulage system running for the short period—say 15 or 20 minutes—during which the first and following full tubs require to be wound out of the mine, emptied on the surface and returned to the pit bottom.

Another assumption upon which the length of siding for empty tubs may be based, is the time before winding would have to cease if the haulage system failed to remove empties from the winding shaft. It is suggested that 45 minutes is a reasonable period for this purpose, which in the case mentioned above would mean standing room for 200 tubs or a length of track of about 750 yd. Similar considerations apply where mine cars are used.

Following a winding shift, a skeleton staff is sometimes employed to return empty tubs from the surface to the pit bottom for use by the repairing gangs and in readiness for the next winding and coal-filling shift, and to move any full tubs that may have accumulated in the districts, in excess of the usual number in circulation. Similar figures may be determined for double-shift winding per day. The crux of the problem is the relative production rate at the coalface and the rate at which the winding plant can raise coal to the surface, which is in turn dependent upon the capacity of the screening and washing plants.

In the case of belt conveyors and hoppers the size of the hoppers would be excessive if such large quantities had to be stored. It is good practice to clear the belt-conveyor system of coal at the end of the last winding and filling shift each day, and since trunk conveyors for large outputs as would be handled by such plant travel at 450 or more ft. per min., the period on a two-mile run is roughly 25 minutes. For such equipment a hopper of 75 tons might be ample if the over-all capacity were 200 tons per hour. Some skip plants, however, have no hopperage.

When rope haulage is used, it is customary to detach the tubs, at a point near the pit-bottom, from which they may gravitate to the cages along tracks graded according to the type of bearings used on the tubs, and their loaded weight. For plain axle bearings lubricated by tub-grease, a gradient of about 1 in 80 is usual; for empty tubs, a gradient of about 1 in 50 is suitable or less for mine cars.

For such a system, the ideal would apparently be to arrange gravity gradients from the detaching point of full tubs from the rope haulage to the attaching point of the empty tubs, but this is not always possible. The tub creeper and the tub retarder are devices of proved worth for assisting in such duties, and may be used to adjust gradients in short lengths of roadway as may be necessary. They are continuous and cheap in operation, and where large outputs are dependent upon them, they should be installed in duplicate. Methods of controlling tubs and cars are dealt with in Chapter 15, Transport.

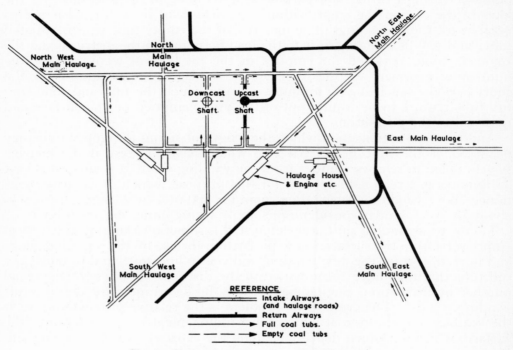

Fig. 6.—Pit-bottom layout for rope-haulage system.

Continuous and smooth shaft operation depends upon a well laid-out arrangement of haulage roads in the shaft-pillar area. It is essential to bring the coal to a single point for each shaft, and when there are two shafts winding simultaneously, there should be easy access for tubs to either shaft.

In the pit-bottom area, various services essential to the working of the mine must be accommodated, such as electrical transformer and switch sub-stations, compressed-air receivers, and locomotive garages. Craftsmen's shops—for sawyers, fitters, electricians, signalmen, rope and track men, conveyor-maintenance men, and girder straighteners—must be provided, and if conditions allow, these should all be placed near enough together to permit efficient supervision. Lunch cabins are necessary, and where horses are used stables must be provided. The offices for timekeepers, checkmen,

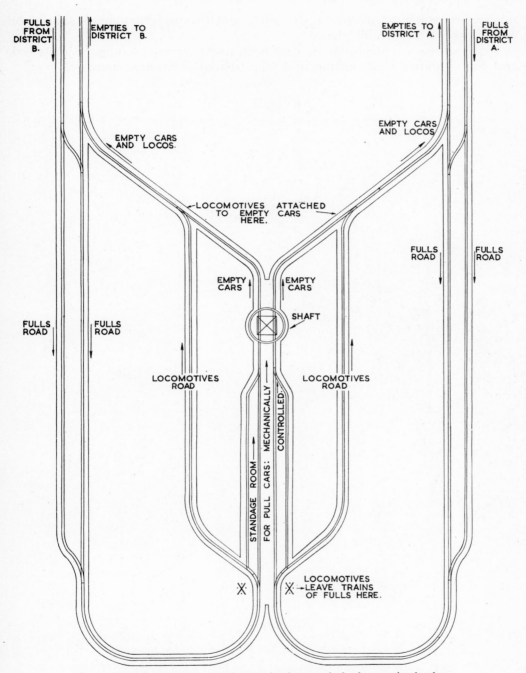

Fig. 7.—An arrangement of pit-bottom haulage roads for locomotive haulage.

259

telephone exchange, overmen, deputies, and the undermanagers should be well lit and strategically placed.

Fig. 6 shows a typical plan of a pit bottom where rope haulage is installed, and Fig. 7 shows a pit bottom in a seam using locomotive haulage.

REFERENCE

[1] Accident at Cresswell Colliery, Derbyshire. Report by Sir Andrew Bryan, D.Sc., F.R.S.E., H.M.S.O. Cmd. 8574. 1952.

CHAPTER 7

METHODS OF WORKING COAL SEAMS

MAIN CLASSIFICATION OF METHODS

THE main classification of methods of working coal seams is as follows:—

(1) Bord and pillar.
(2) Longwall advancing.
(3) Longwall retreating.
(4) Semi-longwall.
(5) Horizon mining.

Hard and fast rules distinguishing between these various methods cannot be laid down in some cases, as so many modifications and combinations of the methods exist at various collieries working under different conditions.

Choice of Method.—The choice of the method to be adopted for working a seam depends upon the following factors:—

(1) The nature of the roof and floor, and their behaviour under different systems of work. Some methods present more favourable results for given conditions than other methods. Although certain general principles afford guidance, the result of experience and trial and error is the only guide to the best working method for a given case.

(2) The depth of the seam from the surface, and the need for, and degree of, support necessary. The prevailing angle of draw (Vol. 2, Chap. 2) will determine the area of coal to be left to support a given area on the surface, but where built-up areas exist it is usual to leave unworked portions of the seam varying from 25 per cent. upwards. In such cases, either pure bord and pillar methods, or a mixture of bord and pillar and longwall working may be pursued.

(3) The geological and physical conditions of the seam: its thickness, quality, dip, depth from surface, strength or hardness and ease of working, the presence of dirt bands and disturbances of the seam such as faults, dykes, washouts, etc.

(4) Current practice in the locality, and the custom prevailing amongst the working population played a large part in the past. The miner of the past was very conservative in his ideas, but today new methods are more readily accepted.

The general principles underlying the three chief systems may be briefly outlined as follows:—

The Bord and Pillar System.—Bord and pillar mining, variously called "room and pillar", "pillar and stall", "post and bank", and "stoop and room", consists of driving "bords", "stalls" or "rooms" to split up the area to be worked, so as to leave "pillars" or "stoops", which may or may not be extracted at a later date. The percentage extraction in the first operation varies according to the width of the bords and walls, and their spacing. Under normal working by this method, no packing is employed; thus pillars when extracted are generally "retreated", that is the pillars farthest away from the shafts are then taken out before those nearer the shafts.

Longwall Advancing.—Longwall advancing working consists of long faces or "wide places" from which all the coal is removed for a given working section, in plan view, and the necessary roads are made through the goaf, or void, left where formerly coal lay. The roof near to the working face is supported by props, bars and chocks, and by packs built up of material which falls from the roof or may be imported as described in Vol. 2, Chap. 2. Packs may be such as to support only the roadways left for the further extractions of the mineral and for ventilation purposes, when the system is referred to as "caving", or they may be built at varying intervals, i.e., "strip packing", or the void or goaf may be packed solid, i.e., "solid packing".

Longwall Retreating.—Longwall retreating working consists of first driving roadways through the solid coal at such intervals as may be necessary for the extraction of the coal in a later operation, and of such lengths as may reach either the boundary of the area of coal to be worked, or an arbitrary boundary. The blocks of coal thus formed are then worked on the longwall principle, but the direction of advance of working is from the boundary towards the shafts.

Packing is thus unnecessary, except in special cases, for example in seams liable to spontaneous combustion, or where roof control offers special difficulty.

The advantages, disadvantages and limitations of the three main systems of working coal seams under different conditions are shown in summarised form in Table I on the following two pages.

CLEAT AND ITS INFLUENCE ON DIRECTION OF WORKING

As they lie *in situ*, most coals exhibit three main planes of cleavage, along which they will break into lumps of varying size. There is the cleavage along the plane of stratification, which lies parallel to the roof and floor, and hence the dip of the seam. At right-angles, or approximately so, to this plane, are two other lines of cleavage, one more defined than the other, both being known as "cleats", and again roughly at right-angles to each other. The more pronounced plane of these latter is the "face" or "bord cleat", known sometimes as the "slynes", and the less pronounced is the "end cleat" (Fig. 1).

Between the two are so-called "awn" at 45° to the cleat, "long awn" and "short awn", nearer respectively to "bord" and "end" directions, as shown

TABLE I. THE THREE SYSTEMS OF WORKING COMPARED

	Bord and Pillar	Longwall Advancing	Longwall Retreating
Seams liable to spontaneous combustion.	Advantageous as panels of work may be arranged to be easily isolated and sealed off, but loss of coal may result in the long run. Crushing of pillars, however, is disadvantageous owing to possibility of air "pulling" through breaks in the pillars and starting oxidation.	Since all the coal of a seam may be removed, prevention of fires from this source is aided. Sealing-off difficulties are more marked than in bord and pillar, except where a panel system is adopted and air tends to leak through packs thus causing oxidation. Special methods of goaf pack sealing can be applied.	By suitable arrangement roadways and faces therein can be sealed-off simply and quickly. Goafs are left behind and little coal need be lost if sealing off an area is necessary. Fires are liable to occur in the solid coal.
Working unknown areas of coal.	Very suitable method for exploration of virgin areas of coal seams.	Fullest knowledge of the area to be worked is desirable, and system best suited to areas undisturbed geologically.	Opening-out headings provide valuable data for setting out faces.
Working other seams in the royalty.	Method generally suitable.	Generally most successful method for all such seams.	Trouble may be experienced with headings, otherwise a successful method for all such cases.
Output capacity and workings concentration.	Large areas of coal in work at the same time required for high outputs, hence lack of concentration.	Highly concentrated working possible and also rapid expansion when required.	Development headings must be well advanced to provide reserve output capacity. Concentrated working practicable.
Percentage extraction ..	There is a tendency to lose coal due to crushed pillars or to abandon areas where roads have fallen-in, or where pillars are difficult to extract.	Approaching 100 per cent. is practicable and can be regularly achieved.	Very high—over 95 per cent. easily possible.
Cost of opening out ..	If a large area is "pillared", the narrow work involved is very costly, but this may be reduced by creating arbitrary boundaries and extracting pillars at the same time as further narrow work proceeds.	Cheap and easy with quick yield on capital expenditure.	Driving headings to form faces very costly in money and time before full production possible. Arbitrary boundaries assist the problem.
Organisation of labour ..	Small teams of men working on contract rates encourages individual effort.	In mechanised faces worked on conventional lines large teams of men may be needed and the majority tend to adopt the speed of the slower workers. In handgot work small working teams are possible.	Headings driven by small teams, but faces may need large teams of men if mechanised. Handgot faces may be worked by small teams.

TABLE I—continued

	Bord and Pillar	Longwall Advancing	Longwall Retreating
Seam thickness	For hand getting, over 4 ft. 6 in. desirable. If mechanised, over 3 ft. desirable. Up to 24 ft. thick may be successfully worked in one "lift" by special methods.	Seams 15 in. to 8 ft. thick may be worked in one "lift". Ripping of roadways usually necessary.	15 in. to 8 ft. usual in one "lift". In thicker range, roadway ripping may be dispensed with if arbitrary boundaries are carefully chosen.
Depth from surface ..	Size of pillar necessary increases with depth, thus more applicable to shallow depths. Is not greatly practised in seams at depths greater than 500 yd., except in isolated special cases. Subsidence effects at the surface may be reduced to a minimum.	No limitations as to depth so far encountered, but not suited to very shallow depths on account of subsidence effects at the surface.	Generally no limitations, except if size of pillars insufficient to withstand load of superincumbent strata. For very shallow depths not recommended on account of subsidence effects at the surface.
Inclination of seam ..	Admirable for inclined seams since no packing is required. May be modified for steeply inclined seams.	Level to 1 in 3 possible by ordinary methods. Special methods or modifications may be necessary for greater inclination of seam.	As for longwall advancing.
Strength of the seam ..	Strong seam desirable to allow pillars to stand without detrimental effect of weathering or pressure.	Immaterial to the system but friable coal is more easily wrought.	Pillars of coal must be of sufficient strength to withstand roof and floor pressures.
Ease of ventilating the workings.	In gassy seams not a simple matter.	In gassy seams ventilation may be accurately planned and operated. Generally simple.	In gassy seams generally as for longwall advancing.
Dirt bands in seam ..	Packing not necessary. Dirt from dirt bands may be left in workings if provision specially made for this, but dirt disposal may be difficult.	Dirt bands not desirable from working point of view, but packing material is essential in majority of cases and extra dirt from dirt bands may be used for packing or left in goaf.	Dirt bands not desirable from working point of view. Packing usually unnecessary.
Floor liable to "creep" ..	Suffers badly as a rule, and the need for much dinting or road repairing is detrimental to the system, as longer roads are involved than in the other systems.	Floors liable to creep can be controlled easier than in other systems, particularly where high rate of face advance can be maintained.	Development headings may have to be remade, when this becomes a serious disadvantage.

in Fig. 1. In British coalfields the direction of the "bord" cleat is roughly NW–SE, and not only the coal seam, but certain surrounding strata, such as shales and binds, bear evidence of having been subjected to the same influence as the coal seam in the formation of cleavage planes.

A face which lies parallel to the "bords" is said to be "on bord" or "on face", whilst one at right-angles to it is said to be "on end" (Fig. 1).

In some coalfields, notably South Wales and North Staffordshire, seams are devoid of normal "cleat" and fracture lines known as "slips" are present. As with cleat, there is a great art in working coal by taking advantage of the "slip".

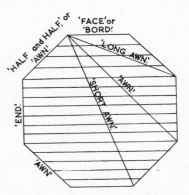

Fig. 1.—Diagram to show relation between cleat and direction. Cleat is indicated by the parallel horizontal lines.

I. BORD AND PILLAR WORKING

General.—This is probably the oldest method of working coal, of which the earliest records come from the North of England coalfields. The simplest plan is one in which a series of roads are driven at regular intervals in the seam, thus forming pillars which in early application of the method were subsequently "robbed" by extracting as much as possible and leaving the rest. Such a method was not however systematic. In the modern bord and pillar system there are two processes involved—first, the driving of coal headings, to form pillars, and second, the extraction of the pillars thus formed.

TERMS USED.—In the bord and pillar system of working certain special terms are used to indicate the various operations and classes of roadways. The meaning of these terms is shown in Fig. 2.

The operation of driving the original headings in the seam, known as "bords" and "walls", for the formation of pillars, is known as "whole working" or "working in the whole". Headings driven in a direction at right-angles to the main cleavage of the coal or the "cleat" are called "bords" whilst those advancing along the cleat are called "walls" or "end" places.

The subsequent extraction of pillars in a second operation is known as "working in the broken" or as "broken working", and special names are given to the roadways or working places. A roadway driven through a pillar to split it into two smaller pillars is known as a "fast jenkin" or sometimes simply a "jenkin". Pillars are extracted by taking slices along their sides which are referred to as "jenkins", "judds" or "lifts". The first slice taken from the side of a pillar is called a skirting jenkin, a first judd or first lift, whilst subsequent slices are called judds or lifts.

If when the headings have been driven there is a tendency for the floor to lift, or so-called "creep" to occur, or for the roof and sides to crush, which is known as "thrust", it is necessary to extract the pillars as quickly as possible, to avoid coal being lost, unless heavy road-repairing expense is to be incurred.

Width of Headings and Size of Pillars.—Sometimes both bords and walls are driven of the same width, but in order to take advantage of the cleat of the coal, the easier working of the two, generally the bord, may be taken wider

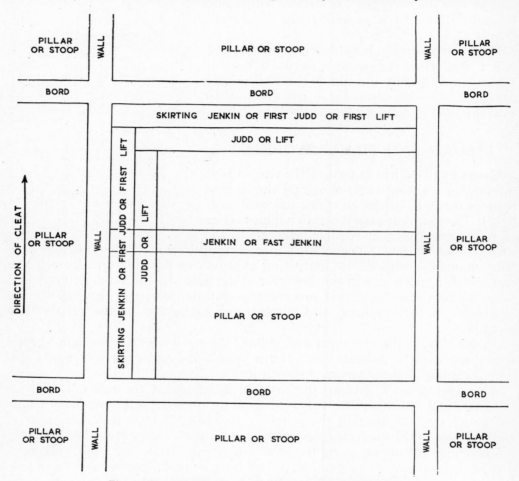

Fig. 2.—Explanation of terms used in bord and pillar mining.

than the wall. Thus the latter may be no more than 6 ft. in width, whilst a bord will be taken at such a width as is economical in roof support under the prevailing conditions, and may be as much as eight or more yards in width. At the junctions of bords and walls, it is advisable not to expose more roof than is necessary—thus the bords may be widened out after passing junctions with the walls as indicated in Fig. 3. But the driving of headings should not be regarded as the main source of output, and it is advisable to leave pillars of adequate size to counteract roof pressures rather than to extract too much coal at this stage. Dirt from dirt bands in the seam may be simply and easily stowed or dumped in the bords.

The best size of pillar to adopt will depend upon local conditions and although experience is the best guide, certain circumstances call for careful consideration. Thus the size of the pillars will be influenced by the following factors:—

(i) *The depth of the seam from the surface.*—This largely governs the weight to be supported and in general the greater the depth the larger the pillars should be made.

At great depth, however, it is questionable whether bord and pillar mining could be profitably employed as the pressure of the overlying strata may exceed the crushing strength of the coal with inevitable crushing of pillars whatever their size. The limiting depth is, however, governed by a number of factors.

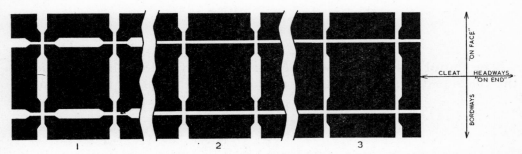

Fig. 3.—Showing methods employed to give increased support at the junction of roadways driven in the whole workings.

1. Bords and walls made narrow at junctions and widened out on each side after passing junctions.
2. As in 1, except that bords only are widened on both sides.
3. As in 2, except that bords are widened out on one side only.

(ii) *The nature of the seam.*—An important factor is the strength of the coal to resist crushing. In soft friable seams larger pillars are required than in hard resistant coals. The effects of atmosphere and escape of gas also influence the size of pillar.

(iii) *The nature of the roof and floor.*—These influence the liability to crush and creep. A strong roof tends to crush the pillar edges whilst a soft floor predisposes to creep and both call for large pillars.

(iv) *The time elapsing between the formation and the extraction of the pillars.*—It is obvious that pillars to be extracted almost immediately need not be as large as those which have to stand for a long period as they will not be so much affected by the various disintegrating agencies.

(v) *Geological considerations.*—The existence of faults and other irregularities usually lead to larger pillars than would otherwise be considered necessary; dip and the presence of water also have their bearing upon the decision as to the size of the pillars.

(vi) *The proportion of coal to be gotten in the whole workings.*—This is influenced by both underground and surface considerations. It also affects the sizes of the bords and walls in that they must be arranged to ensure successful working and, in many cases, avoidance of surface damage due to subsidence.

Various rules are adopted for fixing the sizes of pillars. In one of these the area of the pillar is fixed in relation to the depth so as to give one square yard of pillar for each foot of depth and arranging the shape of the pillar so that one side is not greater than twice another, with a minimum pillar area of about 300 sq. yd.

Another rule fixes percentage extraction in the whole workings at 20 per cent. for a depth of 500 yd. with an addition of 3 per cent. for each decrease of 100 yd. in depth. Thus for a seam 200 yd. deep the percentage extraction would be 29 per cent., say 30 per cent. In such a case with bords 20 ft. in width and walls 6 ft. in width the size of square pillar would be as follows:—

Let x = length of side of pillar

then $x^2 = \cdot 7\ (x + 20)\ (x + 6)$

and $x = 66$ ft.

$= 22$ yd. approx.

The Panel System.—It was recognised as early as 1809, by John Buddle, the celebrated North of England mining engineer, that by working coal in

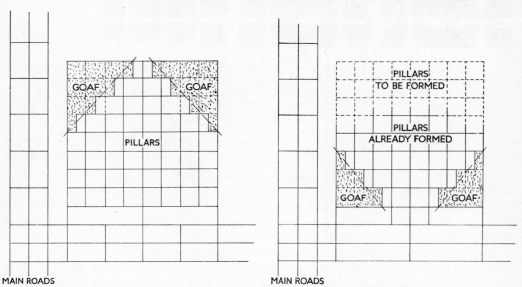

Fig. 4a.—Bord and pillar panel. Pillars retreated after completion of whole working.

Fig. 4b.—Bord and pillar panel. Following the whole with the broken pillars extracted behind whole working.

panels great advantages could be gained over the then prevalent method of driving headings and forming pillars throughout a coal royalty before commencing pillar extraction. Not only was the cost of the heading, often thus fruitlessly spent, eliminated to a major extent, but crushing of the pillars was avoided or reduced, and it was possible to work in the "whole" as well as in the "broken" at the same time. If creep or thrust (crush) commenced in any part of the mine they were arrested in their course, and isolated in their action. Ventilation difficulties were eased, and risk of loss through fire and explosion was limited.

A block of pillars, or a panel, might be up to 30 acres in extent and would be separated from its neighbour by a barrier of coal of sufficient dimensions according to the depth, which barrier would later be extracted.

Figs. 4a, b and c show diagrammatically, in single line, the layout of bord and pillar panels and indicate the various systems of pillar extraction.

In the system shown in Fig. 4a the whole working is completed first and the pillars are retreated subsequently as indicated. Fig. 4b shows the system of "following up the whole with the broken". The full lines show pillars already formed, while the roads to be driven to form the remaining pillars are shown in dotted lines. In this scheme the pillars are worked soon after their formation and are thus less likely to suffer crush due to standing. Furthermore depillaring, which is usually more profitable than driving headings, commences earlier than in the system shown in Fig. 4a. In both these cases the pillars are extracted systematically from each side of the panel causing two distinct fracture lines in the overlying strata, and trouble with roof control is likely to occur where these fracture lines intersect.

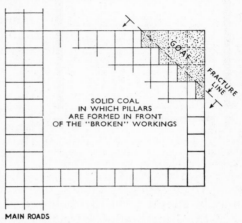

Fig. 4c.—Bord and pillar panel. Pillars formed and extracted on retreating system. Note fracture line.

In the scheme shown in Fig. 4c the broken work or depillaring again follows closely behind the completed whole working, but the pillars are retreated in such a way as to give a single fracture line across the whole panel which reduces the likelihood of roof trouble. Attention to the maintenance of a suitable fracture line is of vital importance.

Methods of Pillar Extraction.—Success in "working the broken", or "pillar extraction" lies in two directions:—

(a) by encouraging the roof to break diagonally across the pillars and panels, and thus diagonally to the cleavage planes in the strata and coal seam. American mining engineers term this "the fracture line", and the longer this "diagonal" or "fracture line" the better. The theory is that roof strata movement is more regular and more easily controlled into the correct fracture line.

(b) by regulating the speed at which the fracture line traverses across a pillar, and panel or series of panels. The faster the travel the better, so that the weight of the roof strata is thrown into the goaf, and not forward on to the coal left to be extracted. Whatever system is adopted, there is inevitably a loss of coal, varying according to the method employed, but usually not less than 15 per cent. to 20 per cent. of the total coal in the seam. This figure does not include sections of the seam unworked, such as roof coal or inferior floor coal.

For a square pillar, "lifts" or "judds" are normally taken off each of two adjacent sides, these being from four to eight, usually five, yards wide, this

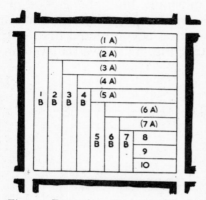

Fig. 5.—Extraction of square pillar by judding. Lifts or judds are taken in the order indicated by the numbers.

being an exact sub-multiple of the length of side of the pillar. Fig. 5 shows this method. The first lift to be taken alongside a bord, or a wall, is known as a "skirting jenkin" (Fig. 2). The order of working the lifts is shown by numbers. Where two lifts bear the same number followed by the letter A or B, it is essential, in the interests of safety and good practice, that the lift marked A (Fig. 5) is extracted before lift B reaches the line which these two lifts have in common. Further, lift 2A may be extracted only after lift 1B has been removed along the line common to the two, and lift 2A must be also extracted before lift 2B reaches its common line with 2A and similarly for the remaining lifts.

With rectangular pillars, the order of working the lifts shown in Fig. 6 may be adopted, the lifts being worked forward in the direction of the arrows.

A third method of extracting pillars is to drive a road through the centre of the pillar, known as a "jenkin" or a "fast jenkin", thus providing access to the pillar for two additional sets of men, making four sets altogether, Fig. 7 shows this method.

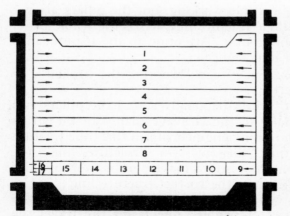

Fig. 6.—Order of removal of lifts in the extraction of rectangular pillar.

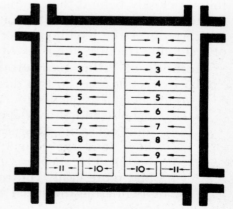

Fig. 7.—Extraction of pillar using centre road or jenkin to split the pillar.

It will be appreciated that to maintain the diagonal break or fracture line across a panel, work must proceed at first upon one of them and then upon three of them, etc., simultaneously (Figs. 4a, b and c), but the work upon each lift must be carefully timed and arranged. In taking lifts from pillars it is always wise to be liberal with the quantity of timber or steel supports, and/or chocks, used for the support of the roof. When this is withdrawn, there is likelihood of emission of gas as the roof breaks and falls in the goaf, and it is advisable that this operation is carried out at a time when there is a minimum number of men in the mine. Lifts

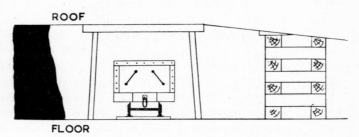

Fig. 8.—A method of support at the edge of a pillar in course of extraction.

should be short therefore to facilitate the process of "drawing off", and as many supports as possible should be recovered. Fig. 8 shows a typical method of support at a pillar edge in course of extraction.

American Coal Mining Conditions.—Bord and pillar working of coal seams is greatly favoured in the United States of America, where roughly 95 per cent. of the output of coal is wrought by this system, for which many advantages are claimed by the mining engineer. It is, however, natural that the system should be chosen on account of the shallow depth of working encountered. Thickness of cover rarely exceeds 600 ft., except under hills and in isolated cases, when a modified longwall system is adopted at depths greater than about 1,800 ft.

Very few royalties have more than one seam being worked, or likely to be worked for some years subsequently, and seam thickness, as worked, ranges from 3 ft. to 23 ft. Thinner seams are normally disregarded owing to the more favourable working conditions in the abundant thicker seams. Gradients are such that only a small percentage of the coal mined is wrought from seams whose grade exceeds 1 in 20, although working in seams with gradients up to 1 in 5 is carried on in some few cases. The excellence of the roof and floor encountered in most mines is illustrated by the fact that working places 15 ft. to 40 ft. in width are driven without supports, and pillars are so arranged as to preclude the necessity of expensive roadway and face supports. Wood props are cheap and plentiful and are thus used almost universally; steel props, bars and arches are seldom employed. Hard floors are such that locomotive track, which requires a high standard of laying practice is, when once laid, permanent in the majority of cases and should not afterwards require great attention. Cases are on record, however, where bord and walls have for one reason and another closed in before pillars have been extracted.

Geological disturbances are not so troublesome in American coalfields as in Britain. Dirtbands exist in some of the seams being worked, and selective mining (p. 317) may be used: faults are comparatively few, and have little effect upon the economics and technicalities of mining, or upon the predominant locomotive haulage. Seams generally maintain constant thickness and washouts are not encountered to any great extent. Spontaneous combustion is almost unknown, and apart from a few mines, gas emission is generally less than in the majority of seams in Great Britain.

American Methods of Working.—Bord and pillar working under the conditions described above has led, over a period of many years, to a highly developed, and still developing system of mechanised mining, and the output per manshift exceeds 6 tons per man for the whole industry, compared with about 25 cwt. per manshift in the British coal-mining industry. Certainly, natural conditions are more favourable in America, but it is only fair to point out that the full advantage taken of the application of machines contributes in no small way to the efficiency figures achieved.

Whilst cleat is present in most coal seams in the United States, some mining engineers plan their workings without regard to its direction, but others attach great importance to it.

ENTRIES.—From the bottom of the shaft, or slope, "main butt entries", or coal headings, are driven in the seam from two to eight in number, or maybe more in some circumstances. Their direction depends upon the gradient, the method of haulage to be used, the cleavage in some cases, and the type of machinery to be used in getting and transporting the coal to the haulage system.

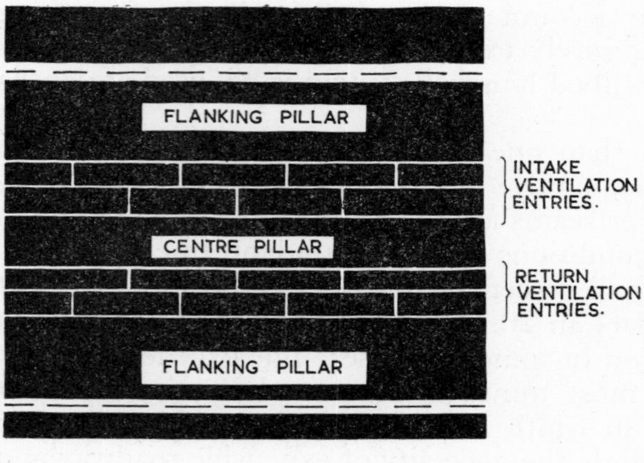

The importance of the gradient of these entries is such that should the gradient of the seam alter temporarily, or a "roll" be met, drifts, or "gradings", are driven through the stone. The number of drifts is governed largely by the amount of ventilation required for the area of the mine which the entries serve. The height of the entries is determined by the seam thickness, but where this is approximately equal to or less than the height of the mine cars or the locomotives

Fig. 9.—Showing six entries with flanking and centre pillars as employed in American mines.

used, a sufficient roof clearance is necessary and ripping or dinting is performed. The amount of ripping is reduced where conveyors form the main haulage system. Entries normally vary in width from 10 ft. to 25 ft., and are arranged on centres from 15 ft. to 40 ft. apart. Extra entries may be driven in order to consume ripping dirt, or dirt from bands in the seam. Multiple entries also have the advantage of reducing the unprofitable period at the commencement of the life of a new seam; also the mechanical plant used to drive the entries is employed to the best advantage when it is fully occupied as it is with seven or eight places working simultaneously.

According to the nature of the roof, floor and coal, and to ensure the minimum leakage of air between entries of differing ventilation function, a centre pillar is advisable, as shown in Fig. 9. Pillars are also necessary at either side of the entries to protect them from crushing due to coal extraction to left and right. These are known as the "flanking pillars". In driving the entries "throughcuts" or "crosscuts" are made at regular intervals to comply

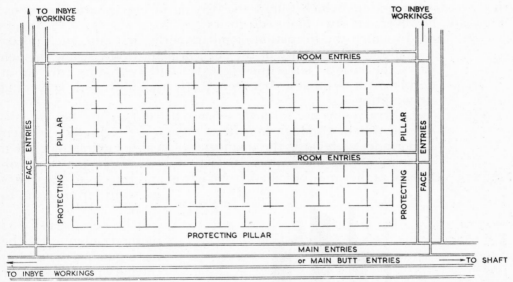

Fig. 10.—Layout of main, face and room entries for formation of pillars adopted in American mines.
Note.—Cross-cuts between main entries, for ventilation, are not shown.

with the various State Mining Laws, either at right-angles, or at a convenient turn-out angle to the entries. Brattice cloth stoppings are inserted as necessary in the crosscuts, or in better practice, these are walled-off between intakes and returns. Auxiliary fans are used for ventilation purposes during the driving of entries.

At right-angles to the main butt entries, the face entries are driven—commonly three in number—one in the middle for intake haulage, and two for returns. Of the latter, one will serve the adjacent block of pillars. Face entries are laid off anything from 600 to 1,500 yd. apart.

Proceeding down the face entries for the distance represented by the thickness of the pillar left to protect the main butt entries, the face entries continue until the distance for setting off the first "room entries" is reached, and from these, which are at right-angles to the face entries and parallel with the main butt entries, the pillars are formed. Fig. 10 shows a typical arrangement of entries.

Pillars of coal left as supports for entries and to form barriers between panels vary in width according to the importance of the duty of the entries concerned, the friability of the coal, the nature of the roof and floor, the depth and the gradient of the seam, and the anticipated life of the entries. They may be from 50 ft. to 300 ft. in width, but it is advisable to err on the generous side in laying them out, as they will be extracted when the panels have been worked, and any extra coal in the pillars will not necessarily be lost.

ROOMS.—The principles underlying the layout of entries described above are fairly generally applied throughout American coal-mining practice, but the layouts of workings which follow the driving of entries are numerous. They fall, however, into two main categories:—

   (i) those in which the formation of pillars is the first aim, such pillars containing the majority of the coal, in plan, in the seam. In such cases the coal is subsequently extracted by rooms, driven at normal widths—that is between 10 ft. and 25 ft. wide according to conditions.

   (ii) those where rooms are formed, separated from each other by ribs of coal which, although known as pillars, are secondary in their importance as regards the quantities of coal for extraction, when compared with the rooms. In fact, it is common for these rib pillars, as they may be called, to be left in and thus lost. They vary in width from 6 ft. to 20 ft.

These different methods may also be distinguished since in category (i), from 15 per cent. to 35 per cent. of the seam is extracted in the first mining operation, and in category (ii), the percentage so extracted is much higher according to conditions. Other systems combining both types of working are sometimes adopted. An example is shown in Fig. 11, in which rooms advance to an arbitrary boundary leaving intermediate pillars to be extracted by retreating. This method of pillar extraction is known as "pillar slabbing", and is suitable for mobile loaders with flight-and-chain conveyors, or for duckbills. The room is driven to an arbitrary boundary, the

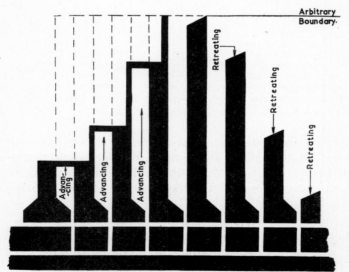

Fig. 11.—Showing so-called pillar slabbing, in which rooms are advanced to an arbitrary boundary, leaving pillars between adjacent rooms to be extracted by retreating, using conveyors.

conveyor or duckbill being extended as necessary and the pillar between adjacent rooms is retreated and the conveyor shortened in the process.

MECHANISATION OF COALFACE OPERATIONS.—Variations of systems of working develop according to conditions, often being products of the equipment employed. Handgetting methods have been largely the foundation upon which mechanical getting and handling of the coal has hitherto been based, but of late, machines have been introduced which have been found to be more suitable when applied in layouts and methods peculiar to them. Such are the Joy loader, the duckbill, the shuttle car, and latterly, getting-and-filling machinery such as the Jeffrey, the Colmol and other machines (see Chapter 9).

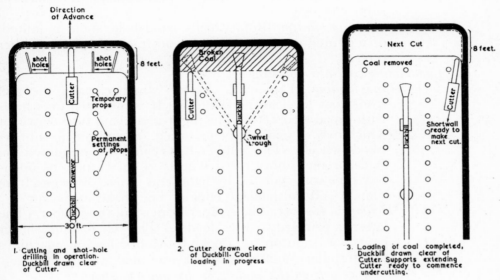

Fig. 12.—Cycle of operations for driving rooms (or entries).

A typical cycle of operations for driving rooms or entries is shown in Fig. 12. The room is first undercut with a "shortwall" machine, the coal is blasted and then filled off by a mechanical loader (duckbill in this case). A crew of men is provided for each machine, and these cut, or fill off and support the roof where necessary, in up to as many as eight places per shift. In the organisation of the work, good management and balanced-capacity machinery are essential to high output. By balanced-capacity machinery is meant that the capacity and duties of the cutting machinery and those of the loading machinery match, and in addition, the duties of the working crews synchronise. Similarly the haulage system for this equipment must be such as to enable the loading machinery to perform its task efficiently, and thus of a slightly greater capacity to compensate for minor hold-ups and possible breakdowns. Coal preparation for loading is of vital importance, primarily for the maintenance of an uninterrupted coal-loading cycle, but also for market requirements.

AVAILABLE MACHINERY.—The successful mechanisation of American mines is inseparable from the room and pillar system of working. Available machinery is listed below, and elsewhere in this work (Chapter 9) details will be found of the plant here mentioned:—

(i) *For the preparation of coal for loading.*
    (1) *Cutting:* The "Shortwall" cutter which may be skid mounted, and is used for undercutting only. The Universal cutter— either track, caterpillar, or rubber-tyre mounted, for cutting at any horizon or angle. (Skid-mounted cutters may be moved about the mine on specially constructed low flitting trucks running on caterpillars, rail-track or rubber tyres.)
    (2) *Drilling for blasting:* Rotary drills, hand-held, stand-mounted, or mounted on a type of truck on track wheels or rubber tyres.

(ii) *For loading coal after blasting* :—
    (1) *Hand loading:* The pit-car loader, which elevates the coal from floor level to the mine car. It is mounted on wheels with broad steel tyres. The flight-and-chain type conveyor which may or may not be mounted, on skids or on rubber-tyred wheels. The rubber-belt conveyor, mounted on skids or on rubber-tyred wheels. The scraper, or open-box type conveyor fed by hand and moved by ropes from a main-and-tail haulage engine. The shaker conveyor.
    (2) *Mechanical loading:* The scraper loader and the slusher. (The latter is primarily a rock loader.) The self-loading shaker conveyor or automatic duckbill. Mobile loading machines —caterpillar-mounted or track-mounted.

(iii) *For receiving coal from the loading device and transporting it:*—
    (1) From the scraper loader, the slusher, or the mobile caterpillar-mounted loader—the shuttle car, delivering to a conveyor or to the mine car. (2) From the scraper loader, the slusher, or the mobile caterpillar-mounted loader— the conveyor or the mine car directly. (3) From the track-mounted mobile loader—the mine car, directly. (4) From the shaker or automatic duckbill—the conveyor, or the mine car directly.

(iv) *For cutting and loading the coal in one operation:*—
    Automatic loaders such as the Jeffrey, the Colmol, the Automat, the Joy and other types. Some of these machines require a conveyor to receive the coal and transport it away from them.

TIME STUDIES.—In the U.S.A. great stress is laid upon the importance of time studies to achieve maximum efficiency of working in all operations. All stoppages, particularly those connected with the loading of coal, are followed up, and the causes of delay investigated and removed. Some American mining engineers hold the view that a stop-watch is as important as any equipment used directly in the winning of coal.

PILLAR EXTRACTION.—By no means all the coal got in the United States is produced by mechanised mining, and handgot methods are still practised in a number of coalfields. The pit-car loader is regarded as an aid to handgot work rather than as a mechanising of the operation of coal filling. With this exception, handgot mining in the States differs but little in layout and method from that carried out in bord and pillar work in Great Britain. Indeed, nearly all United States coalfields have workers whose ancestors emigrated from the British Isles and are influenced by British methods.

Where roof conditions permit "open-ended mining" is particularly applicable where conveyors are used, or where filling is by hand directly into mine cars, but faster extraction of the seam can be achieved with advantage by the use of loading machines. In Britain, this system would be regarded as retreating a "lift" or a "buttock", on the same plan as in Fig. 7, but in order to prevent debris from the goaf becoming mixed with the coal during loading, a "fender" is left. This is a piece of coal, triangular-shaped in plan, some 4 ft. to 5 ft. wide at one end and tapering almost to nothing in the distance of the depth of the cut taken. This is shown in Fig. 13.

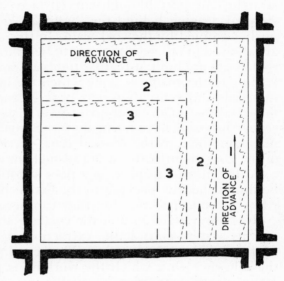

Fig. 13.—Pillar extraction leaving "fenders" to prevent admixture of coal with dust from fallen goaf. The fenders are indicated by the dotted line.

PERCENTAGE EXTRACTION IN AMERICAN COAL MINING.—Generalisation, particularly over the wide field covered by the American coal-mining industry, is difficult. There is one major difference of outlook between American and British mine operators, in that the American enters a mine to bring out coal at the cheapest possible cost, whereas, whilst the British operator is vitally interested in the cheapest possible production cost, he has to spend relatively much more capital to reach the seam, and has to contend with very different and more difficult conditions as well as with other influences, all of which compel him to work every available ton of coal possible, and to conserve as far as practicable the coal resources of the country. It is not surprising therefore that the percentage of extraction is lower on the whole in American mines than in British mines, but exact comparative figures, or even the basis for such figures, is lacking. The basis for comparison is difficult to fix, and differing standards and opinions are common, as for example the fact that the American mining engineer may frequently regard as full extraction what in Britain would be regarded as only 80 per cent. extraction. The term as used in the two countries is thus not relative.

II. LONGWALL ADVANCING WORKING

General Description of the Method.—In the longwall system a continuous line of working-face advances in one direction; the face may be straight, curved (although curved faces are now rarely if ever adopted), or stepped, leaving behind the "waste", "goaf" or "gob", in the space previously occupied by the coal seam. In this area of waste, the nether roof strata are allowed to fall, or if they are to be controlled, "packs" of material from the roof strata are built at regular intervals, and in any event at the sides of roads leading to the coalface, along which the mineral is transported, and persons, materials and ventilation may pass. According to the nature of the roof and floor and the quality and quantity of packing, the thickness and depth of the seam, the roads have normally to be enlarged from time to time, in order to maintain them at the desired cross-sectional area, as the effect of removal of the coal disturbs the strata to such an extent that the packing can only be regarded, in this respect, as a poor substitute for the coal. Such effects may be diminished by packing to the extent of completely and tightly filling the waste by solid packing, but they can never be eliminated entirely.

Roof supports are set at the coalface and in the roads leading to it.

This system aims at the extraction of all the coal in the working section of the plan, in one operation. The actual percentage extracted depends upon the diligence with which the working is pursued: the possibility of around 100 per cent. extraction is usually present if proper care is exercised. Such an achievement involves proper supervision and organisation, including the avoidance of the following practices:—

(*a*) In working a face, leaving coal in the working section and allowing spillage from tubs and conveyors to be left in the waste, or on the roadways.

(*b*) Using coal for packing purposes.

(*c*) Throwing fine coal or gumming slack or cuttings into the waste, rather than transporting it to the surface, and preparing it for the market.

(*d*) Leaving ribs of coal, either due to falls at the face, or between working faces, or against faults.

(*e*) Working panels in such a way that blocks of coal are left between worked areas which upon being crushed by the abnormal roof pressures set up, are rendered unworkable, or, where spontaneous combustion is a liability, develop breaks in which oxidation commences and fires result.

Seam Thickness.—The thinnest seam that may be worked is roughly some 12 to 14 in. in thickness, depending upon the quality of the coal, the prevailing custom in the locality, the nature of the roof and floor, the ability of personnel to move about in the working face, and the type of transport provided at the coalface. The undercutting of the coal is mostly performed by coal-cutting machines whose minimum height is 12 in. Conveyors, of the jigging type or specially constructed belt type, or tray-and-scraper, or flight-and-chain, not more than 6 in. high, are available. In Durham the Victoria Seam is being worked at a thickness of 12 to 14 in. by the use of a scraper. Cases are on record where rolls in the floor and roof or small faults have reduced seam thickness to 12 in. or even, locally, 10 in., and these have been successfully and temporarily negotiated. Workpeople accustomed to these thin seam workings are averse to working in thick seams, and the converse is also true.

Thick seams, over 8 ft. or so in thickness, are not easy subjects for longwall working in one stage or lift. Working thickness is limited to the height at which a man can easily work standing up, although thicker seams than 8 ft. may be worked, according to local custom and usage. A poor roof would seriously mitigate against a seam of such thickness. The ideal thickness of seam for working depends largely upon the upbringing and experience of the miner who is mostly concerned, but if an open mind is kept upon the matter, and judging from the viewpoints of safety, pit economy, and ease of working generally, the author's choice would lie between 3 ft. 3 in. and 4 ft. 3 in. in most British conditions, although some mining engineers may choose a somewhat greater thickness. It is interesting to note that in the United States, a 3 ft. 3 in. seam would be considered "very thin", and any thinner seam would be regarded in the majority of the States as unworkable. In Britain "unworkability" due to thinness of seam has a flexible meaning, depending upon past experience at the colliery concerned. Where tubs 3 ft. 9 in. high, plus rail and sleepers 3 in. thick were used, anything below 4 ft. 3 in. to 4 ft. 6 in. was considered unworkable in many collieries, until the advent of mechanised conveyor mining or the introduction of special systems of transporting coal along the face to the gate, or road ends.

Workable Depth.—The longwall system is suitable for working at depths greater than those possible for bord and pillar. Longwall methods have been found applicable for depths down to about 1,400 yd. from the surface. The latter depth, reached in the Lancashire and in the North Staffordshire coalfields, is so far the deepest in Great Britain.

Inclination of the Seam.—The conventional longwall system is applicable to seams of all inclinations from level to 1 in 3 or approximately 20 degrees to the horizontal. Beyond that, as indicated later, special methods are usually adopted. These are often modifications of ordinary longwall methods, and of what may be termed semi-longwall methods. Faces may be arranged to advance along the strike, or along the line of inclination of the seam, or at an angle between these according to circumstances.

Strength of the Seam.—This is not so important in longwall as in bord and pillar working. In so far as coal is more easily worked in general when on "bord" or "on face" than "on end" (see Fig. 1), the layout of longwall faces is affected by cleats. In handgot workings "end" coalfaces are rarely met with unless the system by which they are worked is such as to allow "face pieces" to be advanced; it is more usual to adopt "awn" or "bord" faces for handgetting. Some seams cannot be worked on "bord" on account of the friability of the roof, which is accentuated by working in this direction of advance.

Ease of Ventilating the Workings.—Compared with bord and pillar, much simpler air circuits are possible with longwall workings. Leakage of air can be reduced to a minimum, and the air is more easily directed to where it is needed to dilute mine gases and to provide fresh air for the men. This is particularly so in machine working with its small number of gates for a given length of face.

Care must be exercised in ventilation planning that provision is made for the face ripping lips of the gates to be included in the circuit. Too often in the past there has been a tendency to neglect this, whereas it is usually a place where much shot-firing is practised and therefore calls for attention in layout as well as operation. Those face rippings which are in gates in which there is a direct air current leading to or from the face should be provided with a hurdle sheet of good design and substantial support, whilst in gates which do not form part of the ventilation system an arrangement of brattice sheets or a pipe system should be fixed at the coalface to deflect a current of air into the face ripping lip, care being taken not to restrict unduly the main current of air in the face.

Dirt Bands in the Seam.—Longwall working is more suitable for seams which contain dirt bands, in that they provide material for the building of packs in the wastes. Naturally, under present methods of working at any rate, disadvantage arises with seam dirt which must be man-handled into the waste, over the conveyor (or tub track), but there is generally space for it there, and unless it exists in more than usual quantities, it is unnecessary to send the dirt out of the working place.

Roof strata may be such that they do not "break" sufficiently to allow enough material to be obtained for packs, and then the dirt from dirt bands in the seam, or immediately above, or immediately below it, is of the highest value.

Floors Liable to "Creep".—Good quality packing by a system which is found advantageous in the circumstances, can considerably reduce the tendency of roads to "creep" owing to the reduced number of roads in longwall compared with the bord and pillar system. Repair work costs are spread over a much larger tonnage than would probably be the case in less concentrated output areas.

Seams Liable to Spontaneous Combustion.—The longwall system is invaluable in these conditions because all the coal may be extracted in the first working operation. Fires, nevertheless, are likely to occur unless preventive measures are taken, many of which concern the day-to-day working and supervision of the coalface (Vol. 4, Chap. 4), but the layout of the workings must be planned to counteract this menace.

The following points are to be observed:—

(a) Faces must advance regularly and at such a speed that packs are buried or sealed within the period of incubation of fires—usually from 6 weeks to 3 months.

(b) Ribs of coal should not be left—either in recovering falls to face, or in the layout of adjacent units. Arrangements should be planned to work out all coal near to faults and other geological disturbances or where the seam may thicken locally.

(c) A straight line of face for each district or unit is essential in order, *inter alia*, to achieve regular subsidence and to facilitate ventilation.

(d) Regular and efficient packing is essential, particularly against pillars, rib sides and fault sides.

(e) Avoidance as far as practicable of air crossings.

(f) Maintenance of large cross-sectional area roadways to keep the ventilating pressure as low as possible.

(g) A return airway is advisable on fault and pillar sides, as any occurrence of fire there can be dealt with without fouling the main intake ventilation current to the coalface.

(h) Sealing of wastes parallel to the face with sand, or packs built with sand, or packs sealed with clay (or "wax" as it is called), every 50 yd. or so of face advance. This assists in excluding air from wastes, and gate-side packs may be similarly treated for successful fire prevention.

(i) The adoption of solid stowing of the waste—performed either by hand or by hydraulic or pneumatic stowing operations.

Further references to spontaneous combustion, hydraulic and pneumatic stowing are made in Vol. 4, Chap. 4 and Vol. 2, Chap. 2.

Working Unproved Areas of Coal.—The longwall system has the great advantages, as already mentioned, that workings may be highly concentrated in a given area, and that the maximum yield per acre of coal seam may be obtained with the shortest possible length of face open and working. The contribution of coal from each face towards the total output of the mine depends upon the seam thickness and upon the length of the face regularly advanced, and in some mines faces of 500 yd. in length in a seam of 4 ft. 6 in. thick, are in operation. Such a face, with a 4 ft. 6 in. undercut, would produce approximately 1,000 tons per day on a 24-hour cycle of operations, which may represent a very high proportion of the output of the mine; even at a large mine in Britain it may contribute of the order of 20 per cent. to 25 per cent. of the total output. To risk so high a proportion of output on one face or one working area, there must be adequate reason for confidence in the system, particularly so far as geological conditions ahead of the face are concerned. The solution lies either in the possession of full and complete geological knowledge of the area to be worked, or in a policy of driving exploratory headings or faces thoroughly to prove the ground. Alternatively, smaller units are advised, which although unable to show the highly economical working possible with longer ones, will not affect so seriously the total output of the mine if disturbance occurs. Long coalfaces, like shorter ones, are liable to suffer from disturbance of output in working—such as the presence of abnormal quantities of gas, falls to face, roadway falls, fires from spontaneous combustion, operating delays and other causes, but speaking generally the longer the face, the better is the supervision and standard of workmanship which tend to eliminate these possibilities. Exploratory headings and faces, coupled with the information obtainable from neighbouring workings, shafts, boreholes (if any), and a study of surface geological features, should provide the necessary data for the planning engineer to lay out the workings. Certain geological features, however, are difficult to locate. These include washouts, abnormally thick sections of seam (swellies), dirt bands running into the seam, local rolls and small faults, and the presence of lenticular, or irregular friable dirt—known as "clod"—below, and particularly above the seam. Water too, in lagoons in the strata either immediately adjacent or some distance above the seam, or contained in conformable or uncomformable water-bearing stratified deposits, such as the Bunter and Keuper Sandstones of the Triassic System, can render areas of coal difficult or impossible to work.

Exploratory headings for locating clod and other irregularities are expensive and have two major disadvantages:—

(1) When the coal is later worked by longwall faces, large areas of coal may have been spoiled by the headings, particularly if floor lift or "creep" has taken place, and further, the coal seam and roof strata will have been disturbed, thereby rendering output difficult to maintain.

(2) Owing to the erratic character of clod deposits, exploratory headings may fail to locate areas of clod which may lie within a very short distance on either side of the heading, or alternatively the headings may be driven entirely through a clod area when a short distance on either side no clod exists. Such an area might thus be wrongly condemned.

Working of seams under clod often calls for special procedure. Methods of handling clod have been attended with varying degrees of success in the past. These include:—

(a) Fore-poling—where steel bars or tubes are placed in holes drilled into the roof at the desired level and for a distance beyond the cut so as to be supported on the coal of the next cut, whilst the other end is supported by a prop.

(b) Overcutting the seam to leave a thickness of coal of six to eight inches or more, depending upon the friability of the coal, to form a roof.

(c) Overcutting the clod itself. Where the clod is lenticular in formation, and therefore of variable thickness, this may involve removing quantities of dirt sometimes thicker than the seam itself in certain areas, with consequent expense.

(*d*) The adoption of short working faces, not more than 30 yd. long, following each other at 30-yd. intervals *en échelon*, and advancing as rapidly as possible under the conditions.

The presence of clod to be taken down, according to its thickness, reduces the output of coal per manshift worked at the coalface—the actual work required to fill off the cut of coal is increased, and the psychological effect on the workpeople is frequently one of frustration and disappointment. The Parkgate Seam and the Warren House Seam of the Yorkshire coalfield and the High Hazel Seam of Yorkshire, Derbyshire and Nottinghamshire are troubled by clod from time to time and the solution generally adopted at collieries so affected in these areas is to have spare faces available immediately, ready equipped with machinery and able to be brought into production at very short notice. In well-organised collieries, there may well be available almost as much spare face room as there is face room actually working. Such a system applies equally effectively where isolated lagoons of water are encountered. The method may be expensive, but continuity of output is of high importance not only to the industry, but in keeping down costs.

Handgot Faces—Layout and Cycle of Operations.—(*a*) DEFINITION. The term "handgot", as the name implies, means that the seam is wrought by handgetting with picks, followed by shovelling the coal into tubs, running on track laid as near to the coalface as possible, and parallel with it. At the present time, however, the use of tubs on the face has been almost wholly superseded by the introduction of conveyors. (See later and Vol. 2, Chap. 7.)

Where tubs are filled at the face they are transferred at the roadheads, or the places where the coalface and the roads leading to it meet, to the track in the roadways or "gates" by means of a sheet of iron, known as a "flat-sheet", or a small turntable may be provided. In the gate, two tracks are usually provided for a distance back from the face, one for the incoming empty tubs and the other for the outgoing full tubs, and the arrangement is known as the "passbye". The length of the passbye varies according to the length of face served, the number of men working on that length, and the frequency with which the tubs are removed from the full side of the passbye and replaced by empty tubs on the empty side.

In level seams the gate serving a length of working face may be centrally situated, but as gradient becomes pronounced the gate is placed in a position where the longer side of the working face is to the rise side, thus easing the work of the men in "tramming" or controlling the tubs along the face to the gate-end. A length of working face in which a number of men are engaged, who join together into a team for the purpose of payment of wages, is called a "stall", whilst the length of face allotted to each man, or each man and his assistant, is known as his "length" or his "stint".

Fig. 14 shows a plan and section of typical handgot longwall stalls in a 5-ft. seam. In this figure the roof bars are omitted from the plan view for

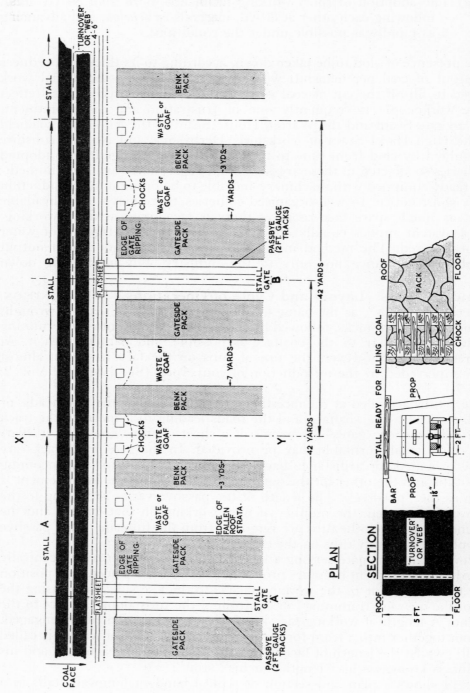

Fig. 14.—Sketch of typical handgot longwall face, showing layout of stalls in relation to stall gates, packing, etc. Gates approximately 3 yd. wide; wastes 7 yd.; gate-side packs 6 yd.; turnover 4 ft. 6 in.; benk or intermediate packs 3 yd. (Face bars omitted from plan.)

the sake of clearness. Mention has already been made of the packs, built in the waste or goaf, and typical roof supports are also shown.

(*b*) DISTANCE APART OF ROADWAYS, OR GATES.—This depends upon the following factors:—

(i) The nature of the roof and floor. The stronger the surrounding strata, the farther apart the gates may be placed; in weak roof measures extra gates may be introduced in order to provide packing material for roof support by means of regularly built packs. Such extra gates may not all be used for traffic to and from the face and those not so used are known as "dummy" gates. The ripping dirt from them provides packing material, and the system is specially useful where the roof stratum does not fall sufficiently to provide enough packing material, as under a rock or very strong roof.

(ii) The thickness of the seam. This factor decides the tonnage of coal per yard run of face, for a given depth of web, strip, turnover or buttock—terms used to denote the strip of coal removed from the face each unit of advance.

Turnovers, or buttocks, may be arranged so that they may be removed per day, usually of three shifts, or at longer intervals up to a week. For handgot faces, one turnover every day is not common, and one turnover every two days is often considered a normal rate of face advance.

According to the rate of advance of the face, the thickness of the seam, and the depth of turnover taken, the number of men required to work the stall may be arranged, a matter which is usually influenced by local custom, or by the fact that if too many men are put to work in a stall they may hinder each other to the detriment of individual output and it is not in the interests of safety. Crowded stalls have the effect of reducing the possible earning capacity of the workers, and in consequence agreements are signed at some collieries limiting the number of men to be employed on a given length of face.

Gates in seams of 4 ft. 6 in. to 6 ft. in thickness may vary from 25 yd. to 80 yd. apart, and the turnover is usually between 4 ft. and 6 ft.

Seams in which the thickness is less than the height of the tubs used have been worked by two handgot methods:—

(*a*) where the coal fillers threw the coal to the gate end, or,

(*b*) a small truck, running on rails, was filled in the stall by a coalface worker, and then hauled by hand rope to the gate end by a youth who transferred the coal to a flat-sheet prior to filling it into tubs. This was known as the "danny" system, and the small truck was called the "danny", being a forerunner of the modern face conveyor by which it has been superseded.

Under such thin seam conditions, gates may be between seven and twenty yards apart.

(iii) The dip of the seam influences the distance apart of the gates because of the desire to assist the men in reaching the gate end with the loaded tubs. If the gates are advanced to the rise or to the dip, the faces will then be on the strike, and transport difficulties on the face are eased.

(*c*) CROSS-GATES.—Stall gates are usually laid out at right-angles to the face or at a slight angle from the normal to the face.

The use of cross-gates eliminates the need to maintain long lengths of gate, and facilitates the removal of coal from the face and gates to the main haulage. Cross-gates are usually carried at an angle of between 30 degrees and 45 degrees to the faces. Their distance apart is such that the maximum effective life is obtained from the gates before they are cut off by the next cross-gate and abandoned, and without the need for undue repairs from which little advantage is gained. Eighty yards may be considered a minimum distance apart, measured along the gates which are to be cut off, and up to 150 yd. as a maximum distance under good conditions. Cross-gates commence from a main gate or haulage plane, as shown diagrammatically in Fig. 15.

Cross-gates may be formed by two methods, the choice of which can best be determined by experience of the seam concerned:—

(i) By packing and forming the road at the desired angle and ripping at the face. The nature of the roof strongly influences the angle which is chosen, as the area of roof exposed varies directly with the angle between the packs and the face. It is usual to erect a line of wood chocks ahead of the cross-gate packs in order to secure the roof at this point, as shown in the lower diagram in Fig. 16.

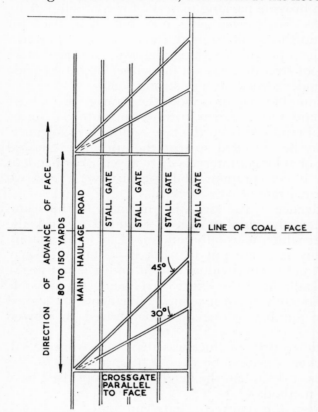

Fig. 15.—Showing varying angles for cross-gates. Cross-gates, as here shown, are set out every 80 to 150 yd., according to conditions, and at angles of 0°, 30° and 45° to the direction of the face line. Cross-gates are seldom set out parallel to the face, due to roof troubles which arise in such cases.

(ii) After the face has passed, and if possible after the initial subsidence has taken place, a cross-gate may be driven through the goaf from the main gate side, at the desired angle to the face, the inbye end of which is not advanced so far as to become damaged by the face subsidence.

The roadway thus formed is called a "scour", and the process is known as "scouring".

It should be mentioned that cross-gates are, in general, more difficult to maintain than gates more nearly at right-angles to the coalface. A cross-gate which is at a small angle to the cleat of the coal is more difficul to maintain than one at a greater angle as it tends to suffer more from the effects of roof subsidence and the presence throughout its length of breaks formed by the advance of the face itself. Cross-gates may be valuable in that they may provide means, if required, of supplying air to the coalfaces. They are useful in extending coalfaces as well as working districts.

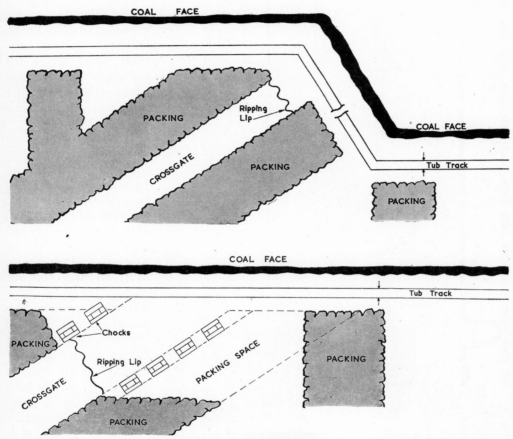

Fig. 16.—Alternative methods of supporting cross-gate ends. In the upper figure packs are built as shown, while in the lower figure chocks are set on the road sides in advance of the packs to give additional support.

(d) GETTING COAL IN THE STALL.—Hand getting represents one of the last surviving arts of the coal miner as a craftsman, and is rapidly becoming a lost art, owing to the introduction of machinery at the coalface. The main methods are as follows, but the miner of past decades may be credited with many variations of these, in order to win his coal more easily, according to his experience:—

(i) *"Ragging"* is a method employed in the thicker seams of the Midland coalfields, particularly the Barnsley Seam in Yorkshire and the Top Hard Seam in Derbyshire and Nottinghamshire. The faces are set out on "long

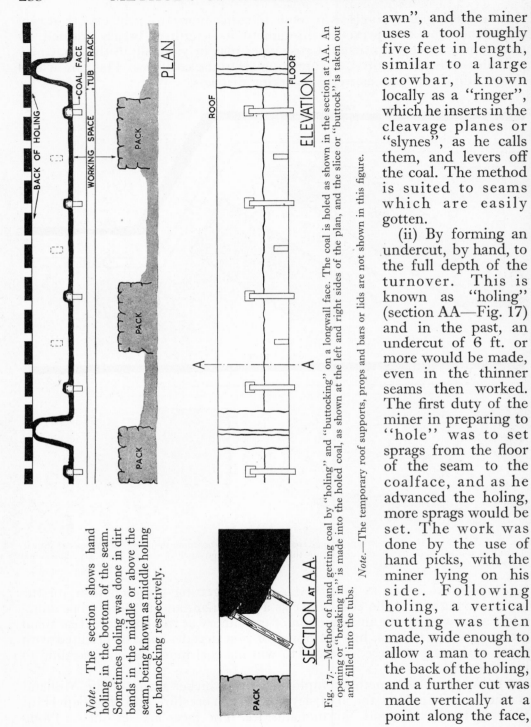

PLAN

BACK OF HOLING

COAL FACE

TUB TRACK

WORKING SPACE

PACK

PACK

PACK

ELEVATION

ROOF

FLOOR

A

A

SECTION at A.A.

Note. The section shows hand holing in the bottom of the seam. Sometimes holing was done in dirt bands in the middle or above the seam, being known as middle holing or bannocking respectively.

PACK

Fig. 17.—Method of hand getting coal by "holing" and "buttocking" on a longwall face. The coal is holed as shown in the section at AA. An opening or "breaking in" is made into the holed coal, as shown at the left and right sides of the plan, and the slice or "buttock" is taken out and filled into the tubs.

Note.—The temporary roof supports, props and bars or lids are not shown in this figure.

awn", and the miner uses a tool roughly five feet in length, similar to a large crowbar, known locally as a "ringer", which he inserts in the cleavage planes or "slynes", as he calls them, and levers off the coal. The method is suited to seams which are easily gotten.

(ii) By forming an undercut, by hand, to the full depth of the turnover. This is known as "holing" (section AA—Fig. 17) and in the past, an undercut of 6 ft. or more would be made, even in the thinner seams then worked. The first duty of the miner in preparing to "hole" was to set sprags from the floor of the seam to the coalface, and as he advanced the holing, more sprags would be set. The work was done by the use of hand picks, with the miner lying on his side. Following holing, a vertical cutting was then made, wide enough to allow a man to reach the back of the holing, and a further cut was made vertically at a point along the face, either by the same man or by his mate in the adjoining stint. If the coal did not fall easily after having had two "loose ends" made, it was necessary to wedge it down, or to use explosives. Fig. 17 illustrates the method. In this way, the face was kept straight throughout its length providing the men work at the same rate over the period of shifts involved in the process.

(iii) The process known as "buttocking" is similar to that described in (ii) above, except that the two vertical cuts are put nearer together, and adjacent to the gate end. The turnover is deeper than in (ii), and the object is to form a length of coal on bord known as a "buttock" which is then worked in a direction parallel to the line of face. It is usual for a buttock to be taken in

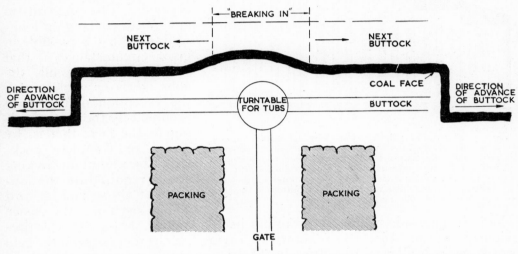

Fig. 18.—Double buttocking: "breaking in" at the gate end. Here the buttock is taken in both directions —to left and right. Flat sheets may be used as alternatives to turntables.

both directions, although in steeply dipping work, where the line of face is on the full inclination of the seam, a single buttock may be taken to the rise as far as the next higher gate.

Double buttocking allows the face to be cleared in front of the gate of each stall, in which the set of men is also responsible for their own gate-side packs. Fig. 18 shows the arrangement.

(iv) A modification of the "buttocking" system known as "continuous buttocking" is worthy of note. A buttock is commenced at one end of a face, for instance, the right-hand end of a series of stalls. It is then advanced, or "taken up", as it is called, until it reaches the end of the stall in which it was started. The next stall and succeeding stalls take up the work in turn, and the first stall commences another buttock at its left-hand end. The buttocks are thus carried in turn across the whole range of stalls until the left-hand side of the district is reached. The system is shown in Fig. 19.

In the last three methods described, the line of face is "on end", and the buttocks form "face" or bord pieces, or the face may be arranged to work on awn, with buttocks also on awn.

Buttocks are normally from 2 to 10 yd. in length. Ventilation of buttock faces is not so simple as for the straight longwall face, and to deflect the air current into the cutting corners brattice cloths are hung at various points along the face. Good packing at the corners is essential, in order to support the roof, which is weakest at such points, and to guide the air current with minimum leakage.

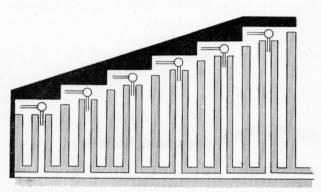

Fig. 19.—Continuous buttocking. The left-hand buttock, which has reached the boundary, has been carried continuously across the six short stalls shown. The men working on this buttock now take over the buttock from the next stall on the right and advance it, and so on throughout the face. Alternatively these men may start a new buttock at the right and carry it through the face.

(e) PACKING ON LONGWALL FACES. — The maximum amount of packing on longwall faces that is possible in given circumstances is that which completely fills the gobs, goafs or wastes, with the exception of the space occupied by the roads leading to the face, that is, by "solid" or "complete" packing. The minimum packing is that required for the support of these roads, and which occupies the space along the gate side, where the seam has been extracted. This system, as previously mentioned (p. 261), is known as "caving", as the roof between the gate roads packs is allowed to fall freely. These systems of packing are shown in Figs. 20 and 21, and in the latter it will be seen that wood chocks, in a straight line, are set in the waste immediately behind the tub or conveyor track. These chocks are advanced as the face advances, and set as close to the face as circumstances permit. Sometimes they are set between the tub track and the face, instead of, or in addition to, the normal props and bars. Between these two systems of solid packing and caving there is the method of partial or strip packing in which packs of appropriate width are built at intervals along the face leaving wastes between them as already shown in Fig. 14 and described fully in Vol. 2, Chap. 2. Various expedients adopted to maintain the roadways leading to the face, and to counteract the effect of roof subsidence, are described in Vol. 2, Chaps. 1 and 2, which also deal fully with the question of packing and face supports.

(f) TRANSPORT SYSTEMS ALONG THE COALFACE.—In the handgot methods of working described above, the tubs are "trammed" along the coalface from the passbye, filled and returned to the passbye, and each stall has its own gate, for which, as far as the outbye end of the passbye, the men in the stall are responsible—they perform all operations including "face" or gate-end ripping, packing and probably one "back" ripping in the gate, the dirt from which is packed at the face. One system previously employed largely in the Midlands, however, modified this haulage arrangement, but not the responsibilities of the workpeople in the gates. This is the "Barry" system, as shown in Fig. 22. Empty tubs were received from the main haulage via gate A, and placed in the right-hand passbye track. The tubs passed along the face, and were filled en route, being delivered in the left-hand passbye track of gate B for transit to the main haulage. Similarly, empty tubs from gate B right-hand passbye track passed

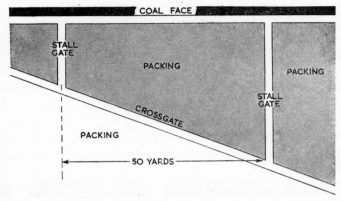

Fig. 20.—Maximum or so-called solid packing in a longwall working.

along the face and reached, when full, gate C left-hand passbye track. Thus the tubs made a complete circuit.

(*g*) LINE OF FACE.—We have seen that the direction of the face is determined *inter alia* by gradient and cleavage, and that various methods of working demand various delineations of the face, in plan. Emphasis should be placed upon the advantages of straight faces, not only in layout and its problem, but in day-to-day working. Straight faces are much easier to ventilate, they are more simple for coal transport, for supports alignment, for supervision and for roof control. This latter is of first importance, particularly as a safety measure, since falls of roof at the face, mostly products of poor roof control, unhappily are one of the most prolific sources of serious and fatal accidents in mines. Packing of the waste is more easily organised

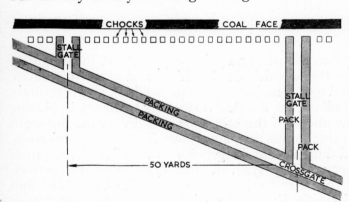

Fig. 21.—Gateside packing and "caving" with the use of chocks in longwall working. It will be noted that in this case no intermediate packs are built.

and carried out with a straight face, and it is to this operation that full attention must be directed for the attainment of good roof control practice.

Curved faces, at one time popular, due to an idea that they facilitated good roof control, have been abandoned due to the advent of mechanisation which necessitates a straight line of face.

(*h*) CYCLE OF OPERATIONS ON HANDGOT FACES.—Operations are generally carried out in the following order, but with modifications to suit local circumstances:—

   (i) Spragging and undercutting the coal.
  (ii) Coal-filling and setting roof supports.
 (iii) Face packing, ripping, including gate-end ripping, and moving up the track towards the coalface.
 (iv) Withdrawing and re-setting chocks where used.
  (v) Withdrawing props, bars, etc., from the waste.

To conform with accepted good practice under-cutting should not be carried out until all the packing in a stall has been completed, even under the safest roof. All the workpeople in a stall are usually paid on the same contract note, and all are thus concerned in the success of their efforts. They

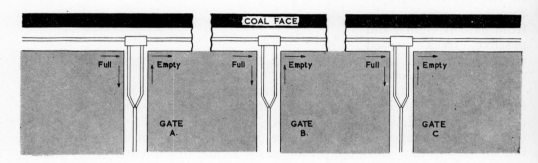

Fig. 22.—"Barry" system of transport at the coalface. Empty tubs entered by one gate, passed along the face where they were filled and then left by the next gate on the right.

are a small team, by today's standards, and pride of work and the filling of clean coal are incentives to them which the machine, and other influences, have unfortunately obscured to no small extent. The machine at the coalface introduced, temporarily at all events, a rather disturbing tendency in placing the filler of coal apparently ahead of the other workers, in status. But sight must not be lost of the fact that unless the packer does his work to perfection, the filler's task is rendered difficult and dangerous, and skill is still required in the operation of efficient packing. With the introduction of coal-cutters, conveyors and other aids, the filler tends to become a skilled shoveller and supports setter, whereas formerly he was one of the most experienced men in the team as a result of long years spent in the art of winning coal from the solid seam without mechanical aids. As previously mentioned, the duration of a cycle of operations depends upon the rate of face advance desired in given circumstances or upon the number of men working a stall.

When the stall workers are all on the same contract note, and usually under a chargeman on each shift, the men become skilled at organising their work amongst themselves in such a way that a minimum of time is lost, and work is prepared, and planned ahead. The prudent team will, within strict and self-imposed safety limits, carry out the various operations as necessity demands.

(*i*) ARRANGEMENT OF FACES—PANEL WORKING.—If, after forming the shaft pillar, faces were advanced in all directions, there would be a progressive

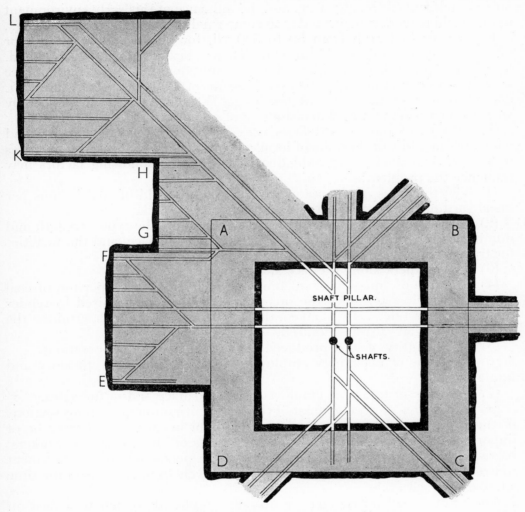

Fig. 23.—A longwall panel layout for handgot working.

output increase as the faces increased in length, as shown by the lines of face ABCDA, in Fig. 23. The layout, if allowed to continue in this way, would result in an unwieldy mine—difficult to ventilate and to provide haulage for, apart from not taking advantage of the possibility of concentration offered by the longwall systems. It is usual therefore to advance only certain lengths of face, which vary from 50 to 500 yd., according to the circumstances, as indicated by the faces EF, GH and KL in Fig. 23. The straggling nature of the mine which would arise from advancing the original faces AB, BC, CD and DA, and the roadways is thus avoided.

Mechanised Mining Layout and Cycles of Operations.—(a) GENERAL.—The first attempts at mechanical mining were carried out on faces laid out for handgetting, and the influence of this early environment upon machine work remains today to some small extent in certain collieries.

Faces vary in length from 50 to 500 yd. for one "conveyor unit", or "conveyor panel", or "face", but experience indicates that a face of 200 yd. long is most suitable for a wide variety of conditions. A 50-yd. length of face may in certain circumstances be used in seams of 7 to 8 ft. thick, using a 4 ft. 6 in. turnover or advance, but the longer 500 yd. face is advisable only where supervision and workmanship are of a high standard.

The length of mechanised faces varies according to many factors, and whilst the majority of these are of local concern and are governed by practices in particular coalfields and individual collieries, the following factors may influence the problem:—

(1) The thickness of the seam, which fixes the yield of coal in tons per lineal yard of face for a given strip, turnover or buttock.

(2) The nature of the roof and floor, which affect the type, strength and number of roof supports required per unit length of face, and the facilities for transporting these materials along the face.

(3) The gradient along the face and in the gates.

(4) The rate of emission of inflammable or noxious gases per ton of coal wrought, which determines the quantity of ventilation required to render these gases harmless. In a given thickness of seam this determines the velocity of the air current required.

(5) The quantity of dust produced in the various mining operations.

(6) The type of machinery employed—its duty, capacity, efficiency and limitations.

(7) The type of transport employed at the coalface and in the gates.

(8) The degree of development of the team spirit amongst various sections of the workers and between worker and worker in each section may be of importance as are also the incidence and effects of absenteeism of workers, particularly key workers, and the ability of the personnel and management to overcome these effects to achieve a regular cycle of operations in the time allotted for each cycle.

The term "mechanised face" is usually employed to denote a face on which the coal is cut by machine and loaded on to a conveyor which delivers it to the gate end from which it is generally transported by a gate-road conveyor to a loading point or transferred to a trunk conveyor. Such faces are referred to as single or double units according to the layout and scheme of working. A *single unit* has a single conveyor along the face which delivers the coal at the gate end at one end of the face as shown in Fig. 24. This gate usually serves as the intake airway and a return airway is provided at the other end of the face as shown in the diagram.

Fig. 25 shows a layout for single-unit faces including four production units and the development face DF from which the production units are opened out as required.

A *double unit* has two conveyors carrying the coal in opposite directions and delivering it to a loader or conveyor gate end at or near the middle of the unit. In this centre gate a conveyor is usually installed to take the coal from the face conveyors to a loading point where it is delivered into tubs or mine cars or on to a trunk conveyor. This gate usually serves as the intake airway and a return airway sometimes called a tail gate is provided at each end of the unit as shown in Fig. 26. Additional or dummy gates (p. 284) may be constructed through the goaf to provide packing material if required. A layout for double-unit faces is shown in Fig. 27. This

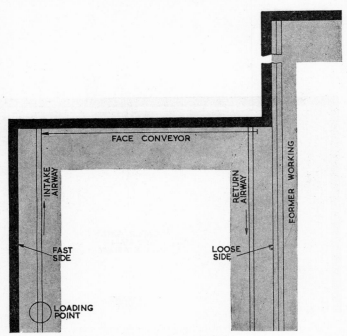

Fig. 24.—Diagram showing typical single-unit conveyor face with "rib side" or "fast side" (solid coal) on left and "loose side" or goaf of former workings on right.

shows four production units and the development unit and indicates the arrangement of gate roads, viz., the centre gates with tail gates at each end of the unit. The centre gate is usually the intake airway and the tail gates serve as returns.

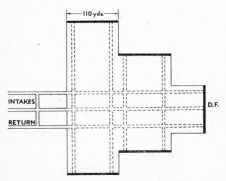

Fig. 25.—Layout of five single-unit faces, including development face DF. Faces shown by heavy black lines, roadways through goaf by dotted lines.

Cross-gates may also be constructed at intervals to reduce the length of conveyors or haulage gates to be maintained as indicated in Fig. 28, which shows two double-unit faces advancing on the same line. Such cross-gates may be formed by scouring across the goaf after the initial subsidence has taken place, as packing-out the cross-gates immediately behind the face gives rise to difficulties owing to the rapid advance of the face, which may move forward 300 to 450 yd. or more per annum depending upon the depth of turn-over and the frequency of the face cycle.

GETTING AND LOADING THE COAL AT THE COALFACE.—The use of machines for under-cutting, middle-cutting, over-cutting, or for cutting

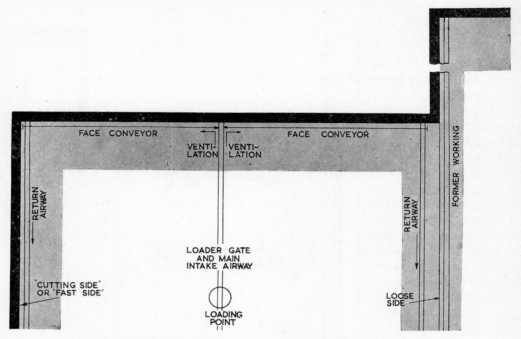

Fig. 26.—Diagram showing typical double-unit conveyor face, with "fast" and "loose" sides.

out dirt bands today replaces almost entirely the hand holing of earlier days, and the conveyor, in its various forms for various duties, replaces the track and tub on the coalface. Shot-firing and its alternatives, Cardox, Hydrox, Hydraulic Bursters, and the like, aid the breaking of the coal for loading, but as yet the majority of the coal is hand-loaded out to the conveyor. Electric power and compressed air are used to drive the machinery. Cleat still plays a part in coal-getting technique, but the part is not so important in machine mining. Of recent years machines known as power-loaders or cutter-loaders have been developed in various forms, for getting

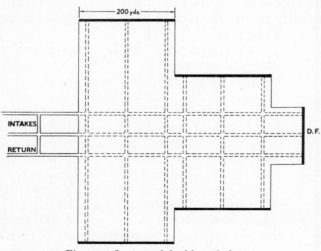

Fig. 27.—Layout of double-unit faces.

the coal and filling it on to the face conveyor. These are described fully in Chapter 9.

TRANSPORT OF COAL FROM THE LOADER GATE END.—The gate conveyor forms the link between the face conveyor or conveyors and the "tub" or "mine car", or the trunk conveyor, as explained in Chapter 9 and Vol. 2, Chap. 7.

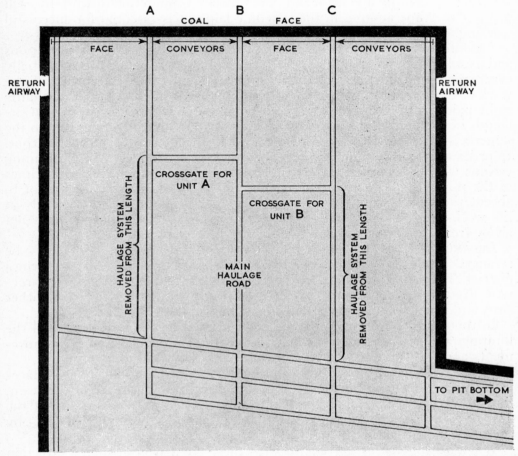

Fig. 28.—Illustrating an arrangement of cross-gates on mechanised faces, designed to reduce the length of haulage roads to be maintained. Coal from face to left of A is conveyed via the cross-gate to road B, where it is joined by coal from face between A and B in the single main haulage road B, which, outbye of the cross-gates, serves for both faces.

LINE OF FACE.—A straight line of face is invariably adopted in mechanised mining as this suits the characteristics of the face conveyor. Opposite sides or faces of a multiple unit are sometimes "stepped" by the depth of one turn-over, and some forms of conveyor demand such an arrangement. This is not, however, recommended where the roof is friable. Systems in which faces are laid out at an angle forming so-called V faces are likewise undesirable as roof pressures tend to become severe at the point where the line of face changes direction.

C.L. I—10*

CYCLE OF OPERATIONS.—These generally follow a similar order to that described for handgot mining, and the same rules apply, but the rigid maintenance of operations to schedule is of much greater importance in mechanised mining. It is vital in machine mining for the work to be highly organised, since a number of teams of men are involved in the tasks which in handgot work are covered by one team and one contract. Completion of work by each team in the time allotted in the schedule laid out is essential for successful working.

Absenteeism of workers seriously disorganises the cycle of operations and results in loss of output. At some collieries this has been partially counteracted by an over-all contract under which a team performs all the work of the unit, but this has the disadvantage that the number of manshifts to be paid for on a single pay note is comparatively large, according to the length of the unit concerned, and unless the team are fully amenable to the scheme, discontent arises amongst them, to the detriment of coal output. In order that teams do not hinder each other, it is usual for men performing various tasks to commence work at times other than the normal shift times of the mine. Such men, and afternoon and night shift workers, are apt to absent themselves from work, without giving prior notice, particularly at the week-ends. This is one of the main reasons why the output does not always reach that planned and possible for a mechanised face.

ARRANGEMENT OF FACES.—In the layout of the mine the faces may be arranged singly or two, three or more may be grouped together to form a district. They may be in one line or *en échelon*, advancing in the same direction. Frequently too, a short developing unit provides access to coal at either side, and units may be opened off to left and right (Figs. 25 and 27).

In this manner workings may be concentrated to a high degree, and the limiting factors of arrangements such as ventilation, haulage, power requirements and the like must be given careful attention during planning.

Opening-out Longwall Faces.—The method of opening-out longwall faces varies with local conditions, including the thickness and depth of the seam, the presence or absence of dirt bands and, maybe, the relationship of the new faces to existing workings. Two chief methods are employed, viz., by narrow workings and by wide workings.

When *opening-out by narrow workings* these are driven in such a direction that the side forms the line from which the new face is started. The opening-up place is made of sufficient width to allow of the installation of a conveyor (or the laying of a tub track in the now rare case of handgetting) plus a width sufficient to allow a coal-cutter to pass and make the first cut in the new face.

Mechanised methods are now generally adopted for the coal-cutting in these narrow opening-up places, using either a shortwall coal-cutter, a Universal coal-cutting machine or in some cases a longwall machine, although the last named is not recommended unless the jib length is such that it will cut the required width by swinging the jib and without having to travel sideways across the face. Details of these machines are given in Chapter 9, and the methods of using them for the purpose under consideration are shown diagrammatically in Figs. 29a, b and c.

After cutting, the coal is blasted preparatory to filling either direct into

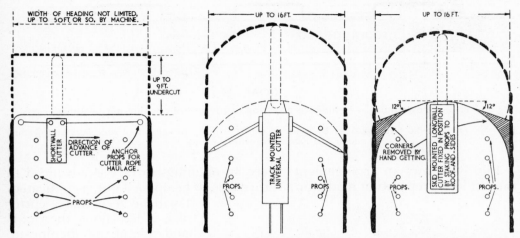

Fig. 29.—Illustrating methods of mechanical undercutting, using (a) a shortwall machine, (b) a Universal machine and (c) jibbing with a longwall machine, not recommended. (Roofbars not shown.)

tubs or on to a conveyor, the tub track or the conveyor being advanced as necessary. Supports are arranged in such a way as to facilitate starting the new face.

Present-day practice is to employ increasingly either power-loading

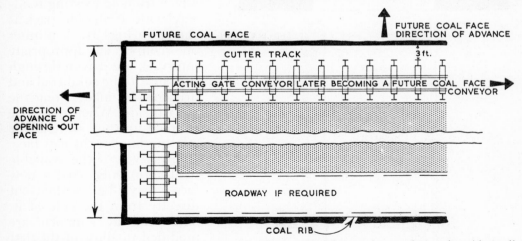

Fig. 30.—Opening out a coalface by "wide-work". The length of the opening-out face varies with conditions. Note that it is equipped with a short conveyor which delivers into the future coalface conveyor.

machines in conjunction with coal-cutters or machines which cut and load the coal in one operation. Details of these are given in Chapter 9.

Opening-up by wide-work is recommended in thin seams and seams containing dirt bands, as the dirt from rippings or from the seam itself may be disposed of by packing.

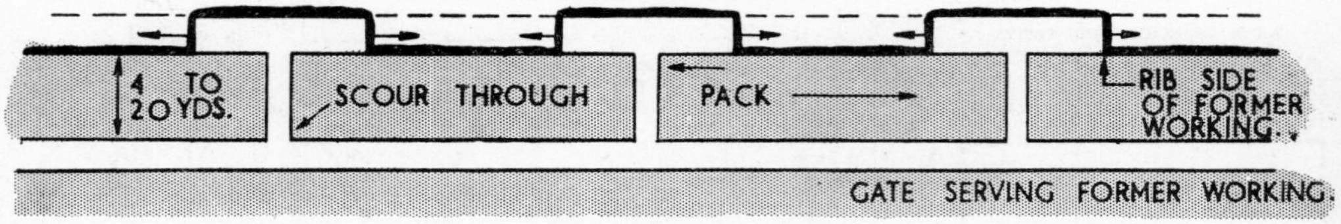

FUTURE COALFACE

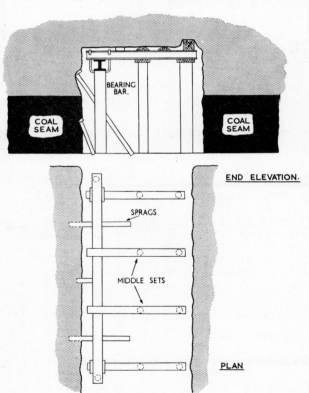

4 TO 20 YDS.   SCOUR THROUGH   PACK ———→   RIB SIDE OF FORMER WORKING.

GATE SERVING FORMER WORKING.

GOAF

N.B. Arrows thus ——→ indicate direction of advance of opening out headings.

Fig. 31.—Opening out future coalface by means of short "scours" throughout rib-side pack and heading along goaf side, as shown by arrows.

Fig. 30 shows an arrangement where an opening-up face is advanced to the left and preparation made for a future face to be opened out, as indicated.

BEARING BAR.

COAL SEAM   COAL SEAM

END ELEVATION.

SPRAGS

MIDDLE SETS

PLAN

Fig. 32.—A method of support when opening-out a coalface from a roadside in the coal.

It will be seen that a cutter track is left along the right-hand side of the opening-up face in readiness for the new face, and the conveyor used for opening up is later employed as the coalface conveyor on the new face.

A method of opening-out a face from an existing roadway with a rib-side pack is shown in Fig. 31. A number of scours, at appropriate intervals, are driven through the pack to the solid coal and drivages are made along the old rib side. When these are coupled up they serve as the starting line for the new face. Alternatively if the available road is in solid coal a new face may be opened-out directly from the side of it. The roadway supports are modified to allow of the first cut being made alongside the road by the coal-cutting machine. Catch props or middle sets are set under the existing bars and bearing bars may be set parallel with the line of the face as shown in Fig. 32.

Where a new face is to be set out from the rib side of a producing unit the method shown in Fig. 33 may be adopted. This is similar in many respects to that shown in Fig. 30. In such cases much depends upon how the rib-side roadway has stood during the period before the new face is started.

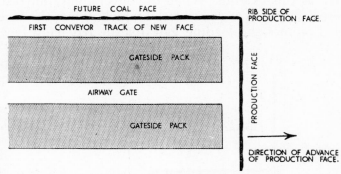

Fig. 33.—Forming a future coalface in an existing working; showing conveyor track for new face left along rib-side of production face.

New faces are sometimes opened out by the extension of cross-gates. An example of this is shown in Fig. 34. It will be seen that connections are made at intervals to the rib-side airway of the former working to afford ventilation for the new face. This airway will suffer damage as the new face advances and will need repair and attention.

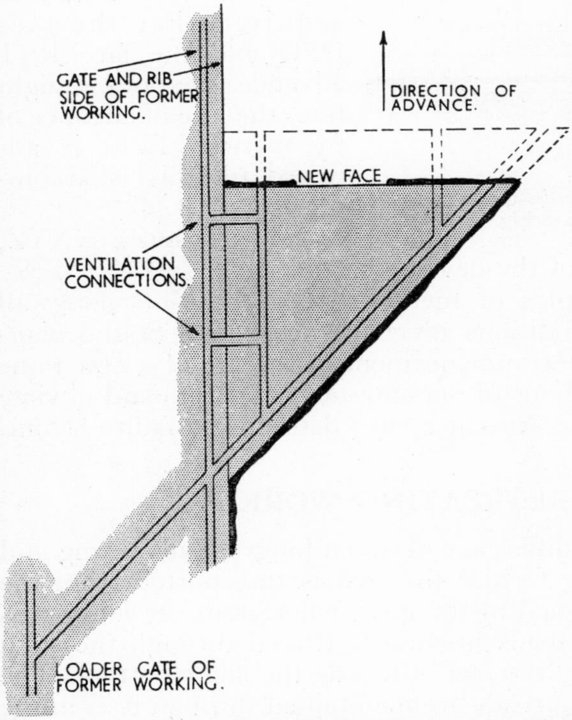

Fig. 35 shows a method which has been used for the formation of two new faces by cross-gate extension. This method is, however, open to the objection that roof troubles are likely to arise at the junction of the two new faces. Such difficulties should be anticipated, and if possible avoided, by planning new faces by other methods from the outset.

Another method of forming faces by cross-gate extension is shown in Fig. 36. The developing face BCD commenced from the scour or road AC which connects with the three main roads leading to the pit bottom. Face BCD is served in this instance by conveyors which are indicated by arrows. On reaching the point E, a cross-gate EF is packed-out to the left from the loader gate ACE. When the cross-gate

Fig. 34.—Forming a future coalface by cross-gate extension. The width of the new face increases as the cross-gate extends.

reaches the point F, a face FG, at right-angles to EF, is formed as shown and a conveyor installed which delivers coal to the cross-gate. Both faces advance so as to keep a constant angle between them on the line of the gate BF as this extends. When the developing unit reaches the point H, another cross-gate HJ is commenced which, when the faces have reached the point J, becomes the loading gate for the left-hand face, whose conveyor is now "turned about" to transport the coal to the new gate. As this latter advances, its right-hand side is developed and the face LMN is formed. The double unit reaches its desired length as face OPQ and is then fully developed. The further face RST is formed, as the original developing unit BCD advances, beyond the point N. If at a later date it is required that the face OPQ and the face RST advance in one straight line, the rate of advance of the various faces is adjusted till this is accomplished.

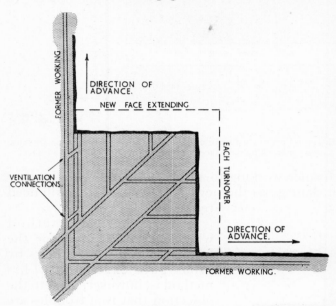

Fig. 35.—Forming two future coalfaces by cross-gate extension; an elaboration of the method shown in Fig. 34.

are formed on the opposite side of the developing unit BCD.

The foregoing selected examples of methods of opening-out longwall faces serve to show how local conditions affect the procedure. Sound planning of all future workings at the commencement of the life of a new mine will include consideration of methods of opening-out new areas and obviate difficulties which would otherwise arise at a later date due to faulty layout.

III. LONGWALL RETREATING WORKING

As already indicated the main difference between longwall advancing and longwall retreating is that in the former the coal is transported from the working face along roadways formed in the goaf, whereas in the latter it is transported from the face along roads previously driven through the solid coal which is worked as that face "retreats" towards the shaft bottom. The goaf or waste is left behind and no roads are maintained through it as in the advancing system.

The general principles of the longwall retreating system in its simplest form are clearly shown in Figs. 37 and 38, which show the method of opening-out a panel or face and the face being brought back or retreated towards the opening-out levels. These levels, *aaa*, are connected by thurlings, *bb*, for ventilation purposes and from them pairs of headings *cc*, connected by thurlings, *dd*, are driven to a prearranged boundary. The distance between these pairs of headings, *c*, governs the length of the face which is fixed according to prevailing circumstances. When the pairs of headings reach the boundary they are connected by levels, *ee*, holed through at intervals for ventilation by the thurlings, *ff*. When these levels have been completed the working face, *gh*, is opened out and retreated as indicated in Fig. 38. The method of support at the face varies with conditions, but is similar to that for ordinary longwall advancing, except that packs are built only in special circumstances, the goaf being normally left open. On the face coal-cutters and conveyors, power-loading machines or cutter-loaders may be employed.

Two special methods of longwall retreating employed in the working of thick seams are described later (see Figs. 44 and 45).

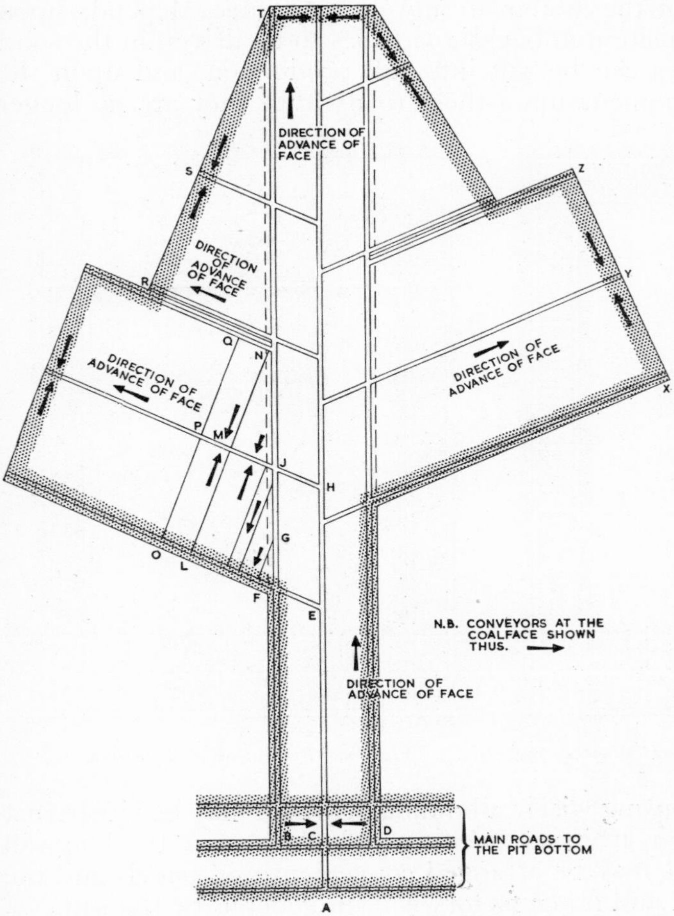

The method is costly in development as roads have to be driven in the solid to the points where faces are opened out for retreating and much capital expenditure has to be incurred before full production is obtained. In consequence it is not so popular as longwall advancing. Another disadvantage is that it is not so flexible as the mechanised bord and pillar and the longwall advancing methods.

The retreating system, however, calls for little or none of the expenditure usually involved in maintaining roads through the goaf, particularly if careful

Fig. 36.—Sketch plan showing another example of the method of forming coalfaces by cross-gate extension.

Note.—For a typical case, face BCD would be about 100 yd. long and faces OPQ, RST and XYZ each 200 yd. long.

planning is combined with accurate observation of strata behaviour and control. The system has much in its favour, and in many cases would probably show a higher over-all profitability than the advancing system. But it must be recognised that such results would not be achieved in every case, especially where technical information of all relevant facts is not available at the outset.

Much of the success of the system in any circumstances depends upon the distance that the requisite number of roads has to be driven in the solid before the retreating faces can be put into full production, and upon the effect of the natural phenomena upon these roads until they are no longer

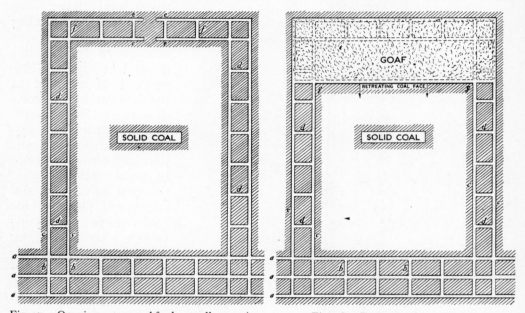

Fig. 37.—Opening out a panel for longwall retreating.   Fig. 38.—Retreating longwall face.

needed. This involves choosing wisely a boundary, which may be either that of the mine, or a natural or arbitrary one from which to start the longwall retreating work. The faces may be arranged conveniently in panels and the number of gates required and other factors will, in general, be the same as for longwall advancing, except for the absence of packing in the waste. Although packing is not carried on as part of the normal retreating system, it may be required where it is necessary to reduce, or to attempt to eliminate, the effect of subsidence at the surface caused by the removal of the seam. Where the seam is liable to spontaneous combustion it may be necessary, as already mentioned, to seal off the wastes by a regular system of packing, or temporary seals across the open wastes will require to be erected at appropriate intervals. In South Derbyshire puddled clay is used for sealing pack walls in retreating work, the method being referred to locally as "wax-walling".

IV. SEMI-LONGWALL METHODS

In considering certain methods of working, it is difficult to distinguish between bord and pillar and longwall systems, and equally difficult is the classification of methods which are neither "narrow work" nor longwall. American mining engineers use the term "shortwall" but this conception does not fully meet those workings where faces vary from 15 to 30 yd. or more in length.

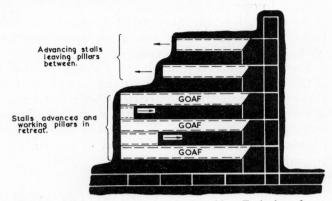

Fig. 39.—The single-stall method of working. Each short face has two roadways for ventilation, but only one of these serves for haulage. The pillars or ribs formed between the stalls are extracted retreating as indicated. Production capacity may be increased by opening up faces to the right as well as to the left as shown.

Two systems calling for special note in this connection are the single-stall and the double-stall systems.

THE SINGLE-STALL SYSTEM.—This is shown in Fig. 39, and is similar in some respects to the American butt-end system. Two roads are driven to the rise of the seam from the main levels or entries, shown at the bottom of the figure. At right-angles to these rise roads and, thus, along the strike of the seam, short faces are opened out and advanced to a predetermined boundary, leaving a barrier adjacent to the next rise headings. Ribs or pillars of coal are left temporarily for support between adjacent stalls and on reaching the boundary a drivage is made through the rib which is extracted by a retreating face, as shown. The faces and ribs are usually only 10 to 15 yd. wide and a haulage road is carried on one side only, with an airway on the other side of the face. On retreating the men from a given face work out the adjacent rib. Alternatively the two rise development roads may be formed by carrying a face to the rise, and furthermore faces may be opened up on both sides of the development roads or face, thus developing the panel in both directions.

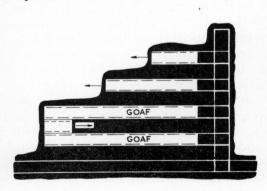

Fig. 40.—Double-stall method of working. Two haulage roads are carried for each face, and, on retreating, half the width of the rib is worked to each of the adjoining stall roads.

THE DOUBLE-STALL SYSTEM.—This is in many respects similar to the single-stall system but in this case a haulage road is carried on each side of the face, which is normally wider than with single-stall, being usually 15 to

30 yd. wide; but it may be wider, depending upon roof conditions. On reaching the predetermined boundary, ribs between adjacent stalls are cut through and the rib retreated as in single-stall, half the width of the rib being worked from each haulage road. Fig. 40 shows a double-stall panel carried in one direction only.

As in single-stall, faces may be opened out in both directions, and the distance the faces are carried depends upon how far the stall roads can advance without undue cost for repairs.

Such methods were in the past employed for handgetting and filling tubs at the face. Of late, however, attention has been turned to the use of modifications of these methods, particularly the double-stall system for the extraction of thin seams by the use of belt conveyors and power loaders following undercutting and shot-firing. The system may not require roof ripping, or the provision of expensive roads and in carefully planned layouts it can be of considerable economic success.

V. HORIZON MINING

Horizon mining consists of sinking the shafts to a point some distance below the seam to be worked, then driving level drifts through the strata to meet the seam. The depth to which the shaft is sunk below the point where it intersects the seam is dependent upon the depth and dip of the seam, and the distance between the seams which determines the distance to be driven on the level to intersect the seam. Integral in the system is the use of staple shafts to reach the seam at intermediate points.

In certain European coalfields, notably those in Holland and the Ruhr, the system is widely practised,[1] and here levels between 250 ft. and 600 ft. apart in sectional view are driven out in the strata on the strike from the shafts as the needs of the seams to be worked dictate, and in order to obtain the maximum quantity of coal from a given horizon, or level. The levels, or "laterals" as they are termed, are driven directly over each other, and their gradient is usually in favour of the loaded cars.

From the laterals, level or slightly rising cross-measure drifts are driven to intersect the seams, which may lie at grades from level to vertical, or thereabouts. Where approximately level, these drifts may or may not be driven through the seams they are to serve. Staple pits then connect with the seams for access and ventilation, and in these pits either cage or skip winding or spiral chutes conduct the coal to the drifts.

Locomotive haulage on the levels is favoured and provides a major advantage of the system in these circumstances. It has been in use in the Ruhr coalfield of Germany for some eighty years.

Fig. 41 shows in general outline the arrangement of shafts and roadways in the horizon method.

The advantages of this system were emphasised in the Report of the Technical Advisory Committee furnished to the Minister of Mines in March 1945 (The Reid Report).[2] The system as practised in Holland is briefly described in this report and illustrated by the plan and section reproduced in Fig. 42, which shows a typical layout for a single seam; the seams being generally worked in descending order. Referring to Fig. 42 the main intake and return drifts are set out from their respective shafts to intercept the seam at points E and F, thus forming the extent to the dip of the first area of coal to be worked, ABCD. The vertical interval between the two drifts in this case is 450 ft., and the full dip of the seam 1 in 4·5.

"Roadways are driven in the seam to form return airways (giving ascensional ventilation), and to open out faces and conveyor roadways successively,

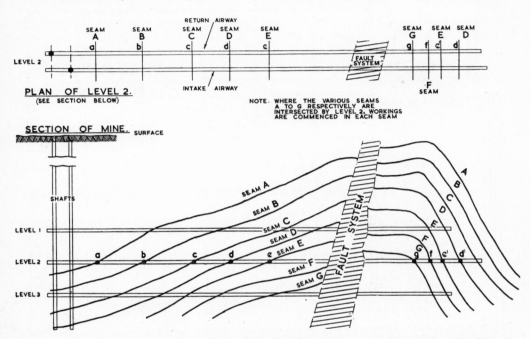

Fig. 41.—Diagram showing the general principles of the layout for the horizon method of working.

ED, EC, GZ and HZ, the latter dividing the area into three strips, each 230 yd. wide, on either side of the main intake roadway, suitable for longwall advancing single-unit working.

"Two 230-yd. wide faces (Strip 1) are worked simultaneously to predetermined distances ZD, ZC—which limit the extent of the first area to be worked—the coal being conveyed down the faces, along the bottom roadway, and loaded into tubs at point E.

"When Strip 1 has been exhausted, Strip 2 is worked in a similar manner, with the exception that the coal is delivered from the roadway conveyor on to a spiral conveyor (or chute) situated in the staple pit at point G, then loaded into tubs on the main intake drift. Strip 2 is replaced by Strip 3, the coal being loaded by way of the staple pit at point H, into tubs on the main intake roadway.

"If stowing material is required [see Chapter 9] it is sent down the up-cast shaft, hauled via the main return airway to point F, and then transported by conveyors along the return airway to the rise end of the faces.

"When the area ABCD is exhausted, another main intake-airway drift is set out from the downcast shaft at a lower level to intercept the seam at point J, in order to work out the area DCKL, the intake roadway for the area ABCD becoming the return airway for the working area DCKL, and so on, progressively.

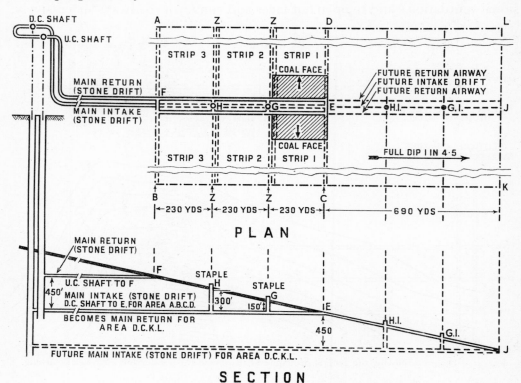

Fig. 42.—Illustrating the horizon method of mining. (Reid Report.[1])

"Man-riding facilities are provided from the shafts to the inbye ends of either the main intake or main-return roadway, points E and F, according to local circumstances."

Certain foreign mining engineers would appear to favour the application of horizon mining to many British coal seams. But there is a balance to be drawn on the relative merits of the system according to the dip of the seams and their distance apart, and hence the capital cost involved in level drivages. With seams of greater dip than 1 in 5 it is feasible that horizon mining would be successful under given conditions, but when the seam dips at 1 in 10 and less, very careful investigation is necessary before its adoption. The success of the system in the Ruhr, and elsewhere, is due to the great number of seams which can be worked to a lateral and its cross-measure drifts, whereas with flatter dips the possibility of reaching seams with staple pits 250 ft. to 600 ft. deep, more especially in those coalfields which are not rich in coal seams, is remote.

VI. THE WORKING OF THICK SEAMS

The methods of working so far described apply, in general, to seams with thicknesses up to about 8 ft. Seams of greater thickness present special problems, and call for special methods of working. Such seams with thicknesses up to 40 ft. or even more occur in Great Britain (South Staffordshire, Warwickshire and Fifeshire), in Europe (France and Poland), in North America (Nova Scotia, Alberta and Pennsylvania), in India (Bengal) and in Australia.

Where seams of this nature occur at or near the surface they are worked, like the thinner ones, by opencast, or "strip" mining methods, but when found at depths greater than roughly 12 to 15 times the thickness of the seam the cover is usually regarded as too thick to allow economic opencast working, although in some cases a higher ratio of rock to coal is taken out (Chapter 9).

Methods applied for the working of thick seams underground vary greatly. In Poland, the room and pillar system is favoured in a 24-ft. seam using, for supports in the rooms, wooden props, to which wooden caps or lids are nailed before the props are set. Men on ladders adjust the top of the prop to the required position whilst two men at the base tighten it by hammering it into the vertical position. Double entry to the rooms is provided by roads 8 ft. or so in height. Hydraulic stowing (Vol. 2, Chap. 2) is used to fill the rooms after the coal has been extracted.

The South Staffordshire Ten-yard Seam, or "Thick Coal".—In working this seam a method known as "squarework" is still practised to some extent.[3] This consists in driving two roads AB and CD, as shown in A, Fig. 43, from a pair of levels, all in the lower portion of the seam. A road BD is then driven as shown, and what is virtually a longwall face is advanced from the side of this road, indicated in B, Fig. 43, by arrows showing its direction of advance; this is known as a "side laning". Next (C, Fig. 43), the road BD is extended to E and F, also the road GH is driven, and square areas of coal marked "1", "2", "3" and "4" are extracted. At the same time the road GH is extended to J and K, and the process of getting down the top coal in the areas "1" and "2" (C, Fig. 43) is started. Vertical grooves are cut in the coal, leaving webs of coal called "spurns" on either one or both sides of the excavation, and then these are removed, by cutting them away with a special tool or by explosives. The process is commenced in the middle of the working place and work continues both ways by advancing a kind of "vertical buttock".

From the road JK (D and E, Fig. 43), excavations numbered "5" to "10" inclusive are made, and from the road marked LM, excavations marked "11" to "13" are made. Work continues until the "side" of work is completed as in E, Fig. 43, whilst the top coal is worked in squares previously prepared. Six pillars are usually formed to constitute a "side".

The method described above is useful where the seam is liable to spon-

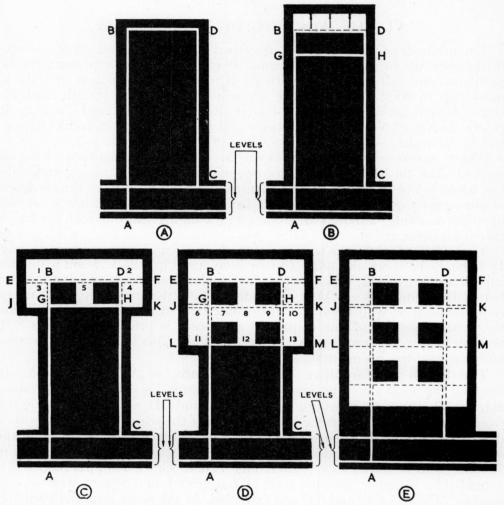

Fig. 43.—Stages in the development of a "side of work" as practised in the working of the Thick Coal of South Staffordshire.

taneous combustion, but is indeed wasteful, extracting, sometimes, only about 40 per cent. of the coal available in the seam.

The South Staffordshire Thick Seam is also worked by first removing the top section by longwall, and after the packs have consolidated, the bottom section is worked. Separating the two working sections is usually a strong dirt band, but roads leading to the face are driven in the lower portions of the seam.

A method of working the South Staffordshire Thick Seam by longwall retreating in panels is described by D. S. Newey.[4] In this method, shown in Fig. 44, three parallel roads are driven roughly 50 yd. apart, in the lower portion of the seam, being connected at intervals of 80 yd. by cross headings for ventilation purposes, Fig. 44a. The roads extend to a natural or arbitrary boundary and are supported as required. The block of pillars at the inbye end are then split, and a type of longwall face is formed along the extreme edge of the pillars, and "retreated" using dirt packing and "cogs" (wooden and rock supports) 8 ft. × 9 ft. in plan, and spaced every 8 ft. along the face. In between the cogs, the top coal is penetrated, and the coal filled out. Cogs are then systematically withdrawn and moved towards the retreating face in the lower portion of the seam, when more top coal is thereby accessible and is filled out.

The Thick Coal of Warwickshire, which comprises three or more seams or layers lying together as shown in the section in Fig. 45, is worked by a special method suitable for use with conveyor mining and less wasteful than those already described. The method is modified longwall retreating (see page 301) and headings are driven in the lower section of the seam (the Slate coal) to the full dip, spaced 30 yd. apart for handworking and

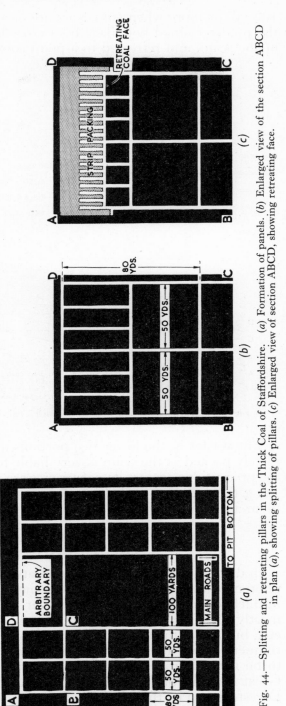

Fig. 44.—Splitting and retreating pillars in the Thick Coal of Staffordshire.   (a) Formation of panels. (b) Enlarged view of the section ABCD in plan (a), showing splitting of pillars. (c) Enlarged view of section ABCD, showing retreating face.

100 yd. or more when conveyors are used (Fig. 45). A face is formed along the predetermined boundary by a cross heading, again in the lower section of the seam, and retreated to a point some 10 to 20 yd. from the boundary;

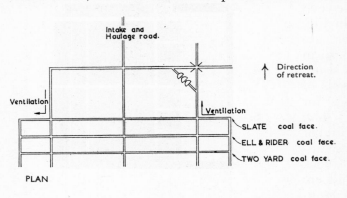

PLAN

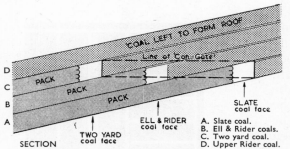

SECTION

A. Slate coal.
B. Ell & Rider coals.
C. Two yard coal.
D. Upper Rider coal.

Fig. 45.—Working the Warwickshire Thick Coal. The coalfaces are immediately above the arrows.

roads are then driven in the coal forming the second section of the seam (the Slate and Ell coals) back to the boundary and on the full dip. These are called "congates", "conduits", or "stall roads", and on reaching the boundaries, faces are formed by cross headings, now graded so as to be in a full section of these seams. The second face is then retreated to a distance of 10 to 20 yd. and the process repeated in order to open out faces in the third and highest worked portion of the seam (the Two-yard coal) and a thickness of Rider coal is usually left for a roof to the working place as shown.

The wastes in the lower two portions of the seam must be well and completely packed as the seam is very liable to spontaneous combustion, and all the precautions against its occurrence are necessary. Fig. 45 shows a section along the congates, and the position of the coalfaces and roads leading to them are indicated in the plan.

VII. WORKING THIN SEAMS

In discussing seam thickness in relation to longwall working, on page 278, reference has been made to the working of thin seams, down to 12 to 14 in. in thickness. These cases are, however, rare and such thin seams are worked mostly because of the special value of the coal, e.g., coking coal, local markets, etc., but as the thicker seams become depleted it becomes necessary to work thinner seams. This trend towards thinner seams, although very gradual, is to be noticed from the statistics showing the percentages of the output in Great Britain won from seams of various thickness as published in Statistical Digests issued by the Ministry of Fuel and Power. The figures are given in Table II.

TABLE II

PERCENTAGES OF COAL FROM SEAMS OF VARIOUS THICKNESSES

Year	Seam thickness					
	Less than 2 ft.	2 ft. to 3 ft.	3 ft. to 4 ft.	4 ft. to 5 ft.	5 ft. to 6 ft.	More than 6 ft.
1913 ..	3·5	15·3	26·5	25·6	17·5	11·6
1924 ..	4·6	17·6	26·9	23·9	17·0	10·0
1944 ..	3·7	22·0	29·3	24·2	12·7	8·1

It will be seen that the percentage worked from seams less than 3 ft. in thickness rose from 18·8 in 1913 to 25·7 in 1944 and during the same period the percentage from seams more than 5 ft. in thickness fell from 29·1 to 20·8.

As previously pointed out, seams less than 3 ft. in thickness are not entirely suited for the bord and pillar method of working, for which a thickness of 4 ft. or more is usually regarded as preferable. In thin seams, working by this method usually gives rise to trouble with dirt disposal. Thin seams are therefore mostly worked by the longwall method and layouts follow the lines previously described, although with the thinner seams it is obviously desirable to keep down the number of roadways to the minimum required for haulage and ventilation on account of the cost of making roads in these seams.

The application of low-type coal-cutters and conveyors and of scraper loaders has greatly facilitated the working of thin seams, and increasing attention is being devoted to the development of special loading or cutter-loading machines as well as stowing machines for use in thinner seams. It appears possible that machines now in course of development may allow of the extraction of thin seams without the necessity for the presence of machine operators on the coalface, leading to what has been aptly described as the "man-less working face".

VIII. WORKING SEAMS IN CLOSE PROXIMITY

Many factors play parts of varying importance in deciding how best to work two seams which lie close together. Questions of quality, nature of surrounding strata, depth from the surface, distance between the seams, relative profitability of working them separately or together, the effect of surface subsidence and the like, all call for consideration.

Contiguous seams are extensively worked in a number of British coal-fields, the method of working depending upon local conditions and customs. It may be pointed out that the Thick Coal of Warwickshire really comprises several contiguous seams, as shown in section in Fig. 45, and is worked by the method already described.

Where the coal beds are separated by intervening dirt beds the method

adopted will depend largely upon their thickness and nature and the intervening beds.

Two seams with up to 3 ft. of rock or shale separating them may be
worked in a variety of ways, two of which are as follows:—

(i) By taking the seams and the rock or shale in one operation, provided
the total height of the working place is not more than about 8 ft.,
so that the men can reach the roof without undue difficulty. The
debris from the rock or shale band is used as packing material.

(ii) By working the lower seam first and supporting the rock or shale,
until a turnover is filled out, then "dropping" the rock or shale by
withdrawing its supports, removing it into the waste and then
working the top seam and filling it out. This may also be done in
another way, by first removing the rock or shale by so-called
"bannocking" and then advancing the top and bottom seams,
either together or singly, setting supports and building waste
packs as required.

If the seams are more than 3 ft. apart it would generally be uneconomic
to remove the intervening strata—in fact 3 ft. may be regarded as a maximum
distance apart for this purpose. Many possibilities are available for working
seams lying close together, e.g., longwall advancing first in one seam and
then in the other, with a suitable interval of time between the two workings
to allow the packs to consolidate, or such an arrangement with some 20 to 30
yd. only between the faces. Or longwall advancing in one seam, and longwall
retreating in the other, with the faces progressively becoming further apart,
may be employed. Local conditions and customs are so diverse as to require
special study before embarking on schemes for extraction of seams in close
proximity to each other.

In parts of the South Staffordshire coalfield the Deep and Shallow seams
lying near together have been worked successfully by longwall advancing
carrying the workings in the Deep seam about 10 yd. in advance of those in
the Shallow seam.

In Scotland the Main seam, 2 ft. 4 in. thick and the overlying Pyotshaw
seam, 2 ft. 7 in. thick, separated by about 2 ft. of dirt, have been successfully
worked as follows:—The Main seam is first worked to the boundary by
longwall advancing and the goaf tightly packed. On reaching the boundary
the Pyotshaw seam is entered and a retreating longwall face brought back
over the goaf of the Main seam using the gates already formed in this seam.
Coal-cutters and conveyors are successfully employed in both the advancing
and retreating faces.

In another case in Ayrshire three seams, in close proximity, as shown in
section in Fig. 46, have been worked by first extracting the bottom seam to
the rise by longwall advancing and following up by working the middle seam
in a similar manner over the goaf of the bottom seam. Finally the top seam
is extracted by retreating over the goaves of the two previously worked seams
as shown in Fig. 47, which shows three districts at various stages of develop-

ment and illustrates the general scheme of working. In District No. 3 the advancing face in the bottom coal is shown, while in District No. 2 the middle coal is being extracted, and in District No. 1 the final working is in progress in the retreating face in the upper seam. The beds dip 1 in 6 and districts

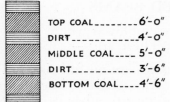

TOP COAL _____ 6'-0"

DIRT _____ 4'-0"

MIDDLE COAL ____ 5'-0"

DIRT _____ 3'-6"

BOTTOM COAL ____ 4'-6"

Fig. 46.—Section of contiguous seams worked as in Fig. 47.

are opened up from pairs of levels AA, BB and CC at intervals of about 120 yd. Pillars are left for the support of these levels as shown. Good packing is essential in the workings of the bottom and middle beds, but even so considerable subsidence occurs and it is advisable to allow ample time between successive workings for settlement to occur. In the third, retreating, working no packing is done and little stone work is necessary. In the case shown the coal was handgot with gate roads about 12 yd. apart, but in present-day working coal-cutters and conveyors would be employed with gate roads about 100 yd. apart.

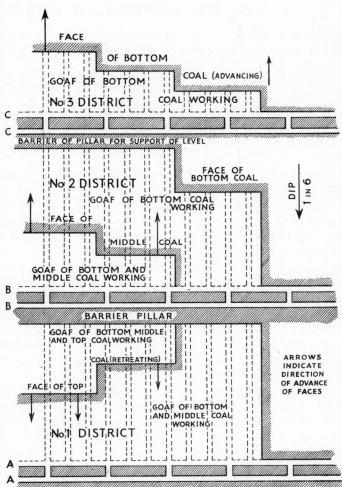

Fig. 47.—Showing method of working three contiguous seams.

In West Yorkshire there are a number of seams separated by thin dirt bands. At Sharlston West Colliery[5] the Lower Haigh Moor Seam is 2 ft. 6 in. to 2 ft. 9 in. thick and the Top Haigh Moor Seam 3 ft. 9 in. to 4 ft. thick with an intervening bed of clunch 6 ft. 10 in. thick. Experiments made by working the seams separately, extracting either the lower or top seam in the first working, and also by working the seams simultaneously, have shown the importance of good packing and the advantages of using mechanical stowing machines. The more extensive use of mechanical and pneumatic stowing plays an important part in working contiguous seams.

IX. THE WORKING OF INCLINED SEAMS

Two methods of face arrangement are commonly employed where seams lie at gradients between roughly 1 in 12 and 1 in 3. These are:—

(i) The face is advanced to the full rise: the gates are on full rise and the face line is on the strike or level line. Alternatively, in certain circumstances it may be essential for the face to advance to the dip, but such working is not easy.

(ii) The face is advanced along the strike, and the face line is thus on the full dip of the seam. The gates are then on the strike.

In the former method where the gradient suffices, use may be made of gravity haulage in which the full tubs descending a gate can be arranged to pull up the empty tubs. The arrangement of the faces is similar to that employed in methods already described, and adaptations to suit the seams having high inclination are mainly of local origin and interest. Chutes may replace tubs and rails in the gates, or the belt conveyor may be used if the gradient is not too steep (i.e., not greater than 1 in 3, at which gradient the coal will roll down the belt). Conveyors on steep gradients are fitted with regenerative braking equipment or at least with braking gear to operate automatically when the current is switched off. On steep gradients the tendency of the coal to roll on the conveyor may be overcome by the use of retarding arrangements. The retarding rope-and-button conveyor, and the chains-and-flight conveyor are useful for conveying on inclinations approaching or greater than 1 in 3 (Vol. 2, Chap. 7).

Coal-cutting machines for working on steeply dipping faces are fitted with means of controlling the travel of the machine by ropes secured to the rise end of the face. The system of work is similar to the *Tailles Montantes* system in use for working seams to the rise on the continent of Europe. Bord and pillar methods may also be used for the working of highly-inclined seams.

The *rearer* method, which basically involves horizon mining (see p. 305), has long been used in North Staffordshire. Two levels, one for intake and haulage and one for return, driven in the seam are connected to the shafts by cross-measure drifts or so-called "cruts" (Fig. 48). A pair of roads is then driven to the full rise for some 100 or 150 yd. and levels are opened off on either side, and pillars formed by rise and dip connections between the levels at a distance of some 60 yd. on the strike. The pillars are extracted by a process known as "entering-up" a pillar. Men commence the operation by standing on ladders and scaffolds, and later stand on the goaf debris which falls as the pillar is removed.

A barrier is left intact above and below the workings, in the plane of the seam, on account of gas and water troubles that may occur if this were removed.

Fig. 48 shows the general layout of the workings. In the rise gates haulage is effected by transporting the tubs on a level platform of a special carriage usually hauled up the grade by a counter weight and braked down it by a band-brake pulley or a jig wheel (Vol. 2, Chap. 6). The percentage of coal extracted from the seam is only about 60 per cent. and is even less where pillars are lost through crushing before they can be worked. The method is suitable only for steep gradients greater than about 45 degrees.

Another system of working, similar in some respects to the "rearer" method, is that in which the formation of pillars in the latter is replaced by short "breastings" which, if the seam were level, would be called "buttocks".

The breastings are taken on the full rise and dip of the seam and advanced along the strike, being roughly 10 yd. in length and following one another *en échelon*. Fig. 49 shows the arrangement. Packing of the gates is a special problem and packs are "interlaced" with wood chocks to prevent them sliding down the dip before roof subsidence can consolidate them.

The main levels are, as before, driven on the strike of the seam. The method is very similar to the *Tailles Chassantes* system used on the Continent for seams dipping 25 to 45 degrees.

GRADINS RENVERSÉS.—This is a modification of the *Tailles Chassantes*

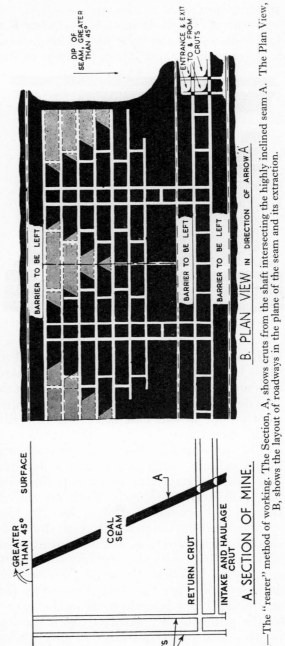

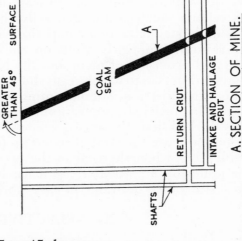

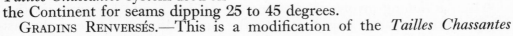

Fig. 48.—The "rearer" method of working. The Section, A, shows cruts from the shaft intersecting the highly inclined seam A. The Plan View, B, shows the layout of roadways in the plane of the seam and its extraction.

system, in which, as already indicated, faces advance on the strike with the uppermost face leading. In the *Gradins Renversés* system, however, the lowest face leads and it is suitable for working seams with gradients between 70 degrees and vertical. Fig. 50 shows the view in the plane of the seam. Men stand on the goaf and advance "steps" or *gradins* each about 3 metres long and spaced 5 metres apart. The coal is drawn away from the workers by chutes constructed through the goaf, which conduct the coal to mine cars in the haulage roadway below.

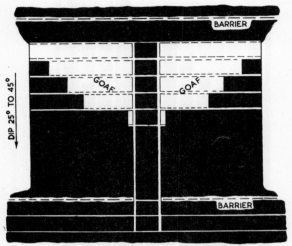

Fig. 49.—Method of working steep seams with "breastings" on the strike.

X. THE ORDER OF WORKING SEAMS

Where seams are less than 3 ft. apart, they may often be worked together as indicated already. If they are more than 3 ft. apart it would not generally be considered economic to attempt to work them simultaneously. Even with seams spaced widely apart the question of interaction of the workings must be considered. Thus a seam 400 yd. or more above one being worked is affected by the result of subsidence from the lower seam. Certain disturbance also occurs to a lower seam when an upper seam is worked, but the zone of interference in this case is very much reduced, and, according to the nature of the strata, may be only a few yards in depth.

The question of which seam to work first was in the past usually decided by its relative quality, and generally the more valuable was worked first. This is understandable in a competitive industry, and in any case, there is a better assurance of early yield on the capital already expended in shaft sinking and provision of plant and the like.

Opinion differs as to which seam should be worked first if the quality is equivalent or is no criterion, but most mining engineers now favour working seams in descending order. In opposition to this view it is argued that when a lower seam is worked first, the area is relieved of occluded gas pressure, but by so doing not only are the strata broken up (and breaks of such a nature are not desirable), but when the coal in the upper seam is worked the coal is said by the miner to be "wooden", as it has lost the liveliness usually found in a virgin seam and so desirable to easy working.

XI. SELECTIVE MINING

Selective mining involves the taking out of dirt bands, by cutting with a machine, as a separate operation, in order to avoid intermixture of the dirt

with the coal. It may be adopted in all methods of working seams where dirt
bands are present in the working section. The dirt band may be taken out
before or after the coal has been removed and the dirt either moved to the
waste or left lying near its original position, as in some bord and pillar
layouts.

The method is widely practised in the United States, using the same
machinery as for normal coal winning. If it is not adopted, large quantities
of dirt may be filled out with the coal and sent to the surface, there to be
separated in the coal preparation plant. In certain mines in the U.S.A., as

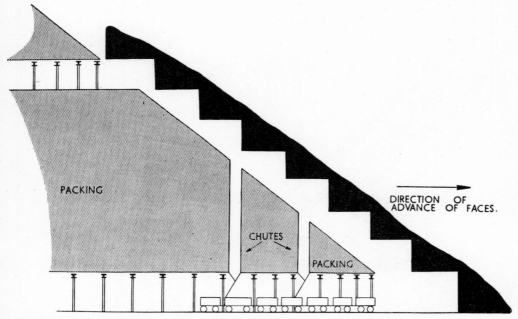

Fig. 50.—*Gradins renversés* system of working steep seams in certain continental countries.

much as 40 per cent. of the gross output of the mine is dirt which has to be taken
out, as necessary, on the surface in the washery or dry cleaning plants. It is
accepted generally that selective mining slows down the over-all speed of
getting coal.

Where hand-filling of coal under contract is adopted, the phrase "selective
mining" is reduced to more practical terms in the colliery contract price
lists by the words "filling coal as free from dirt as practicable" but the extent
to which this is done depends upon a variety of factors.

XII. PROJECTED DEVELOPMENT SCHEMES

The necessity for efficient planning of mining operations is mentioned at
the outset of the previous chapter, and it must be emphasised that its importance cannot be over-rated, whether for entirely new projects, such as

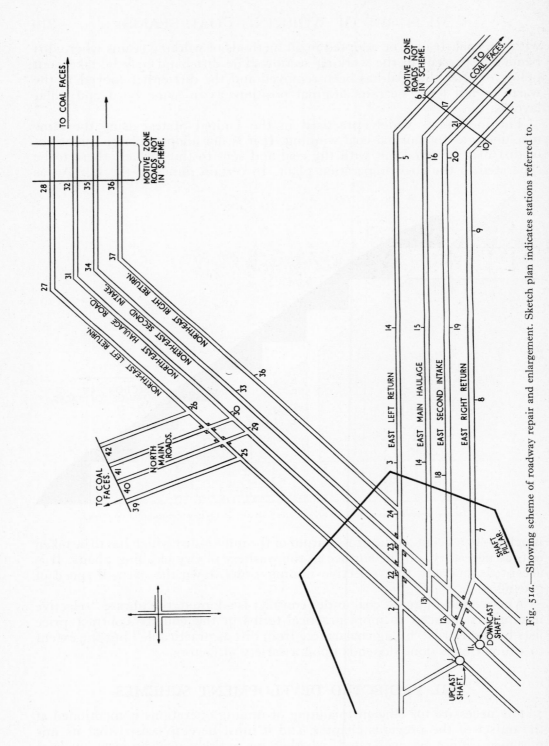

Fig. 51a.—Showing scheme of roadway repair and enlargement. Sketch plan indicates stations referred to.

the laying out of a new mine or working area, or for a reorganisation scheme at an existing colliery. Time spent at the planning table is always amply repaid by saving of time and labour and, maybe, trouble and expense in the future.

It is equally important that the official responsible for the planning should confer with the operational staff, giving full details of the project and their individual and collective responsibility for carrying it out according to plan.

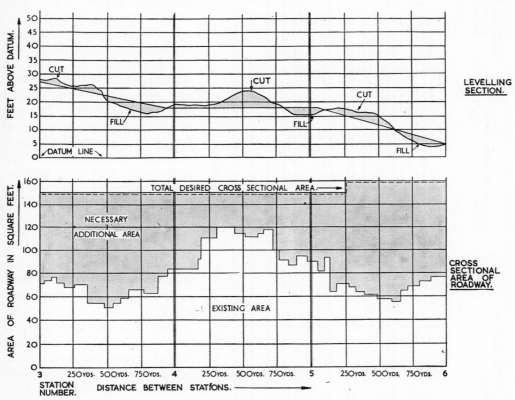

Fig. 51*b*.—Roadway repair and enlargement scheme. Upper figure shows levelling chart and lower figure the cross-sectional area chart.

It is only by getting together for discussion of details that the various points of view concerning it can be appreciated and a spirit of co-operation fostered.

The progress of the scheme should be followed by the responsible official by frequent conferences with the operating staff, for lack of which many a well conceived plan has failed.

The work of the planner must cover every aspect of the operation to be carried out and adequate provision made in advance for all requirements. Winding, haulage, power and ventilation requirements must be catered for in consultation with the various officials, e.g., the mechanical, electrical, mechanisation and ventilation engineers. This is especially necessary where

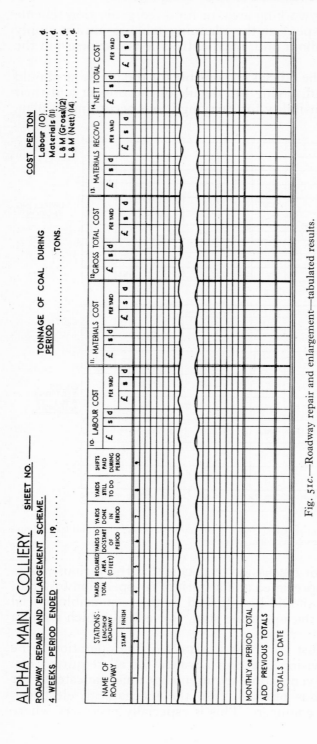

Fig. 51c.—Roadway repair and enlargement—tabulated results.

mechanised methods are to be introduced at the face or a new method of haulage employed, as replacements or additions to existing equipment may be necessary.

PROGRESS RECORDS FOR DEVELOPMENT AND REORGANISATION SCHEMES. — All development and re-organisation schemes should be planned in detail in advance to a time schedule and complete records kept of the progress made. By way of illustration an example of forms of records used for a scheme involving the enlargement, regrading and reconditioning of several miles of roadways is given in Figs. 51 *a* to *d* inclusive. It is only by preparing such plans and records that a check can be kept on the progress of the scheme and adherence to the prearranged schedule ensured.

Fig. 51*a* shows a plan of the roads to be repaired, enlarged, reconditioned or, in certain parts, driven through the solid strata. Each junction is numbered as are also stations between junctions at intervals of not more than 1,000 yd. As the roads are reconditioned or driven, the actual position of the completed lengths is marked on the plan.

Fig. 51*b* shows a levelling section of one of the roadways, together with a graph of the cross-sectional area, and indicates the area of excavation required to give the desired cross-sectional area. Similar diagrams should be made for each roadway in the scheme.

Fig. 51c sets out in tabular form the whole scheme for a predetermined period. Column 1 gives the name of each roadway, and in columns 2 and 3 are inserted the station numbers denoting the particular lengths of roadway. The total yardage between stations is given in column 4, while in column 5 is indicated the required cross-sectional area of the roadway for each length between stations. The number of yards to be completed in each length at the start of each period is shown in column 6, and column 7 gives the number of yards of road *completely* reconditioned and on which no further work is necessary under the scheme. It is important that any part-length inserted in column 7 should indeed be completed, and there should not be included any yardage in respect of lengths of roadway on which partial work only has been carried out. The cost of the latter should be charged to those lengths already completed; thus finally, when the roadway between one station and another has been completed, the cost will include all the work done on that length of the roadway. Column 8 shows the difference between column 6 and column 7, whilst column 9 records the number of shifts paid for during the period, being taken from the deputies' time books. Columns 10 and 11 show the labour and material costs respectively in total amount and also per yard of roadway completed as recorded in column 7. Column 12 is the sum of the entries in columns 10 and 11 and gives the gross total costs. Column 13 records the value of materials recovered during the operation of reconditioning the roadways, such as roof supports retrieved from former workings. Column 14 gives the difference between columns 12 and 13 and is the net total cost in aggregate and per yard.

The period covered by one of the forms shown may be a calendar month, a four-week period, or such other period as may be desired. Each period sheet is numbered, and in the totals at the bottom of the sheet, provision is made for the last period total, previous period totals from previous sheets, and the totals to date. The tonnage of coal wrought during the period, either of the whole mine concerned, or only in the parts of the mine which are served by the roads in the scheme, is recorded on the sheet, and forms the divisor for the aggregate amounts of money in columns 10, 11, 12 and 14, which are then recorded at the top right hand of the sheet.

Fig. 51d shows the yardage rate of progress of the scheme as a whole when compared with the scheduled yardage rate of progress. The time over which the scheme is spread depends upon the total yardage of road to be reconditioned and the speed at which this may be done. It will be seen that the actual period yardage fluctuates considerably in the example shown, a common experience in such cases. Alternative forms of record may be devised to suit any scheme but the example serves to indicate generally the type of data to be recorded.

Finally, it should be made clear to all concerned that when a change of plan and policy is necessary in any scheme due, for instance, to geological disturbance or interruptions of working, such as, say, a large fall or an out-

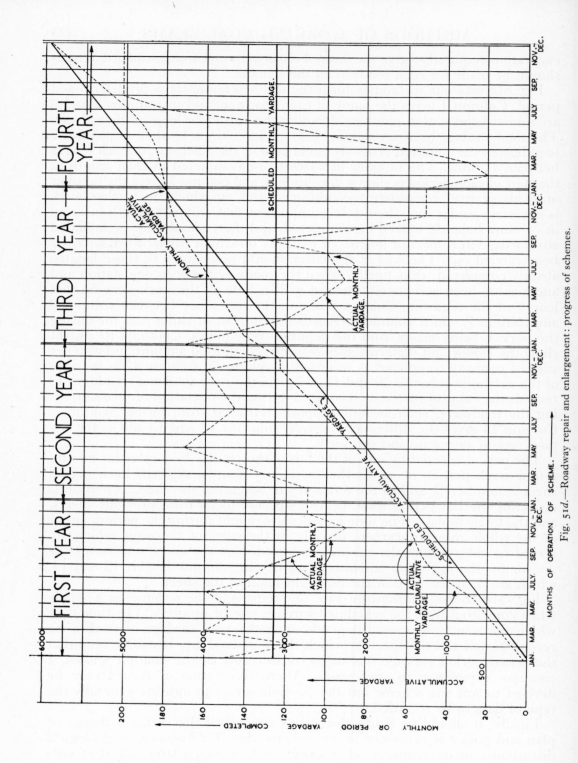

Fig. 51d.—Roadway repair and enlargement: progress of schemes.

break of fire, a revised planning technique must be immediately brought to bear upon the work; and for this reason the necessity for a certain degree of flexibility should be recognised. When a scheme has been planned in all its many aspects, those who will be responsible for working it should be allowed full and free discussion with the originator of the scheme and the higher executives of the mine or group of mines, before the scheme is embarked upon. But once such discussion has taken place, the plan must be regarded as fixed and definite, from which no deviation is permissible unless demanded by unforeseen circumstances; and even then only with the knowledge and consent of the responsible higher executive. It is only by fixity of purpose that any future projection or development scheme can succeed.

REFERENCES

[1] *Horizon Mining*, by C. H. Fritsche and E. L. J. Potts, Allen & Unwin, London, 1954.
[2] Coal Mining. Report of the Technical Advisory Committee. H.M.S.O. Cmd. 6601. 1945. See also "Planning for Horizon Mining", National Coal Board.
[3] Practical Experience in Working the South Staffordshire Thick Coal Seam, B. Price, *Trans. Inst. Min. Eng.*, Vol. 108, 1949, p. 150.
[4] A New Method of Working Thick Coal Seams with special reference to the South Staffordshire Thick Coal at Beggeridge Colliery, *Trans. Inst. Min. Eng.*, Vol. 58, 1919–20, p. 257.
[5] The Working of Seams in Close Proximity, H. Saul and J. J. Gill, *Trans. Inst. Min. Eng.*, Vol. 113 1954, p. 1089.

CHAPTER 8

BREAKING GROUND—I. TOOLS AND EXPLOSIVES

TOOLS AND HAND DRILLS

History.—Evidence from prehistoric surface excavations suggests that even in Neolithic times 10,000 or so years ago, man was faced with the problem of breaking ground in his search for the flints which he fashioned into arrow heads, axes and knives. Excavation was entirely by hand. About 6,000 years ago flint tools gave way to those of bronze, and these were later superseded by tools made from iron.

Fire-Setting.—Undoubtedly, one of man's earliest discoveries was that a hard rock face could be disintegrated by setting fire to wooden faggots piled against it and throwing water on the heated rock.[1] This practice persisted even to the 17th century, but was gradually discarded in favour of blasting with gunpowder.

Those pioneer miners who delved for coal on the south shore of the Firth of Forth in 1200 A.D., must have used very rudimentary tools. It is recorded that even during the 16th century, when mining of coal was developing slowly but surely in almost every coalfield in the country, picks were so dear on account of the difficulty of obtaining iron, that often they were rented annually. During the 17th century, sinking through rock was, in all probability, wholly carried out by hand labour, heavy iron hammers and picks being the only implements available apart from wedges, which at first were made of wood. Later years have seen a continuous improvement in the design and manufacture of the implements employed, and today basic tools are vastly superior in all respects to their prototypes.

Basic Tools.—A group of such tools is shown in Fig. 1, which includes representatives of the following classes:—

PICKS.—Item No. 3 illustrates the most simple type of pick, a tool which the miner may employ to cut into any kind of rock that is not too hard. It is still used in some areas of Scotland, the Midlands and South Wales. It consists of a metal blade fitted to a wooden "helve" or shaft. A hole or "eye" in the middle of the blade receives the wide end of the helve. This end is split for a short distance, and when the blade is in position, it is secured by the driving of a wooden wedge into the split. Picks are manufactured in a variety of shapes and sizes to provide suitable tools for any class of work. The blade of the holing pick or "pricker" is about 15 in. long and is curved

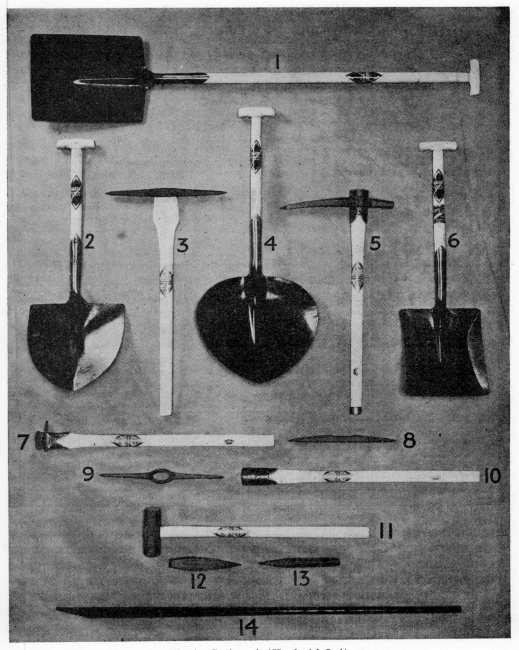

Fig. 1.—Basic tools (*Hardypick Ltd.*).

1. "Scufting" or "Gumming" shovel.
2. Round-nosed pit shovel.
3. Simple miner's pick.
4. "Pit Pan" or "Durham" shovel, etc.
5. Dresser or "Poll Tomahawk".
6. Square-mouthed shovel.
7. "Acme" pick handle, shaft or "helve".

8. "Acme" pick blade.
9. Universal pick blade.
10. Universal pick handle.
11. Sledge hammer.
12. Wedge.
13. Wedge.
14. "Ringer".

approximately to the circumference of the circle it partially describes when a pickman swings it to and fro in hewing dirt from beneath a seam of coal. For narrow work and in corners, a shorter blade is employed. Helves are usually made from American hickory and are from 24 in. to 32 in. in length. Helves were originally made from ash or other locally grown timbers, but with the introduction of interchangeable miners' picks and helves, hickory was adopted. This timber is the finest in the world for tool handles over 16 in. in length, and it is preferred for small hammers where shafts are 16 in. or less in length. Hickory is flexible and tough, and it is said to be "easy on the muscles" of the worker. No satisfactory substitute has been found, and as the supply is waning and many still think that the red hickory wood is not so strong or tough as the white, it is well to remember that weight for weight, sound hickory has the same strength, toughness and resistance to shock, regardless of whether it is red, white or mixed red and white. A test for a good tool handle is to drop it on end on a good hard surface, when it should emit a clear ringing tone, not the dull sound of inferior wood. Sometimes the head of the helve must stand great strain, and it may be covered with a metal sheath. Moreover, such sheaths permit the use of detachable blades, thus (a) simplifying the transport of blades for sharpening, (b) eliminating the possibility of burning the hickory shaft during forging, and (c) permitting rapid substitution of a sharp blade for a dull one. Nos. 7 and 8 show the "Acme" type of sheath, slotted or eyeless blade and wedging key. Nos. 9 and 10 show the Universal type of blade and sheath. The latter is expanded towards the end and the eye of the blade is similarly expanded to afford a firm grip when passed over the small end of and along the hickory shaft into position on the metal sheath. Shafts are usually 32 in. in length, and the blade weights vary from $1\frac{1}{2}$ to $3\frac{1}{2}$ lb.

SHOVELS.—These vary in design with locality and according to the purpose and condition of employment. No. 1 is a "Scufting" or "Gumming" shovel having a flat blade in line with the handle. It is used to clear from the machine cut the cuttings or "gummings" left behind the machine. No. 2 is a "Round-Nosed Pit Shovel," usually fitted with a 24-in. handle, and a standard lift, but for a few mines a 10-in. lift is supplied. It is used chiefly in the Midlands. The "lift" of a shovel is the height of the top of the handle when the blade lies flat on the floor. A standard lift is usually 15 in. to 17 in., according to the length of the handle. A miner's shovel with a 24-in. handle has a lift of 15 in., but for a few mines, shovels with a 10-in. lift are supplied. Similarly the "rise" of a shovel is the height of the bottom edge of the blade when the top of the handle and the top of the blade both rest upon the floor. Blade sizes vary from 12 in. $\times$ $12\frac{1}{2}$ in. to 14 in. $\times$ 16 in. No. 4 is known as the "Pit Pan," "Frying Pan," "Oscar" or "Durham" shovel. It is fitted with a 24-in. handle and is popular in Durham, Northumberland and Yorkshire. Sizes vary from 13 in. $\times$ 13 in. to 18 in $\times$ 18 in. No. 6 is a "Square-Mouthed Miner's Shovel", usually fitted with a 24-in. handle which may be arranged to afford a low lift. It is very popular in the East Midlands where it is used chiefly for conveyor loading.

Other Tools.—DRESSERS.—A "Dresser" or "Poll Tomahawk" is somewhat similar to a pick, half the blade being of pick design, the other half being shaped like a hammer. As will be seen from No. 5, the metal sheath connection between blade and helve is employed. Dressers are normally used for breaking down oversize pieces of coal and rock, and are therefore heavier than picks. Shafts are usually 32 in. in length, but the heads vary in weight from $2\frac{1}{2}$ to $3\frac{1}{2}$ lb.

SLEDGE HAMMERS.—As will be seen from No. 11, a sledge hammer consists of a metal head with a central eye into which the handle fits tightly. Heads vary in pattern, but in almost all types the edges are chamfered off. The head may taper towards the striking faces to enable it to follow a wedge into a narrow channel. Handles are usually 30 in. long and heads vary in weight from 4 to 7 lb.

WEDGES.—These are usually of the types shown in Nos. 12 and 13, but sizes vary; the harder the rock the smaller is the wedge employed. From the section of maximum thickness the wedge tapers slowly in one direction to a flat striking head and in the other towards a chisel shape, but ultimately it sinks to a point. For coal, the longer octagon wedge is usually employed. Weights vary from 1 to $3\frac{1}{2}$ lb.

RINGERS.—These are steel levers, usually 4 ft. 6 in. in length, and 1 in.–$1\frac{1}{2}$in. in diameter. No 14 shows a typical example. Each is round in section at the handle end, passing to octagon and then to square section towards the opposite end which is shaped as a chisel. Ringers are used for many purposes, but particularly for levering large lumps of coal or rock away from the main body when once a crack produced by a wedge or other means permits a bite to be obtained with the end of the tool.

HAND SAWS.—Hand saws are almost indispensable wherever and whenever timber is used underground, e.g., in the erection of sprags, bars, legs, struts, chocks, etc., but they must be very strong to withstand rough treatment and poor maintenance conditions in the working places. The need for saws is, however, greatly reduced by the supply of timber cut to the requisite size and shape and by the increased use of steel supports.

Hand Drills.—THE JUMPER. Throughout the earlier history of the use of gunpowder for mining purposes, holes were drilled by hand by means of a "jumper". This was a bar of iron about 5 ft. in length and $\frac{3}{4}$ in. in thickness, fashioned at one end into a broad curved bit with a hard sharp cutting edge (Fig. 2 E). Taking hold of the bar with both hands, striking the rock therewith repeatedly and rotating the bit a little between the blows, the miner could drill a hole into relatively soft rock. In harder rock, hammer blows on the head of the jumper were required, and in very hard rock it was necessary for one miner to strike the blow with a sledge hammer while another held and rotated the tool. Such "jumper drills" are employed today only in exceptional circumstances; they are now made of steel, usually octagonal in section, with the outer end slightly reduced to centralise the blow received.

Stemming Gear for Shot Firing.—A common type of stemming gear consists of a scraper and rammer. Both are made of copper and each may be fitted to a long wooden handle, or alternatively they may be fitted to opposite ends of a common handle (Fig. 2, A, B, C and D). Some experts in the use of explosives advise the use of the wooden handle alone as a rammer, dispensing entirely with the metal head. (See Ministry of Fuel and Power report of the Committee of Enquiry into the precautions necessary to secure safety in the use of explosives in coal mines, p. 18, "Shot-firing Tools".)

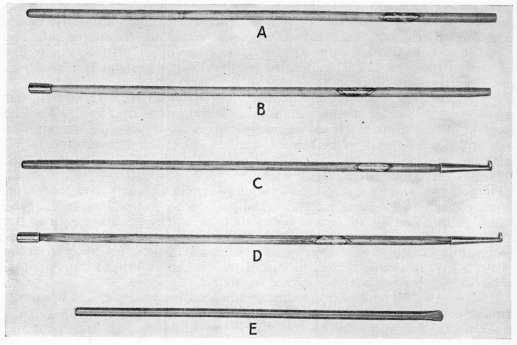

Fig. 2.

A. Wooden rammer.
B. Copper-headed rammer.
C. Scraper with wooden handle.
D. Combined scraper and rammer.
E. Hand drill or jumper.

Scrapers are used periodically during the process of hand drilling to clear the hole free from debris and thus permit the drill to strike a more effective blow on the bottom. They are also used for cleaning drillings from shot-holes before inserting the explosive charge and for the detection of cracks. When drilling is completed and all the drillings have been removed, the rammer is used to push the explosive charge with its primer cartridge to the bottom of the hole and then to "ram", tamp or stem the remaining space to the mouth of the hole with a tamping medium.

Hand Machine for Drilling in Coal or Rock.—The simplest form of hand-machine drill for drilling in coal is the ratchet machine shown in Fig. 3. It consists of a simple feed-screw which works through a screw-nut collar forming the end of a cylindrical metal sheath which houses the screw. The outward end of the screw is fashioned to receive the shank end of the drill. Rotary motion is imparted via a ratchet handle. To drill a hole the pointed end of the sheath must bear against a prop or other support offering adequate

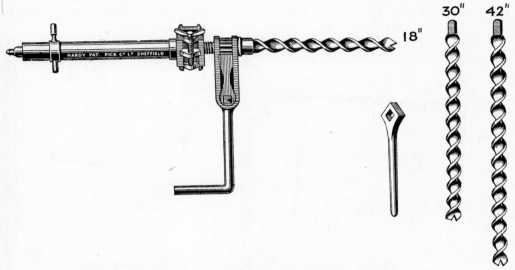

Fig. 3.—Simple ratchet type hand-drilling machine.

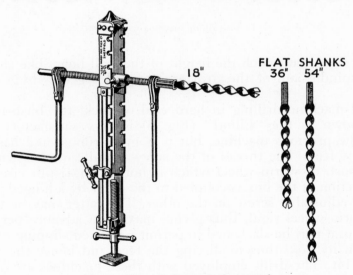

Fig. 4.—Hand drill mounted on stand.

resistance. As the depth of the hole increases longer drills are substituted as required, the screw being run back into its sheath for each exchange. The employment of a telescopic stand (Fig. 4) for the support of the screw and drill expedites and simplifies the operation of drilling. Primary adjustment between roof and floor is made by sliding one half of the stand relative to the other, and securing them together with the clamping screw shown. Secondary adjustment and tightening is by means of the jack-screw at the foot of the stand. In this machine the screw spindle works through a screw thimble or sleeve, the lateral arms of which may be located in any pair of

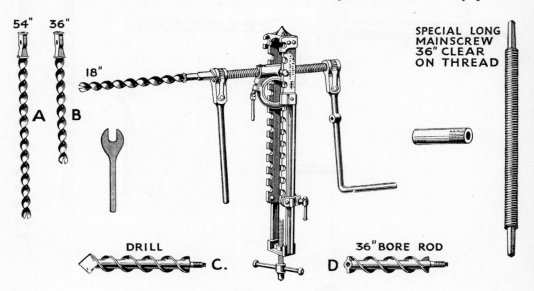

Fig. 5.—Elliott drilling machine with "bush" feed.

the bearing slots that match the height of the drill hole. The shank ends of the screw spindle and of the drill are coupled together by a loose sleeve box.

For hand-machine drilling in hard coal or rock, the bush-feed type of machine known as the "Elliott" (Fig. 5) is very satisfactory. It is very similar to the previous machine, but it is more robust and has a superior type of screw feed. The thread of the screw spindle meshes with the teeth of a brass bush or worm-wheel which is housed in a split circular slipper box. One section of the box is coupled to the other by a hinged joint on one side and an adjustable screw on the other. The latter may be tightened to hold the worm-wheel rigid, thus giving maximum advance per rotation of the spindle, or it may be slackened to permit regulated slipping of the worm-wheel within its box, thus modifying the feed and hence the pressure on the drilling bit. The drills employed with these machines are usually fashioned from flat oval or "fish-belly" drill steel twisted into a spiral, with a flat shank at one end and two cutting teeth at the other (Fig. 5, A and B). The latter are formed by cutting a broad V shape out of the end, its maximum width being about one-third of the width of the steel, and by sharpening the cutting edges and points. Alternatively, twist bore-rods of the type shown in Fig. 5, C and D, may be employed.

POWER DRILLING

History of Drilling.—The more important facts, discoveries and events associated with the history of the development of the art of drilling, arranged in chronological order, are given in the following list:—

1700–1860		The drilling of holes was by hand, using jumper bars. Plug and feather wedges were still employed.
1849	..	The first percussive power-drill was made by Couch of Philadelphia.
1851	..	Fowle, also of Philadelphia, produced a percussive drill using a direct stroke and the principle of self rotation.
1851	..	The driving of the Mount Cenis tunnel focused attention on rock drilling.
1866	..	Nobel produced the explosive dynamite.
1870	..	The Ingersoll and Rand drills were produced. Rotary boring by diamond bits was introduced.
1879	..	Many rock drills had been developed, some with automatic rotation, some with automatic advancement, but nearly all had failed because of the immature state of metallurgical science and of machine-tool production. Hesse and Harting found that water directed at the point of drilling diminished the volume of dust.
1880	..	The Holman drill was first employed in Cornish mines. In these early drilling machines a cylinder was employed housing a piston from which a piston rod extended through the end cover of the cylinder. A chuck was fitted to the end of this rod and served to couple the piston and the drill in tandem. Thus the drill itself reciprocated in the hole and tended to remove the cuttings.
1897	..	The Leyner drill was introduced in which the drill was held loosely in the chuck attached to the head of the cylinder. The piston inside reciprocated freely, striking blows on the shank of the drill at the rate of about 1,500 per minute. The drill no longer reciprocated, friction was avoided and a lighter machine could be employed.
1898	..	Leyner introduced hollow drill-steel to permit removal of the cuttings from the hole by blowing air down the centre of the drill. Due to the intensity of the dust cloud produced, the drill was modified to pass water and air down the central channel. Such drills were lighter and faster than the old piston type.
1913	..	Leyner's patent rights lapsed and his design became almost universally standard.
1919	..	The South African Phthisis Prevention Committee ruled that dry drilling should be prohibited, that only axial water-fed types should be permitted in raising and boxholing and that other drills should have a water pipe in the hole.
1921	..	South Africa prohibited the use, in any part of the mine, of drills which passed air only down the drill steels. Detachable bits were patented.
1926	..	South Africa prohibited the use of machines having internal water tubes without the provision of air-release ports in the front head of the drill. The object was to prevent the passage of air down the drill steel, only to return via the hole in the form of bubbles charged with fine and dangerous dust. During recent years an automatic rock-drifter machine has been developed and put into use in which (*a*) water and air are turned on simultaneously, (*b*) the drill feeds itself forward and controls its own rate of advance according to the hardness of the ground and (*c*) the reversal of a lever compels the drill to retract itself from the hole. Also, "long piston" hammer drills are sometimes employed which, by virtue of their longer pistons, reduce the quantity of air which can penetrate to the vicinity of the chuck, thus reducing the discharge through the venting ports and adding to safety.
1936	..	The Demag Company of Germany produced drilling bits tipped with tungsten

carbide (Widia) of such a nature that they could be used for percussive drilling of rock with light jack-hammers.

1938 .. The P.M. detachable bit was produced by Rip Bits Ltd. Two years later it had become established in many countries.

1943 .. Experiments were made with alloy drilling steels such as a carbon, chrome and molybdenum steel, but no alloy steel was produced which possessed the requisite combination of toughness for resistance to shock, and hardness for resistance to abrasion.

1943 .. Diamond-impregnated crowns and sinter-set diamond crowns attached to the ends of the tubes were available for blast-hole drilling. The diamonds were kept cool by water flush.

1945 .. Rotary drilling with carbide-tipped heads employed in some stone drivages in British collieries.

1947 .. German firms considered that carbide-tips were very serviceable when fitted to alloy steel containing nickel, vanadium and molybdenum, but for a really sound joint a cushioning material of alloy consisting of 40 per cent. nickel and 60 per cent. iron was required.

1951 .. Electric rotary drilling of very hard rocks, e.g. granites, proved economic.

TYPES OF DRILLING MACHINES

Compressed-Air Percussive Machines.—There are three main classes of machines driven by compressed air, namely: Jack-hammers, drifters and stopers.

JACK-HAMMERS are sometimes subdivided into two classes, hand drills and sinkers. All the machines are very similar in design; they vary principally in size, power and methods of support.

Handril.—This is the name sometimes applied to the hand-held hammer drill. Such drills vary in weight from 20 to 80 lb., are applied to coal or rock and may be controlled or partially controlled, according to circumstances, by hand, foot, or shoulder (Fig. 6).

Sinker.—This is a heavy-type hand drill and as the name implies, is used extensively for sinking. It is useful for deep holes and for hard ground. To modify heavy vibration effects, "sinkers" are fitted with spring handles. Fig. 7 shows such a heavy hand drill.

DRIFTER.—This is a rock drill mounted in a cradle in order that it may be secured to a column, tripod, or other structure (Fig. 8). Drifters are classified according to the bore of the cylinder which is usually $2\frac{3}{4}$–4 in.

STOPER.—This is a drill with a telescopic air-feed usually employed for raising and for drilling vertical or nearly vertical holes where the floor is the most convenient support (Fig. 9). It may be regarded as a handril machine floating upon and in tandem with a telescopic air-cylinder.

The Handril Airleg, Holbit Unit.—This drilling unit, shown in Fig. 10, represents a considerable advance in drilling technique. As the name implies, a handril type of machine is supported on the end of a piston rod which extends through the top of a compressed-air cylinder. The air control for the airleg cylinder is located near the top of the piston rod and is always in the same position relative to the machine. An air vent near the top of the airleg cylinder allows the escape of air when the limit of the feed of the leg

Fig. 7.—Holman heavy "handril" or "sinker".

Fig. 6.—Holman "handril".

has been reached. Thus warned, the operator releases the air pressure in the leg, which is easily and quickly retelescoped, moved forward, readjusted by pressure and thus prepared for continued drilling. This unit, when using Holbits, is capable of fast drilling speeds.[2]

Fig. 11 shows the Holman Vented Drill, the various components of which are shown in Fig. 12.

It may be noted that the body casing of the machine consists of three main parts, (a) the cylinder in the middle, housing the piston, (b) the cylinder head, containing entrance ports for air and water, and (c) the cylinder bottom or chuck casing, which is bushed to receive the shank end of the drill. Figs. 13, 14 and 15 show the piston, the twist bar and the ratchet and pawl rotation mechanism.

The oscillations of the piston, numbering 1,500 to 2,000 per minute, are controlled by the valve mechanism and the arrangement of delivery and exhaust channels. The rotations of the piston numbering about 150 per min. are obtained by fitting the big end of the piston with a twist nut which is internally grooved to mesh with the splines shown in the twist bar. The head of this twist bar is fitted with pawls, each with its spring and plunger; it rotates intermittently within a fixed ratchet ring. The piston does not rotate as it moves forward to deliver each blow on the end of the drill, but the twist bar is rotated by the passage of the twist

Fig. 8.—The Holman "drifter".

nut over the splines. On the return journey, the twist nut attempts to turn the twist bar back again, but is prevented from doing so by the interlocking of the pawls and ratchet. As the twist bar remains stationary during this backward stroke of the piston, the twist nut, and with it the piston, are rotated. The rotary motion of the piston is transmitted by the splines in its forward end to the chuck and thence to the drill steel.

Most rock drilling is now done wet, and Fig. 12 shows how the water enters through a central swivel stem, passes down the machine through the central water tube to enter the hollow drill-steel and emerge at the bottom of the drill hole. Such are the basic features of these machines, but there are many minor differences.

Fig. 9.—Stoper drill with telescopic air-feed for drilling vertical or highly-inclined holes.

Chucks.—Chucks, for example, vary according to the drill steel employed and are classified as follows:—

   (a) Chucks for collared shanks—are open, the collar preventing the drills from being inserted too far and permitting the use of a retainer to assist in withdrawing the drill from the hole.

   (b) Chucks for lugged shanks—are fitted with a slotted nose; the slots permitting passage of the lugs up to the chuck bush. The lugs transmit rotary motion from the bush to the drill; also, as they are located between the nose and the bush, they serve to pull the drill from the hole.

   (c) Chucks of the anvil-block type—have a so-called anvil or metal bobbin interposed between the piston and the end of the drill-steel. They have the great advantage of requiring only plain-shank drills. They are used with stopers and with some drifters.

   (d) Chucks of the bolster type—interpose a perforated metal block between the drill and the piston to limit the insertion of the drill steel. The drill-shank is turned down to pass through the hole on the bolster and thus make contact with the piston. The shoulder formed by the turning limits the insertion. Here again, shank forging is avoided.[2]

Drill Steels for Percussive Drilling.—From Fig. 16, it will be observed that mining drill steel is supplied in many forms according to the work it has to do. Its composition varies for the same reason, but in all cases it should be such that the greatest hardness for cutting and resistance to wear should be obtainable without depreciating its other properties too much, so that excessive brittleness is avoided. To a great extent, good steel means steel with a low percentage of such impurities as sulphur and phosphorus.

The central hole of the hollow rods, so commonly used for water flush drilling in rock, was originally formed by rolling a billet which had previously

Fig. 10.—Handril airleg (*Holman Bros. Ltd.*).

been bored and filled with sand. Because of the resulting roughness of bore surface (Fig. 17) and its liability to initiate fractures, this method was superseded by the use of an inserted bar of copper or austenitic steel in place of the sand, as indicated in Fig. 18.

Occasionally, the central hole may have a stainless steel lining which is made by casting the billets for rolling around a stainless steel tube.

The steel in general use is a carbon tool-steel with a carbon content in the range of 0·7–0·8 per cent. and manganese below 0·35 per cent. The cutting edge is hardened by quenching in water from a temperature of about 780° C., and the composition is such that the surface hardness is very high whilst its depth is small so as to provide a tough backing to a hard edge, thereby preventing chipping away of the edge in service.

The shank or striking edge of the drill must be sufficiently hard to resist spreading under the hammer blows, but ductile enough to prevent failure under shock. It is therefore usual to harden this portion by quenching in oil from about 830° C. The bulk of the drill between the shank and the point is left in its normal condition which is relatively soft. One development which has taken place in recent years, particularly in South African mines, is the use of an alloy steel containing approximately 1 per cent. carbon, $1\frac{1}{4}$ per cent. chromium and 2 per cent. molybdenum. In its natural state it is appreciably harder than carbon steel, and requires no treatment at the shank end. The hardness at the point is developed by oil quenching. This type of drill is frequently used without an integral collar, a hard rubber collar being fitted instead.[3]

Percussive Drilling Bits.—Fig. 19 shows a few of the many different types of bits employed for percussive drilling in the almost infinite variety of rocks encountered in the crust of the earth.

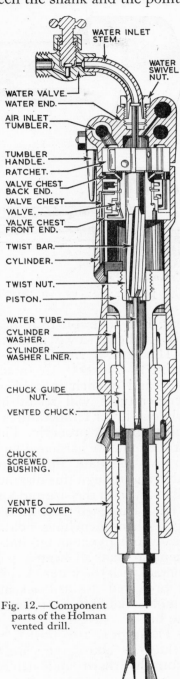

WATER INLET STEM.
WATER SWIVEL NUT.
WATER VALVE.
WATER END.
AIR INLET TUMBLER.
TUMBLER HANDLE.
RATCHET.
VALVE CHEST BACK END.
VALVE CHEST.
VALVE.
VALVE CHEST FRONT END.
TWIST BAR.
CYLINDER.
TWIST NUT.
PISTON.
WATER TUBE.
CYLINDER WASHER.
CYLINDER WASHER LINER.
CHUCK GUIDE NUT.
VENTED CHUCK.
CHUCK SCREWED BUSHING.
VENTED FRONT COVER.

Fig. 12.—Component parts of the Holman vented drill.

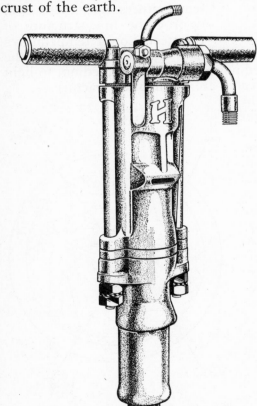

Fig. 11.—Holman vented drill.

These bits are forged from the drilling rod, and since with some drills the shanks also must be forged, it is obvious that for large mining projects,

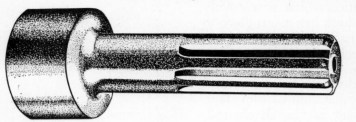

Fig. 13.—Piston of Holman drill.

both forging and sharpening must be done by machine.

Heat Treatment of Drilling Steels.—For heat treatment of drilling steels the maker's instructions should be followed precisely. The following are such instructions for Hadfields "Hecla 18" mining drill steel:—

Forging Shanks and Points.—Heat uniformly and forge at 1,000° C. (orange to yellow). Carefully avoid higher temperatures as these will destroy the fine structure of the steel. Lower temperatures may lead to bursting of the

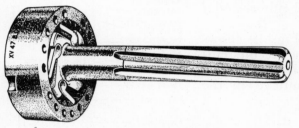

Fig. 14.—Twist bar and ratchet of Holman drill.

bar. It is advisable to re-heat the forged portion to 800° C. (medium to light red) and cool slowly in air. Drills so treated are less liable to fracture.

Hardening the Point.—Re-heat the point to 780–800° C. (medium to light red) and quench in cold water. Higher temperatures will result in brittleness, while at lower temperatures the steel will fail to harden properly. The end of the drill should be hardened far enough back to give adequate support to the cutting edge and though this distance will naturally vary with the size and form of the bit, $\frac{3}{4}$ in. of hardened material is a good average. When quenching, hold the drill vertically and give it an up-and-down movement so that all heated parts come in contact with the water. A suitable furnace is preferred to a blacksmith's hearth which is liable to burn the thin edges of the bit.

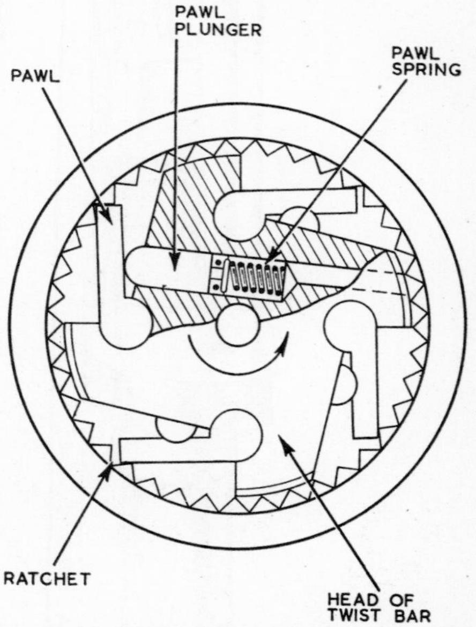

Tempering the Point.—If drills are treated as above they are found to be somewhat hard and liable to spall in use; tempering may be resorted to by

PAWL
PLUNGER

PAWL

PAWL
SPRING

RATCHET

HEAD OF
TWIST BAR

Fig. 15.—Rotation mechanism of Holman drill. The twist bar is free to rotate in direction of arrow only.

heating the point to about 200° C. after hardening. This can be effected by allowing a part of the heated portion to remain out of the water when quenching after forging. When the point is cold, withdraw the drill and clean a section with emery. The heat will flow from the hot part and the usual temper colours will appear via the cleaned part. When a straw colour is reached, the whole point should be quenched in water.

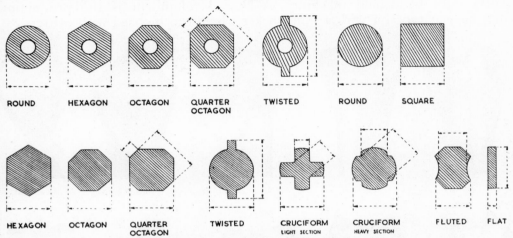

ROUND   HEXAGON   OCTAGON   QUARTER OCTAGON   TWISTED   ROUND   SQUARE

HEXAGON   OCTAGON   QUARTER OCTAGON   TWISTED   CRUCIFORM LIGHT SECTION   CRUCIFORM HEAVY SECTION   FLUTED   FLAT

Fig. 16.—Mining drill steels showing various sections.

Fig. 17.—Drill rod produced by sand-core process.

Fig. 18.—Drill rod produced by metal-core process.

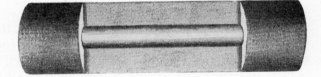

TREATMENT OF THE SHANK.—The shank, including the collar or lugs and 1 in. beyond, is hardened by heating up to 830–850° C. (bright cherry red) and quenching in oil. The shank should not be quenched in water as this will give too great a degree of hardness.

Percussive Drill-Steel Detachable Bits.—ONE-PASS-BITS.—Since most of the wear of a drill steel takes place at the bit end, the use of a detachable bit saves much labour and expense in transporting the whole drill steel every time it requires resharpening. To be successful, however, the bit must be coupled to the rod in an efficient manner, and it must cost no more than the resharpening of a one-piece drill steel so that when blunt, it can be scrapped and replaced by a new one. Such a bit is the "P.M." bit (Fig. 20), designed by Rip Bits, Ltd., Sheffield, in 1938, which is very popular in South African gold mines. It is a steel pressing weighing only 3 oz., and it is attached to the rod by a plug and $\frac{7}{8}$-in. socket fitment, which achieves an even grip by using the principle of differing tapers. Such bits are used with fairly light hand-held machines. A later development is the production of a heavier type bit with a 1-in. socket which can be used with drifters.

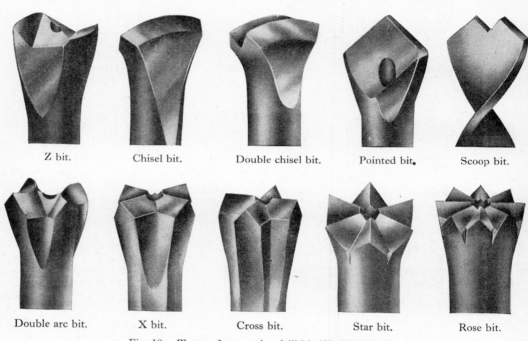

| Z bit. | Chisel bit. | Double chisel bit. | Pointed bit. | Scoop bit. |

| Double arc bit. | X bit. | Cross bit. | Star bit. | Rose bit. |

Fig. 19.—Types of percussive drill bit (*Hadfields Ltd.*).

RESERVICEABLE BITS.—Fig. 21 shows the "Rip bit", which can and should be resharpened until the gauge is too small for further use. The illustration shows that the bit is fitted with a forged stud.

Percussive Drill-Steels, Carbide-tipped Bits.—German mining engineers attempted to reduce the wear of steel tools by tipping with cemented tungsten carbide or Widia metal, which was very hard, but also very brittle, and contained about 95 per cent. metallic carbide fused together with a cobalt bond. About 1936, they developed a grade of tungsten carbide sufficiently tough to be used for percussive drilling of rock if the hammer drill employed was of a very light type. Further research led German mining engineers to adopt carbide bits, mostly of the detachable type, for percussive drilling. They consider the best steel for tipping is alloy steel containing nickel, vanadium and molybdenum, but owing to differential contraction and expansion with heat changes, a sandwiching material is required to accommodate the variations. "Ferry metal", containing 40 per cent. nickel and 60 per cent. iron, seems to be best for this purpose. The drilling machine should be one giving a light rapid blow and a rapid rotation.

One German method of tipping a bit is as follows:—

(*a*) A slot is milled and lined each side with a shim of copper 2–3 thousandths of an inch thick.

(*b*) A layer of ferry metal of about 10 thousandths of an inch thick is placed on either side.

(*c*) A further shim of copper is added to each side.

Fig. 20.—Detachable drill bit (*Padley & Venables Ltd.*).

Fig. 21.—The "Rip Bit" (*Padley & Venables Ltd.*).

(*d*) The carbide tip is placed in the middle; this tip consists of about 89 per cent. tungsten carbide and 11 per cent. cobalt.

It is possible that the future lies with the detachable carbide-tipped bit used in conjunction with drilling machines of light, rapid stroke and rapid rotation, but this combination is opposed in England, South Africa, Canada, the United States and Australia, by some users who already possess heavy equipment. It is claimed that in each of these countries, machines of full drifter size, i.e., 3-in. diam. cylinder and in some cases $3\frac{1}{2}$ in., are being used successfully. The normal size being used is of $2\frac{1}{2}$ in. and $2\frac{5}{8}$ in. diam., with a minimum rate of rotation. However, this claim is not accepted by some manufacturers of carbide tools.

One-piece drill steels with blades of tungsten carbide brazed directly into them are used extensively in Sweden, and have become popular in South Africa. Carbide bits of the percussive type are very expensive. It appears probable that they become economical only when they drill 100 times as far as the ordinary bit. It may be cheaper to drill many ordinary rock formations with the conventional detachable steel bit, but such a bit may be useless in certain granites, cherts and pure silica rock, which render the use of the carbide-tipped drill, or some form of diamond drill, imperative.

There are three types of bit attachment:—(*a*) an internally threaded bit screwing to a male thread on the rod; (*b*) the loose rope-thread stud screwing to the bit and also into a female threaded rod; and (*c*) a plain socket type of bit which pushes on to the tapered end of the rod. Various types of bits are used, but at present the chisel bit and the cross bit, shown in Figs. 22 and 23, are favoured. Some of the advantages claimed for the use of such carbide-tipped percussive drilling bits are as follows:—(*a*) a higher average drilling speed is maintained, (*b*) the necessity for frequent drill-steel changing is eliminated, (*c*) over-all drilling time is reduced, (*d*) smaller rock drills are employed, (*e*) less compressed air is used by the smaller drills, (*f*) fewer drill rods are required, (*g*) transport of drill rods is reduced, (*h*) drill sharpening is eliminated, (*i*) over-all blasting efficiency is increased.

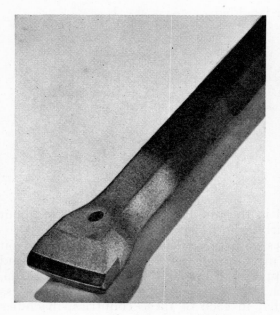

Fig. 22.—Holman tungsten-carbide tipped chisel bit.

Fig. 23.—Latest type cross Holbit with large tungsten-carbide inserts.

Special advantages claimed for detachable carbide drilling bits over one-piece carbide drills are:—(*a*) the life of such a bit exceeds the normal life of drill steel before failure due to fatigue ; (*b*) it is impracticable to extract inserts from a broken steel and rebraze them in another, but if a drill rod breaks, the detachable head can be transferred to another rod ; (*c*) less time and labour is required in transporting detachable bits than in transporting one-piece drills ; (*e*) they can be more easily handled in re-dressing the tips; (*f*) they are stored more easily; (*g*) the lower initial capital outlay—one bit and a set of rods are a much cheaper proposition than a complete set of tipped rods.[4, 5]

Electrically-Driven Percussive Machines.—Although much attention has been devoted to the matter, it appears to be the general opinion that, as yet, no really successful electrically-driven percussive drill has been devised.

ROTARY MACHINES

Compressed-Air Rotary Machines for use in Coal and in Stone.—
When first introduced, hand-held rotary drilling machines had a very limited application in collieries. Only steel drilling bits were available, and much depended upon the care given to the correct grinding of the drilling bits.

Today, on mechanised faces, particularly with power loading, mechanical drilling is a real necessity. On longwall faces in thin seams, portability is extremely important and has presented no difficulty where electric power is used at the coalface. The introduction of the compressed-air rotary drill, combined with the use of tungsten-carbide tipped bits has also solved the drilling problem on faces supplied only with compressed-air power.

Fig. 24.—Huwood compressed-air rotary drill for coal, in use.

A typical example of such a machine is shown in Figs. 24, 25 and 26.

The machine illustrated in Fig. 25a consists of (a) the main casing at the back, which houses the power unit, to which a handle is attached at each side, and (b) the front casing which envelops the gear and the chuck. The casing is of special alloy. The principle on which the air motor operates is illustrated in Fig. 25b. An air-rotor C is set eccentrically within the motor chamber and light vanes B of plastic material are free to move radially under centrifugal force in the radial slots of the rotor. Air enters at A, the rotor turns and the vanes fly out to maintain rubbing contact with the liner of the chamber; the compressed air expands and finally escapes at the exhaust ports, as indicated by arrows, but before a vane reaches the first exhaust port, another vane is under high pressure from the feed port. One of the handles of the machine functions as a twist control for the admission of air. The rotor motion is transmitted by epicyclic gears to the chuck, Fig. 26. Two types of gears are available; one for coal gives a reduction to 700 r.p.m., the other for stone gives a reduction to 350 r.p.m. Chucks are made to suit the shanks of the drill rods, but where wet drilling is employed, a special chuck fitted with a wet-drilling adaptation is used. Mechanical feed, if desired, can be arranged most simply by the use of (a) an extensible prop fitted with tightening screws and (b) a special feeder-chain mounted on sprockets to run inside the trough of a channel iron, which extends from the prop to the coalface. Operation of the chain is by ratchet handle.

Electric Rotary Machines for Coal and Stone.—As with compressed-air rotary drilling machines, so with those driven by electricity, designs suitable for coal are, with slight modifications, also suitable for rock.

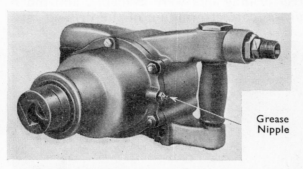

Grease Nipple

Fig. 25a.—Huwood compressed-air rotary drill.

It must be remembered that the complete equipment required at the face for the electric drilling-machine is more complicated and expensive than for the compressed-air drill and normally includes a gate-end drill panel with an a.c. transformer to give the required voltage. In general, the electric machines are similar in appearance to the compressed-air machines; the cable replaces the hose, the drills for dry work are of necessity spiralled in both cases, and the detachable drilling bits employed are similar in outward appearance.

The Siemens-Schuckert electric drilling machine, Type E438/1, shown in Fig. 27 is a fan-cooled electric machine suitable for drilling in coal or hard stone. The main casing is of light metal and is ribbed for strength and dissipation of heat, although the light metal fan, housed under the cowl at the back of the machine, ensures efficient cooling. This casing envelops a squirrel-cage motor in a flame-proof housing which incorporates the two hand grips, a switch chamber with cable gland, and a gear-box. The standard motor is $1\frac{1}{4}$ h.p., half-hour rated, and is wound for 110–125 volts, 3-phase, 50 cycles. It is officially approved for use

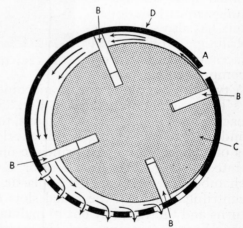

Fig. 25b.—Showing course of air taken in drill shown in Fig. 25a.

in British mines. The switch is operated by a lever mounted on one of the hand grips, and, as with most drilling systems on a coalface, it operates the main switch in the gate-end panel by remote control. The gear-box and motor are separated in a flame-proof manner by an intermediate plate. There are two types of machines, and in the one suitable for coal, the gears give reduction of rotor speed down to 700 r.p.m., and in the other, for rock, to speeds between 600 and 320 r.p.m., the precise speed adopted being in accordance with the nature of the work. The drilling spindle of a machine ends in a slotted nose cap which engages directly with the wings of the spiral drilling rod.

The stone-drilling attachment employed when the nature of the stone renders hand drilling too arduous is shown in Fig. 28. The machine is clamped in a carrier mounted on the rack-feed bar, and is fed forward by the ratchet handle and a pinion meshing with the rack teeth. The drill and carrier are pulled back in a single quick movement on releasing the ratchet pawl.

The drill shown in Fig. 29 is readily adapted to wet drilling by the use of a small water coupling having

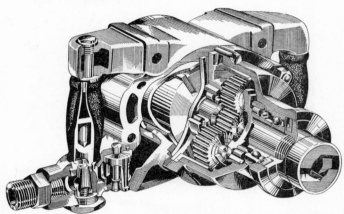

Fig. 26.—The Huwood compressed-air rotary machine (sectionalised).

a shank at one end for the insertion of the chuck, and at the other end a slotted nosecap to take the drilling rod. The coupling is of course supplied with a stopcock. Hollow rods of turbine or diamond-section spiral types are employed, outlets for the water being made near the bit end of the rod about $3\frac{1}{2}$ in. from the cutting tips of the bit.

Rotary Drilling Bits.—The use of detachable bits tipped with tungsten carbide in rotary drilling by hand machines, proved to be an enormous advance in drilling technique and many makers have produced bits in a variety of grades and shapes to suit different purposes.

Fig. 30 shows different Siemens-Schuckert bits of which type K is most popular for general

Fig. 27.—Electric fan-cooled drilling machine (*Siemens-Schuckert (Gt. Britain) Ltd.*).

purposes. It should be observed that the points of the bit are eccentric to the centre line, the result being that the borings produced are of a coarse nature. Type "KE" differs from type "K" only in that the points of the tips are equidistant from the centre-line.

Fig. 28. — Electric drill with mechanical feed mounted on adjustable stand, Type DA42, for drilling in hard stone (*Siemens - Schuckert* (*Gt. Britain*) *Ltd.*).

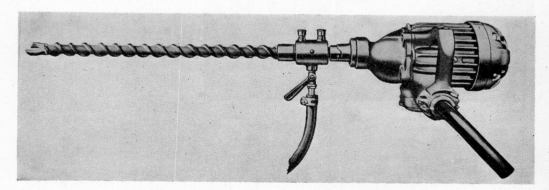

Fig. 29.—Hand-held electric drill with water-coupling, hollow drill rod and Wimet bit, for drilling in rock (*Siemens-Schuckert* (*Gt. Britain*) *Ltd.*).

Results achieved depend to a large extent on the care given to the drilling bit, the manner of regrinding and the precision with which it is achieved. It must be realised that tungsten carbide cannot be heat-treated or worked in any way. For regrinding, which should be wet, special abrasive wheels of green silicon carbide of appropriate grit and grade are required. The makers recommend a specially designed grinding machine, such as the one illustrated in Fig. 31, in order to ensure (*a*) the use of a correct grade of grinding wheel, (*b*) maintenance of the original tip angles in all directions, and (*c*) regular grinding before the edges become too dull; avoidance of excessive grinding is also recommended.

Siemens-Schuckert electric drilling machines are said to give results such as the following:—

(1) In shales with the 430-r.p.m. machine hand-held—2 ft. 4 in. per min.

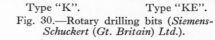

Type "K".   Type "KE".

Fig. 30.—Rotary drilling bits (*Siemens-Schuckert (Gt. Britain) Ltd.*).

(2) In medium sandstone with the same machine—mounted on a feed bar—1 ft. 6 in. per min.

(3) In hard rock with the 180-r.p.m. machine—mounted on a feed bar—3 in. per min.[4,5]

Fig. 31.—Siemens-Schuckert bit grinder.

Dr. H. S. Alpan,[6] after investigation of the factors affecting rotary drilling, has established the following:—

(1) The standard two-winged rotary bits, with certain modifications, are quite satisfactory in coals, shales, sandstones and soft rocks.

(2) The thrusts attained normally by one or two men are insufficient to obtain rapid penetration of harder rock. Without sufficient thrust the bit is worn away at an excessive rate by abrasion rather than by cutting action.

(3) For each type of rock there appears to be a critical thrust which affords rapid penetration due to the breakdown of the crystal structure of the rock.

(4) The critical thrust for hard rocks such as granite is about 3,500 lb. and for such a thrust a tubular bit of the coring type appears to be necessary. Moreover, the drilling machine must be of 3 to 6 h.p.

(5) The tubular drilling bit should be provided with two tungsten-carbide cutting inserts, with curved profiles, negative rake, and well backed by metal to take the strain. With such a drilling bit operated by a machine of 5 h.p. a penetration speed of 13·4 in. per minute has been achieved in hard granite.

(6) Electric rotary drilling of hard rocks

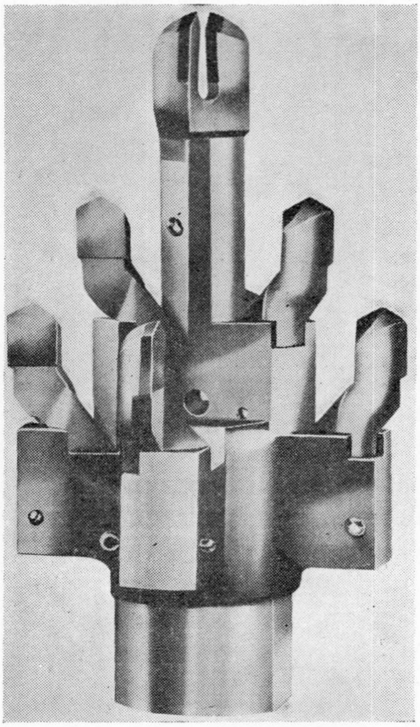

Fig. 32.—Siemens-Schuckert 6-in. dia. bit for rotary drilling machine.

Fig. 33.—Single-wing nut used with 6-in. bit (Fig. 32).

has been proved economically possible and may be used for drilling in fields previously monopolised by the percussive machine.

(7) To attain the heavy thrusts required, more robust and mobile structures will be needed to carry and position the drills and to withstand their severe reactions.

Large Diameter Drill Holes.—These may be required for Cardox or Hydrox blasting, for the Gullick burster (or hydraulic wedge) or for the purposes of forepoling at the face. The holes may be drilled by hand-held rotary drilling machines, and the larger drilling bits may be of special types such as the Gullick "split shank" alloy-tipped drilling bit for holes $3\frac{7}{8}$ in. in diameter (see Chapter 9, Fig. 26).

Messrs. Siemens-Schuckert produce a 6-in. bit, shown in Fig. 32. It consists of a standard two-way bit assisted by a number of single-wing bits, one of which is shown separately (Fig. 33). This bit should prove to be particularly useful in drilling horizontal blast holes in opencast workings (See Chapter 9, Fig. 31).

EXPLOSIVES

History of Explosives.—The following is an outline of the history of the development of explosives and the art of blasting as practiced in the mining of coal.

1242 A.D. Roger Bacon wrote of gunpowder.

1627 . . Casper Windt used gunpowder for breaking ground at Schemnitz, Hungary.

1636 . . Holes for blasting were hand drilled about 3 in. in diameter and were sealed with wooden shooting plugs. Some form of drilling machine had been tried already.

1685 . . Clay tamping was introduced.

1771 . . Picric acid was discovered by Woulfe.

1781 . . Schele, a Swedish chemist, manufactured glycerine.

1799 . . Howard produced fulminate of mercury.

1814 . . Percussion caps primed with mercury fulminate were used with fire-arms.

1831 . . Bickford devised his safety fuse.

1838 . . Pelouze treated cotton with strong nitric acid and initiated the study of nitro-celluloses.

1846 . . Gun-cotton was produced by Schönbein.

1846 . . Sobrero, an Italian chemist, prepared nitro-glycerine by nitrating glycerine.

1863 . . Nobel applied nitro-glycerine as a blasting explosive.

1864 . . Nobel invented the detonator.

1865 . . Sir Frederick Abel succeeded in making gun-cotton a practical explosive.

1866 . . Nobel produced dynamite.

1872 . . The Coal Mines Regulation Act placed certain restrictions on shot-firing where inflammable gas had been found, and thus initiated many attempts to render the use of gunpowder safe in the presence of methane. Tampings of cylinders containing water, water-jelly, wet moss and liquid carbon dioxide were suggested.

1875 . . Nobel produced blasting gelatine.

1877–1891 The reports of various commissions in Great Britain and abroad, appointed to investigate accidents in mines, seemed to agree that high explosives, when used with the water cartridge, were safer than black powder, but that water tamping in any form afforded security, if used in conjunction with black powder.

1881 . . Electric detonators were first employed.

1881–1886 The Royal Commission on Accidents in Mines, emphasised that blown-out shots were particularly dangerous.

1887 . . The British Coal Mines Regulation Act prohibited the firing of shots unless the explosive was of such a nature that it would not inflame gas or coal dust, or was so used with water or other contrivance as to prevent it inflaming gas or coal dust.

1888 . . Jicinski used sand or kieselguhr saturated with water as a sheathing material.

1888 . . Lohmann, carrying out research work for a German Government Commission, proposed that washing soda should be substituted for water tamping cartridges.

1889–1890 Abel and Dewar produced Cordite.

1890 . . The first experimental testing gallery was used in Great Britain, built at Hebburn-on-Tyne by the North of England Institute of Mining and Mechanical Engineers.

1890 . . The "French Doctrine" for the production of safe explosives, stipulated that (a) the explosive must be over-oxidised, (b) preferably, it should be of a binary nature and (c) for explosives to be used in coal, the calculated detonation temperature must not exceed 1,500° C.

1894	..	The Royal Commission on Explosives in Mines reported that whatever minor objections might be established against the use of high explosives in mines, their general employment would greatly limit the risks of explosions in dry and dusty mines.
1896	..	A committee was appointed in Great Britain "to enquire into the best means of estimating the safety of explosives in coal mines and as to the means to be adopted for applying such tests".
1897	..	At Woolwich, the Home Office carried out its first tests on the safety of explosives used in coal mines, as a result of which the first list of "Permitted Explosives" for use in fiery and dusty mines was issued.
1898	..	Elephant Brand Gunpowder No. 2 was authorised by the Home Office for use in coal mines, provided that the cartridge was surrounded by a layer of sodium carbonate, the whole to be contained in a casing of paper and the gunpowder to be separated from the sodium carbonate by a suitable diaphragm.
1902	..	A dynamite of low freezing point was first produced.
1908	..	The lead azide detonator was placed on the market.
1911	..	The Home Office testing station was tranferred to Rotherham.
1911	..	Delay action detonators were introduced.
1920	..	About this time Cordeau Bickford fuse was introduced into this country. Also, detonators with an A.S.A. (Chapter 9) initiating and a Tetryl base charge became available to the mining world. The initiation charge was made up of lead azide, lead styphnate and aluminium powder.
1921	..	The Home Office testing of explosives was transferred to Ardeer.
1929	..	The Home Office testing station was transferred to Buxton.
1931	..	Low-density explosives were produced in Britain.
1931	..	Cardox was first introduced into this country from America.
1933	..	Capped fuses were introduced from South Africa.
1934	..	Sheathed explosives appeared on market in Britain.
1938	..	The bicarbonate felt sheathing was introduced.
1938	..	Electric detonators were first sealed with neoprene plugs.
1938	..	Gasless delay detonators became available.
1946	..	Short delay (milliseconds) detonators were first used in the field, on a commercial basis.
1949	..	"Eq. S" explosives, i.e., explosives equivalent in safety to sheathed explosives, were certified permissible for use in coal mines.
1950	..	Water infusion/blasting introduced.

Definition of an Explosive.—An explosive is a substance which, under the influence of heat, shock, or both, is capable of generating a large volume of gas at high temperature in an extremely short space of time. It is, therefore, capable of exerting a very high pressure almost instantaneously and of doing work.

Constituents of an Explosive.—Normally, but not invariably, an explosive has two ingredients : a combustible substance and an oxidising agent. Common combustibles employed are charcoal C., cellulose $(C_6H_{10}O_5)_n$, benzene C_6H_6, naphthalene $C_{10}H_8$ and glycerine $C_3H_5(OH)_3$. Oxidising agents may be nitric acid HNO_3, potassium nitrate KNO_3, sodium nitrate $NaNO_3$, barium nitrate $Ba(NO_3)_2$, ammonium nitrate NH_4NO_3, potassium chlorate $KClO_3$, potassium perchlorate $KClO_4$ and ammonium perchlorate NH_4ClO_4. On the application of heat, the oxidising agents release free oxygen to combine with the constituents of the combustible substance for which it has a great affinity. A third ingredient may be employed to keep down the temperature of the gases produced. It may be a salt, such as sodium chloride, NaCl, ammonium oxalate, $C_2H_8O_4N_2$, ammonium chloride, NH_4Cl, or possibly a salt with water of crystallisation. Such salts were introduced as "coolers", but in regard to some of them at least, it is now clear that their action cannot be accounted for in this manner alone.[7]

Action of an Explosive.—The reaction which takes place between the essential ingredients of an explosive in blasting operations, produces an explosion which is usually, although not always, a very rapid oxidation resulting in the formation of large volumes of gas at high temperature. The speed of the oxidation varies very considerably for different explosives.

LOW EXPLOSIVES.—Where combining substances are intermixed and the oxidation must be propagated by rapid combustion from particle to particle through the mass, the rate of explosion is relatively low, and such explosives are classified as "low explosives." They are usually fired by simple ignition. Gunpowder is the most common explosive of this type, with a speed of burning not exceeding 400 metres per second.

INITIATING EXPLOSIVES.—Are those explosives which ignite from a flame but accelerate their reaction to full detonation in an exceedingly short space of time and are used for initiating high explosives.

HIGH EXPLOSIVES.—These are explosives which react with high velocity under the influence of a shock wave passing through them.

TEMPERATURE OF GASES.—The temperature of the gases produced varies with the nature of the explosive used. For gunpowder the value is 4,000° F., and for dynamite 5,400° F.

IGNITION TIME LAG.—In order to ignite a gas mixture, the source of heat must be in contact with the gas for a minimum time. The period varies,[8] but it is much greater for CH_4 than for H_2. However, the duration and length of the flame produced by equal weights of different explosives vary. Obviously, the shorter the flame the lower the temperature, and the less its duration the less will be the risk of ignition of gas.

Comparative figures for 100 grams of various explosive are as follows:—

Explosive	Approximate date used	Length of flame	Duration of flame
		mm.	sec.
Gunpowder	Up to 1888	110	0·777
Blasting gelatine	,, 1901	224	0·0097
A modern permitted explosive ..	Present	40	0·0003

The Safety of an Explosive.—From the foregoing it will be inferred that the safety of an explosive in methane-air mixtures is proportional to the "time contact period," and inversely proportional to the "temperature" which the gases attain. Actually, the safety of an explosive lies in the effective cooling of the gases immediately they are formed. Some success has attended the admixture of volatile salts with modern explosives, but effective cooling would be ensured if the explosive could be compelled to do fully the work of which it is capable. Imperfect detonation of a high explosive reduces it to the level of a gunpowder as regards safety. Danger lies in that the work may be accomplished already, while the charge is still burning. With complete detonation, a high explosive is instantly and fully decomposed and the hot gases expand so rapidly and cool so quickly that the temperature is reduced long before the time element has reached a high value. Incomplete detonation is the danger, and that is why a detonator of approved type and ample power must always be used.

CONDITIONS OF EMPLOYMENT.—It must be realised that the conditions of employment of the explosive are of far greater importance than its actual constitution. Safety depends very much upon the correct placing of shot-holes, testing for gas, freedom from coal dust and breaks in the holes, and correct undercutting, correct proportioning of the charge and stemming, and other matters. The shot-hole driller normally has control of the placing of the shot-hole, but the suitability of the hole and all questions concerning charging and firing are for the duly appointed shot-firer alone to decide.

Low Explosives.—GUNPOWDER.—Gunpowder is a typical low explosive, and is a mixture of 75 per cent. of sodium or potassium nitrate, 15 per cent. of charcoal and 10 per cent. of sulphur. When nitrate of soda is used, the black powder is known as N.S. powder, and when nitrate of potassium is used, it is known as N.P. powder. Sulphur is obtained from natural sources, and when impure, it is mixed with limestone, melted out and purified by distillation. Sulphur from Louisiana is 99·5 per cent. pure and may be used directly. Charcoal is of course obtained by heating wood in a closed vessel to drive off the volatiles. The nature of the charcoal has an effect upon the rapidity of the burning of the powder, and willow, elder and dogwood are preferred.

The ingredients are powdered separately, mixed in correct proportions and then ground in a mill consisting of two heavy rollers running in a shallow pan. A little water is added for safety. The "millcake" thus formed is broken down by gunmetal rollers and pressed to bind the particles together, forming a second compact cake which is then granulated by passing it through a series of rollers. Glazing is effected in a rotating wooden drum, a little graphite being added to obtain a polish and to impart a waterproofing effect. After a final drying in a warm stove, the powder is blended and graded. The coarser grades are compressed into the form of pellets, etc., for use in blasting. Usually two "pellets" are wrapped together to form a cartridge of from $1\frac{1}{4}$ in. to $1\frac{3}{4}$ in. diameter, requiring 4, 5, 6 or 8 to 1 lb. Cartridges are packed in cases containing 50 lb.

Gunpowder is a stable compound which ignites at about 300° C. Owing to the relative slowness of the reaction of its constituents, it rends rather than shatters, thereby producing lump coal, and is therefore eminently suited for coal getting. Objections to its use are that it produces a marked quantity of smoke, a hot flame which will ignite a methane-air mixture, and also poison-ous gases. The reaction is usually expressed thus:—

$$2KNO_3 + S + 3C = K_2S + 3CO_2 + N_2$$

Actually the decomposition is far more complex than this equation indicates. This is shown by the following analyses of the resultant gases as determined by Nobel and Abel.

Gases produced by the firing of gunpowder :—

In normal condition %	In inferior condition or improperly fired %
CO_2 .. 48·0	CO_2 .. 32·0
CO .. 13·0	CO .. 34·0
N_2 .. 32·25	N_2 .. 19·0
H_2S .. 2·55	H_2S .. 7·0
CH_4 .. 0·25	CH_4 .. 3·0
H_2 .. 4·0	H_2 .. 5·0

It should be noted that a man may easily be overcome by entering a badly ventilated heading after shot-firing, if sufficient time is not allowed for the clearance of noxious gases. N.P. gunpowder is not so hygroscopic as N.S. and is better in storage. It is not quite so strong, but it is quicker in action than the N.S. type, and is, therefore, better for fissured rocks. A limited amount of black powder is still used per annum in Great Britain, and of this a small proportion is used in deep mines. In both mines and quarries however the use of gunpowder is giving way gradually to that of high explosives on account of their increased safety and efficiency.

High Explosive.—NITRO-GLYCERINE.—Nitro-glycerine is a high explo-sive. It is not used alone, but is a basic constituent of some and an integral part of many other high explosives.

The chemical basis of the manufacture of nitro-glycerine, $C_3H_5(NO_3)_3$, involves the nitration of glycerine by the use of strong nitric and sulphuric acids in fixed proportions. In the continuous process of manufacture the reaction takes place in a continuous nitrator, to which the glycerine is ad-mitted at the top and the mixed acid at the bottom. They are stirred together in a central mixing chamber where the nitro-glycerine is produced, and after being discharged it is separated, washed and filtered through flannel before passing to storage tanks.

Nitro-glycerine is an oily liquid of specific gravity of 1·6. Its viscosity is two and a half times that of water. It is colourless when pure, but is usually slightly yellow. It has little or no smell, a sweet taste, and it freezes at about 55° F. As it is non-hygroscopic, it is useful in the presence of water. It is an organic poison which seems to pass rapidly through the skin, and small doses produce headache and nausea.

The reaction of ordinary nitro-glycerine to a fall in temperature is very important. Its temperature may be lowered below its known freezing point without actually freezing, and then for no apparent reason it may freeze.

In the frozen state, the crystals may be in a state of stress, and therefore, dangerous to handle. During thawing, droplets of nitro-glycerine are exuded and this again is evidence of a highly dangerous condition. It is natural therefore that some explosives of high nitro-glycerine content, for this and for other reasons, are not permitted for use in the coal mines of Great Britain. Fig. 34 illustrates a sheathed cartridge of a low freezing type of nitro-glycerine explosive which is permitted. Typical brands are:—

Polar Ajax .. .. ⎫
Polar Saxonite No. 3 .. ⎬ Nitro-glycerine gelatines.

Polar Thames Powder ⎫
Polar Viking .. .. ⎬ Nitro-glycerine powders.
Polar Dynobel No. 2 .. ⎭
A. 1. Rounkol .. .. Low density nitro-glycerine powder.

CLASSIFICATION OF HIGH EXPLOSIVES

Nitro-Glycerine Explosives.—DYNAMITE.—Consists of nitro-glycerine absorbed in varying percentages of kieselguhr, which is a very porous diatomaceous earth. This is really the only straight "nitro-glycerine" explosive used. As kieselguhr is inert and incombustible, the Americans use woodmeal instead, adding a nitrate to restore the oxygen balance and calling the product "straight dynamite". Obviously, an explosive might be substituted for kieselguhr; thus, according to the nature of the absorbent used, dynamites may have an inert, a combustible or an explosive base.

BLASTING GELATINE.—Consists of 7 per cent. of nitro-cellulose dissolved in nitro-glycerine. This forms a stiff, pale yellow and transparent jelly which is the most powerful commercial explosive used for blasting the hardest of rocks. It has the great advantage of being unaffected by water. Pure blasting gelatine is too strong for most purposes, much energy being wasted in shattering and local pulverising; it is therefore graded down by the addition of woodmeal and the further addition of nitrates to preserve the oxygen balance.

GELATINE DYNAMITES AND GELIGNITES.—These lower-grade explosives are known as gelatine dynamites and gelignites, and they are manufactured in varying strengths as shown by the following table of typical British products.

Constituents	Blasting gelatine	Gelatine dynamite	Gelignite	Ammon. gelignite
	%	%	%	%
Nitro-glycerine ..	92	72	50	36
Collodion cotton ..	8	4	2	1
Sodium nitrate ..	—	18	39	16
Ammon. nitrate ..	—	—	—	40
Woodmeal ..	—	6	9	7

Permitted Explosives.—These may, with appropriate precautions, be used in the coal mines of Great Britain and are sometimes grouped as follows:—

1. NITRO-GLYCERINE GELATINES.—These have a high resistance to water and are easy to handle. They have a high density which permits of a concentrated charge at the back of the shot-hole. All modern gelatines are of the non-freezing type, and do not produce adverse physiological effects (headache, etc.) when handled, unless they are taken out of the wrapper. Such action should be forbidden. Typical members of this group are Polar Ajax, Eversoft Driftex, Antifrost Nitrox No. 2 and No. 3.

2. NITRO-GLYCERINE POWDERS AND SEMI-GELATINES.—These are less dense than the gelatinous type and are not very highly water resistant, although they can be used in damp conditions, providing the explosive in contact with the detonator is kept dry. This group includes the explosives most generally used for the blasting of coal in Great Britain, and also the low-density explosives which are mentioned later. Typical members of this group are Polar Viking, Unigex, Unifrax, Minex, etc.

3. NON-NITRO-GLYCERINE POWDERS.—This group contains all the Ammonium nitrate TNT (Tri-nitro-toluene) explosives which are of a slightly higher density than nitro-glycerine powders and semi-gelatines, but still lower than the gelatines themselves. They have a higher velocity of detonation than the nitro-glycerine types, and are particularly useful for breaking through hard bands. They should not be used in wet conditions and must be stored in a perfectly dry place. A typical member of this group is XL Hawkite.

Low-Density Explosives.—These were developed in the U.S.A. to replace black powder and to reduce the weight of explosive used per hole. They were introduced into Great Britain in 1932 but are no longer available. They incorporate low-density cellulose such as balsa or bungo wood sawdusts and having a density of 0·6–0·7 that of ordinary explosives, the cartridges are larger per unit weight. The pressure produced is lower per unit area of shot-hole; the area of shot-hole subjected to pressure is greater and the spread of the explosive force is extended. Such explosives are very useful in soft to medium hard coal where shattering must be avoided, and where the distance from the shot-hole to the undercut is short. They are not applicable to hard seams, seams containing hard resilient layers, or to shale, and they are not recommended for use in the presence of water. They have a velocity of detonation of about 1,700 metres per sec., and in their effects they resemble gunpowder more nearly than any other explosive.

Sheathed Explosives—The sheathing of cartridges of permitted explosives is the result of experimental work undertaken to reduce the risks of blasting in gassy mines. A sheathed cartridge is one which has been sheathed for its whole length, but not its ends, by a layer of incombustible material, the whole then being wrapped in an outer layer of paper as shown in Fig. 34.

As a result of research in Great Britain, Naylor and Wheeler (1933–4) concluded that sodium bicarbonate could be employed as an efficient and practical sheathing material which, by its blanketing and cooling effect, would substantially increase safety in the use of explosives in mines. The sheathing may be in a simple powder form or in the form of a "felt" in which 90 per cent. sodium bicarbonate is held together by a 10 per cent. binding of cellulose.

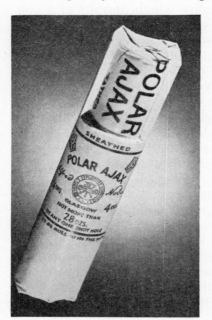

Fig. 34.—Sheathed explosive cartridge.

"Eq. S." Explosives.—Further research has shown that the sheathing constituents may be incorporated directly and uniformly into the explosive itself, thereby producing an explosive equivalent in safety to the sheathed explosives. The official designation "Eq. S." has been accorded to each new explosive admitted to this class. Such explosives should be safer and possess the great advantage that they have no sheath which can be stripped off accidentally or otherwise.

Over 80 per cent. of the permitted explosives used in Great Britain are now sheathed or equivalent and this percentage is increasing.

Testing of Permitted Explosives.—Until about 60 years ago, gunpowder, or black blasting powder, was the only explosive used in coal mines. With this "slow-burning" type of explosive, there was considerable risk of causing explosions of firedamp, of coal dust, or both.

About 1880–90 it was realised that the risk was less with new types of explosive known as "high" or detonating explosives such as dynamite, blasting gelatine and ammonal, and that the risk could be still further reduced by incorporating a proportion of cooling agent such as common salt in these explosives.

In 1896 a committee was appointed in Great Britain, "to enquire into the best means of estimating the safety of explosives in coal mines, and as to the means to be adopted for applying such tests". In 1897 the principle of direct-gallery testing was established, that is to say, explosives were fired into firedamp and coal dust under conditions approximating to those of practice. With those explosives which did not cause ignition under test conditions, it was considered that the risk could reasonably be small enough in practice, and accordingly, they were permitted for use in mines in which safety lamps were employed. Such mines are coal mines in which inflammable gas has been found within the previous three months in such quantity as to be indicative of danger, or which are not naturally wet throughout. It was of course stipulated that the explosives should be used properly; for example, they were to be well stemmed. The official gallery testing was inaugurated at

Woolwich in 1897; in modified form (the Rotherham Test) it was continued at Rotherham from 1911 until 1920, and at Ardeer from 1921 to 1929. The Buxton Test, a further modification, has been in operation from 1929 to the present day.

The "Permitted List" of explosives is divided into two parts, namely:

Part I: Explosives permitted for general use.

Part II: Explosives permitted only for bringing down coal.

It should be noted that the latter group includes the explosives generally known as low-density explosives.

BUXTON TEST.—The cylindrical testing gallery is 50 ft. long, 5 ft. in diameter, and constructed of mild steel plates. At one end a length of 18 ft. constitutes the explosion chamber into which a steel gun, located outside, fires through the end plate of the gallery. The gun bore is 55 mm. dia. and 120 cm. long. A diaphragm of oiled brown paper seals the end of the explosion chamber.

Gas.—A gasholder adjoins the gallery, and is connected therewith by piping, fitted with valves, in such manner as to permit the filling of the explosion chamber with the inflammable gas-air mixtures required. A fan is fitted into the end of the pipe-lines to propel the mixtures. Pressure-relief ports are provided along the top of the gallery and are closed by paper sheets. Observation windows are fitted to the sides. Thus the explosion chamber can be filled quite readily with the required gas mixture. The desired charge of explosive can be placed within the gun and fired, with or without stemming, into the gas mixture. For the standard test, this consists of air mixed with 9 per cent. ($\pm$ 0·25 per cent.) methane or with coal dust. When testing with coal dust, a plank 10 ft. long by 10 in. wide is placed 6 in. below the bore of the gun and covered with coal dust at the rate of 4 oz. per ft. run. The dust is also spread, at the rate of 2 oz. per ft. run, along the rest of the gallery to the far end. For the standard test, the coal dust used contains not less than 35 per cent. of volatile matter, calculated on an ash-free dry basis, and ground to such fineness that 90 per cent. by weight passes through a 150-mesh sieve (I.M.M. standard).

Gallery Test.—The procedure is as follows:—

(1) Five shots, each of 8 oz., are fired unstemmed into the gas mixture.

(2) Five shots, each of 28 oz. in the case of explosives submitted for Part I of the Permitted List, or 18 oz. for explosives submitted for Part II of that list, are stemmed with a clay plug and fired into the gas mixture.

(3) Five shots, each of 28 oz. in the case of explosives submitted for Part I of the Permitted List, or 18 oz. for explosives submitted for Part II of that list, are fired unstemmed into the coal dust.

Explosive.—The cartridges are of not less than $1\frac{1}{4}$ in. in diameter, and are fired in their normal wrappings. Each cartridge is pierced through its envelope, the detonator is completely inserted flush with the end of the cartridge and the firing wires are given a half hitch round the cartridge. A clay plug of $\frac{3}{4}$ in. to 1 in. in length is placed first in the gun followed by the charge, the primer cartridge of which enters last with the detonator at the end of the cartridge nearest the muzzle. Finally, when the shot requires to be stemmed, a clay plug which fits the bore and is 1 in. in length, is gently pushed on to the charge, but in such manner as not to distort the cartridge. All the shots are fired electrically.

Ballistic Pendulum Test.—This test is carried out to obtain a rough measure of the power of the explosive. A small gun, bored 35 mm. diam. for a depth of 60 cm. is charged with 4 oz. of explosive and then stemmed with 2 lb. of dry clay. The gun is run to within 2 in. of a 5-tons mortar, which is suitably suspended as a pendulum on ball bearings. The discharge of the gun displaces the mortar, the swing of which is recorded. The mean of two swings produced by the explosive being tested is compared with the standard given by 4 oz. of gelignite containing 60 per cent. of nitro-glycerine.

Liquid Oxygen Blasting.—This method of blasting has not been employed in Great Britain since 1932, as its employment is more hazardous than normal practice. An absorbent, such as sawdust, may be made into cartridges which are placed in a dipping tank containing liquid oxygen. These are removed after a given time and loaded straight into the shot-hole. Vaporisation of the oxygen takes place continuously, and to avoid accumulations of excessive pressure and the possibility of a consequent premature explosion, the stemming material employed must be of a pervious nature. These cartridges are very susceptible to friction, and produce a hot flame of

LIST OF EXPLOSIVES, 1956

The following table gives the list of non-permitted and of permitted explosives, but it is important to remember that none of these explosives is absolutely safe in atmospheres containing inflammable gases. It should be noted that all the explosives appearing in the official list are not necessarily being manufactured at the present time.

Non-Permitted	Non-Permitted
Nitro-glycerine Explosives:	*Non-Nitro-Glycerine Explosives:*
Antifrost Ammon. Gelatine Dynamite.	Aluminite, No. 2.*
Antifrost Ammon. Gelignite.	Aluminite, No. 3.*
Antifrost Ammon. Gelignite, No. 2.	Ammonal, No. 3.*
Eversoft Gelamex, No. 1	Blasting Abelite.*
Eversoft Gelamex, No. 2.	Burrowite.
Eversoft Gelamex, No. 3.	Celmonal.
Gelignol.	Gradely Powder.*
Nobels Explosive, No. 695A.	Modified Sabulite, A.*
Opencast Gelignite.	Nobels Explosive, No. 704.
Polar Ammon. Gelignite Dynamite.	Ripping Ammonite, No. 1.
Polar Ammon. Gelignite.	Sabulite, No. 1A.*
Rockrift Powder.	Thameite, No. 1.*
Submarine Blasting Gelignite.	Thameite, No. 4.*
Victor Powder.	Thameite, No. 5.*
Winrox.	Tuthill Powder, No. 1.*

Note.—Explosives marked * are supplied either in cartridges or grain.

LIST OF EXPLOSIVES, 1956 (*continued*)

Explosives on the permitted list issued by Min. of Power, 31st December, 1956

Part I.—Permitted for general use. Permissible maximum charge, 28 oz.

Section A(1). Nitro-glycerine Explosives, Gelatinous Type:

Ajax (S).*
Antifrost Gelammonite, No. 2 (S).
Antifrost Nitrox, No. 2 (S).
Denespex (Eq.S).
Driftex (S).
Driftex P. (S).
Hydrobel (S).
Infugel
Nobels Explosive, No. 1186 (S).
Nobels Explosive, No. 1213 (Eq.S).
Oakley's Explosive, No. 561.
Oakley's Explosive, No. 562.
Pentregel.
Plastex No. 1 (S).
Plastex P. (S).
Polar Ajax (S).
Polar Ajax C (S).
Polar Saxonite, No. 3 (S).
Samsonite, No. 3 (S).*
Saxonite (S).*
Saxonite, No. 1.*
Stonobel (S).*
Unigel (Eq.S.).
Unigel, M.

Section A(2). Nitro-glycerine Explosives, Powdery Type:

Antifrost Penrhyn Powder (S).
Antifrost Penrhyn Powder, No. 2 (S).
Bettacol (S).
Colespex (Eq.S.).
Colex, No. 1 (S).
Colex, No. 2 (S).
Compex, No. 1 (Eq.S).
Dynobel, No. 2 (S).*
Equicol (Eq.S).
Equinox (Eq.S).
Eversoft Tees Powder (S).
Lesslak (Eq.S).
Lodespex (Eq.S).

Minex (S).
Monobel, No. 1.*
Morcol.*
Nobels Explosive, No. 944.
Nobels Explosive, No. 964.
Nobels Explosive, No. 1105.
Nobels Explosive, No. 1181 (Eq.S).
Nobels Explosive, No. 1200 (Eq.S).
Nobels Explosive, No. 1201 (Eq.S).
Nobels Explosive, No. 1220 (Eq.S).
Pencol (Eq.S).
Polar A2. Monobel (S).*
Polar A3. Monobel (S).
Polar Dynobel, No. 2 (S).
Polar Viking (S).
Simex, No. 3 (S).
Super Ammodyne.*
Unibel (Eq.S).
Unifrax (Eq.S).
Unigex (Eq.S).
Unigex H (Eq.S).
Unikol (Eq.S).
Wincoal Extra (S).

Section B. Non-nitro-glycerine Explosives:
Celmonite.
Douglas Powder (S).
Equamite (S).
Hawkite, No. 2 (S).
Hawkite, No. 3 (S).
Unirend (Eq.S).
Norsabite (S).
Tolumite, No. 1 (Eq.S).
Trinite W. (Eq.S.)
Tuthilite.
XL Hawkite (S).

Part II.—Permitted only for bringing down coal. Maximum charge, 18 oz. N.G. powdery type.

A.1. Rounkol (S).
Antislak P. (S).
Lodensite, No. 2.
Lodex (S).

Notes.—(S) means permitted with or without external sheaths. (Eq.S.) means not less safe than a sheathed explosive of the same group. * Means explosives not manufactured in Great Britain, or for export only. For certain explosives the charge limit for use in stone is 48 oz.

C.L. I—12*

comparatively long duration that will readily ignite gas. Enrichment of the oxygen content of a mine atmosphere by vaporisation, and the possible spillage of liquid oxygen upon coal dust, increases the risk of a fire and of explosion in gassy and dusty mines. The cartridge becomes weaker with lapse of time, and results in general are not as good as those obtained by ordinary explosive. Electric ignition is usually employed, but fuse firing may be adopted if good quality fuse is used.

Consumption of Explosives in Coal Mines.—The importance of blasting in coal mines is indicated by the large amount of explosives used for this purpose which has increased considerably during recent years.

Relevant data for the years 1938 and 1954, taken from the Statistical Digest published by the Ministry of Fuel and Power, are given below:—

USE OF EXPLOSIVES IN BRITISH COAL MINES

Explosives used (thousand lb.)	1938	1954
Permitted:		
Sheathed	8,654	22,806
Equisheathed (Eq.S)		16,510
Unsheathed	14,220	7,633
Total	22,874	46,949
Other	7,144	4,979
Total	30,018	51,928
Estimated number (thousands) of shots fired ..	63,707	99,379
Output of saleable coal (thousands of tons)	226,993	213,994
Explosive (lb.) used per 100 tons of saleable coal ..	13	24·4

It will be seen that the consumption of permitted explosives has increased greatly from about 29 per cent. of the total in 1938 to about 90 per cent. in 1954, so that the amount of permitted explosives used in 1954 was some nine times that of the non-permitted type; the total amount of explosives used for 100 tons of output in 1954 was almost twice that for 1938.

CHOICE OF EXPLOSIVE

The choice of explosives for use frequently calls for the help and advice of the specialist engineer of the service department of an explosive manufacturing company which is readily available and valuable, but the major factors to be taken into consideration may be enumerated.

1. Nature of the Mine.—Coal mines are classified under either Part I or Part II of the Explosives in Mines Order, and whereas almost any explosive may be employed in other mines, only those on the Permitted List may be used in mines which come under Part II of the Order.

2. Moisture and Water.—In moist atmospheres, and particularly in wet ground, the hygroscopic types of explosive such as some of the ammonium nitrates are unsuitable and a high-density water-resisting type such as Polar Ajax should be chosen.

3. Oxygen Balance.—When there is a deficiency of oxygen in the explosive, incomplete combustion results in the production of deleterious gases. This must be avoided in explosives which are to be used underground. The paper wrapper must be allowed for in the calculation. Sufficient oxygen should be present to minimise the formation of CO, but there should be no excess to permit the production of oxides of nitrogen.

4. Sensitivity.—Normally, the explosive should be safe to handle, but it must be sufficiently sensitive to ensure complete detonation in use.

5. Nature of the Ground.—(A) Rock Work in Shafts.—A hard rock, such as whinstone, requires an explosive which is high in density, bulk strength and velocity, namely, a gelatine. When the situation allows for the use of a non-permitted type as, perhaps, in sinking a shaft, a Polar Ammon Gelignite may be used, and for excessively hard rock, it may be necessary to choose a Polar Ammon Gelignite Dynamite. It is a useful coincidence that the gelatines are also water resisting. Powder types of explosives are unsuitable for the wet conditions so often found in sinkings. Should a "permitted" type be necessary, then Polar Ajax may be chosen, although of necessity such explosives are lower in strength and velocity of detonation by reason of the addition of cooling salts, etc. Here it may be noted that if, as is usual, the shot-holes for blasting in a sinking are in concentric rings, with sumpers near the centre, then a ring of easers and finally an outside ring of trimmers, it may be good practice to select a full-strength gelignite for the sumpers, say Polar Ammon Gelignite Dynamite, and for the easers and trimmers, say Polar Ammon Gelignite, with slightly less weight and bulk strength, but with the same density and velocity of detonation, thus effecting an economy in blasting costs.

(B) For Stone Heading or Crutting.—The same conditions apply, but when a "permitted" must be used for hard rock, Polar Ajax would again show advantage.

(C) For Softer Shale Measures.—A weaker gelatine such as Unigel, or an ammonium nitrate TNT powder, as for example Unirend, might be used. For ripping, the same line of reasoning holds, but the problem is normally simpler, as the measures vary from a hard compact sandstone down to a soft laminated shale. For hard ripping the choice naturally falls on the high-strength permitted explosives. For ripping operations, however, the cutting action as determined by velocity of detonation of the explosive must be taken into account. Hard bands may be present which demand a sharp cutting action. Also, where side holes have to be used, it is desirable that the explosive shall cut down cleanly through the stone to square the road sides without spreading beyond, over the roadside packs. This cutting ability is possessed by the explosives such as Unigel in the gelatines or Polar Viking (sheathed) in the N.G. powders, and Douglas and XL Hawkite (sheathed) in the ammonium nitrate/TNT powders. On the other hand, strata conditions may occur where the ripping is "short" in nature and breaks out small in blasting. In such a case, to obtain better building stone for pack walls, an explosive with a slower velocity of detonation might be used with advantage, as for example, Unifrax, etc.

(D) COAL.—Where high explosives are used in naked-light mines, the choice is usually one of the gelatinous type like Polar Ammon Gelignite, or occasionally, an N.G. powder like Gelignol.

Factors of Importance.—For use in mines where safety lamps are required to be used a remarkably wide range of explosives has been developed to meet the diversity of coal-seam conditions, some of which will now be considered.

1. NATURE OF THE COAL.—For hard splint coal, an explosive of both high weight and bulk strength is desirable, such as Polar Ajax (sheathed) or Driftex (sheathed).

For medium hard coals, explosives of lesser weight and bulk strength may be used, such as Polar Viking and Unigel.

For softer coals, less strength is required, and Unifrax or Lesslak give better results.

2. THICKNESS OF THE SEAM.—Where the seam is 5 ft. thick or upwards, it may be good blasting practice to use two rows of holes, upper and lower, when the problem resolves itself as for seams of average thickness. With seams of 4 ft. in thickness, it may be possible to win the coal with one row of holes, but here both strength and high velocity of detonation is desirable in order to cut down through the coal to the undercut or holing. Thus Unirend with its high velocity of detonation of 3,000 metres per sec. shows good results.

For thin seams a low density explosive such as Unifrax is more suitable.

3. COAL STRUCTURE.—Well-established cleavage planes make blasting conditions easier on the whole, and generally allow for a reduced strength of explosive, but the presence of "slips" in close proximity may call for an increase in velocity of detonation, in order to cut sharply across them in addition to cutting downward.

4. PRESENCE OF HARD BANDS.—Here again, high velocity of detonation is a desirable characteristic together with good strength in order that the explosive shall smash through the hard bands.

5. WET CONDITIONS.—As already mentioned, wet conditions definitely call for the use of a gelatinous explosive.

6. GRADES OF COAL REQUIRED.—This consideration has a decided bearing on the selection of the most suitable type of explosive. Occasionally, as with coking coals, good fragmentation may be an advantage, but usually lump coal is required, and for this, the bulk strength of the explosive is a most important characteristic where low power per unit volume is essential. The "low density" explosives with their bulk strengths and low velocities meet this requirement; so do the low-power normal density explosives.

The following standard list of Permitted Explosives, specified by the National Coal Board for use in British coal mines, serves as a useful guide in the selection of explosives for normal purposes.

STANDARD LIST OF PERMITTED EXPLOSIVES SUPPLIED BY VARIOUS MANUFACTURERS TO THE N.C.B., JANUARY 1957

Type	Manufacturer			
	Imperial Chemical Industries Limited	Cooke's Explosives Limited	The Colliery Explosives Company Limited	Explosives and Chemical Products Limited
Eq. S explosives	Unigex Unifrax Unirend Unigel	Lesslak Pencol Equinox Pentregel	Compex No. 2 Compex No. 1 Trinite No. 1	Denespex Minespex Colespex Lodespex
Sheathed explosives	Polar Ajax Polar Viking	Anti-frost Nitrox No. 2 Anti-frost Penrhyn Powder No. 2	XL Hawkite Simex No. 3	Driftex Minex
Unsheathed explosives	Polar Ajax	Anti-frost Nitrox No. 2	Simex No. 3	Driftex
Explosives for firing under water	Hydrobel			

REFERENCES

1 Historical relationship of mining, silicosis and rock removal, Treve Holman, *British Journal of Industrial Medicine*, Vol. 4, No. 1, 1947.
2 Messrs. Holman Bros. Ltd., Camborne, Catalogues.
3 Messrs. Hadfield Ltd., Sheffield, Catalogues and letters.
4 Development in drill steels and bits, O. C. Gambling (Technical Reunion of the B.C.A.S.).
5 The introduction and development of carbide percussive detachable bits, H. M. Griffiths, Supplement to *Mine and Quarry Engineering* of March, 1947.
6 Factors affecting the speed of penetration of bits in rotary drilling, H. S. Alpan, *Trans. Inst. Min. Eng.*, Vol. 109, 1950, p. 1119, and Improving the efficiency of rotary drilling of shot-holes, R. Shepherd, *ibid.*, Vol. 113, 1954, p. 1029.
7 Shot-firing and explosives in coal mines, J. Taylor and J. Hancock, *Trans. Inst. Min. Eng.* Vol. 106, 1947, p. 678.
8 The lag on ignition of firedamp, Naylor and Wheeler, Safety in Mines Research Board Paper No. 9, 1925.

CHAPTER 9

BREAKING GROUND—II. THE APPLICATION OF EXPLOSIVES AND OTHER MEANS

FIRING OF EXPLOSIVES

Firing by Flame.—In naked-light mines, low explosives may be fired by squib, fuse or cap.

THE SQUIB.—This consists of a tube of suitably coated paper, closed at one end and almost filled with black powder. The open end is then twisted up and treated with sulphur and saltpetre. On charging the hole, a long copper needle is inserted with the last cartridge. The needle remains in position until stemming is completed, and is then withdrawn leaving an open channel of small diameter for the passage of the squib to make contact with the charge. Squibs are still used to a limited extent; only about 43,000 were fired in 1954.

SAFETY FUSE.—This consists of a thin core of gunpowder, enclosed in a covering of thread or thread tape, rendered impervious to moisture by gutta percha or bitumen. The specially blended powder has a normal burning speed of one yard in 90 seconds, which time must not vary more than 10 sec. either way. It is the spit of flame from the fuse which ignites the black powder pellets, and the spit is about 1 in. in length. Stemming of the hole is done with the fuse in position. The fuse may be lit from any suitable flame.

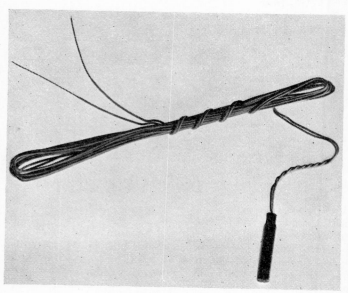

Fig. 1.—Electrical detonator and wires or leads.

CAPPED FUSE.—Capped fuse is the name given to a length of fuse to which a plain detonator has been attached by crimping. It is used for the firing of

366

a high explosive. All detonators consist primarily of a thin-walled copper or aluminium tube of about $\frac{1}{4}$ in. diameter, closed at one end and containing a small charge of explosive. When buried in a charge of high explosive and ignited, it explodes with sufficient violence to produce detonation of that charge. A plain detonator is fired by the flash from the end of the safety fuse. Such methods of ignition cannot be used in safety-lamp mines.[1]

Firing by Electricity.—ELECTRIC POWDER FUSES.—These are used to ignite charges consisting of pellets of black powder. They are constructed

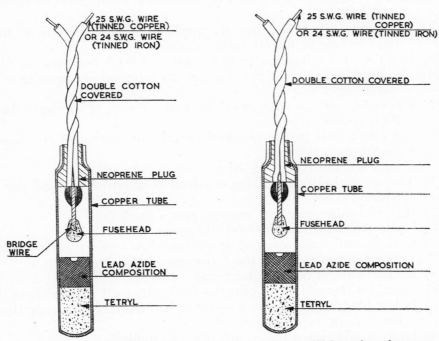

Fig. 2.—Low-tension detonator.

Fig. 3.—High-tension detonator.
Note absence of bridge wire.

on the same principles as electric detonators, but the tube of the powder fuse is made of paper and contains gunpowder.

THE ELECTRIC DETONATOR.—This is simply a plain metal tube containing an electric fusehead which is attached to insulated wires, or leads, which extend through the sealing compound at the end, and may be coupled to the firing cable, Fig. 1. The metal tube may be of copper or aluminium, but only copper ones may be used in gassy mines, as those of aluminium are of an incendiary nature. The charge within the detonator may be divided into initiating and base components, each separately consolidated. For initiation, the so-called A.S.A. mixture is employed. It is made up of lead azide, lead styphnate and aluminium powder. The base charge is usually trinitrophenyl-nitro-amine, otherwise known as "tetryl". In 1938, neoprene was employed for sealing detonators hermetically, thus preventing the possibility of a slow reaction between lead azide and the copper tubing.[2]

Electric detonators may be divided into two classes, low-tension and high-tension, and the more important facts concerning each of them are as follows:—

A. The low-tension type (Fig. 2):—

(1) Both conducting wires or leads are covered with white insulating material.

(2) Has a bridge wire embedded in a flash composition.

(3) Has a resistance of 0·9 to 1·6 ohms with 48-in. 25 S.W.G. copper wire leads.

(4) For single firing, requires the application of a current of not less than 0·6 amps. for 50 milliseconds.

(5) Requires 1·5–2·0 amps. to fire a series of 20 detonators.

(6) Should pass a current of 0·1 amps. for a period of one minute without firing.

(7) Offers less risk of stray sparking and ignition of methane than the high-tension type.

(8) May be tested before use and permits of testing of the complete circuit before firing.

B. The high-tension type (Fig. 3):—

(1) The insulating material for one lead is coloured red and the other white.

(2) Has no bridge wire but incorporates a spark gap.

(3) Has a resistance of 1,500–50,000 ohms.

(4) Usually has lead wires of iron, but their resistance is negligible when compared with the resistance of the circuit.

(5) Requires about 50 volts for firing.

(6) Should withstand the application of 5 volts for 1 min. without firing.

(7) Is less likely to misfire as a result of bad contact resistance than the low-tension type.

(8) Is not easily tested for completion of circuit.

The number of high-tension detonators used in Great Britain is gradually decreasing in favour of the low-tension type, which is used for about 95 per cent. of the shots fired.

COUPLING SHOTS—SERIES OR PARALLEL.—Shots may be coupled up for firing in series or in parallel, but in practice, series firing is adopted almost invariably. When coupling in series, one lead of the cable is coupled to one wire of detonator No. 1 and the second wire of that detonator is coupled to the first wire of detonator No. 2, and so on (Fig. 4), until the second wire of the last detonator in the round of shots is coupled to the other lead of the cable. The whole of the firing current passes through each detonator. When coupling in parallel, one wire of each detonator is attached directly to the first conductor of the cable. The remaining wires, one from each detonator, are attached to the second conductor of the cable.

Parallel firing offers a greater liability to serious variations in the resistance of the parallel circuits, and misfires are more likely to occur. In firing a charge, there are four time intervals of importance. Three of these commence with the beginning of the flow of current. The *"excitation time"* is the period up to the moment of ignition of the fusehead, the *"lag time"* is the period up to the termination of current flow (either by fusion of the bridge wire or by detonation), and the *"bursting time"* is the period up to the detonation. Thus the bursting time may be equal to, or slightly greater than, the lag time. The difference between the two is known as the *"induction time"*. In order to ensure that all the electric detonators in the circuit will fire suc-

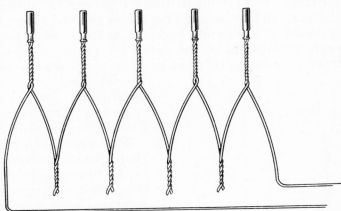

Fig. 4.—Diagram showing method of coupling shots in series. The two leads at the right are twisted to the two cores of the wiring cable.

cessfully, it is essential that "the shortest lag time of any of them must exceed the longest excitation time of any of them".[2]

GASLESS-DELAY DETONATORS.—Gasless-delay detonators differ from normal type detonators in that a delay sleeve filled with a slow-burning composition is interposed between the fuse head and the detonating compound (Fig. 5). Owing to the nature of the delay composition and the perfect sealing, no sparks or hot gases can escape from the detonator, and regularity of burning time is ensured. The delay periods range from No. 0, instantaneous, by half-second intervals, up to No. 10, but delays up to 4 seconds only are permitted in gassy mines. The current employed for firing a series of these should never be less than 1·5 amps., and for 20 shots or more, should not be less than 2 amps. The use of an exploder with excess capacity is advocated. The circumstances in which gasless delay-action detonators are employed are referred to later.

SHORT-DELAY DETONATORS.—These were introduced in the autumn of 1945. They are very similar in construction to the ordinary gasless-delay detonator having delays graduated in half seconds. The main difference is that the delay interval increases in steps of 25 millisecs. (0·025 secs.) or 50 millisecs. (0·05 secs.). These detonators have been largely used for reducing the vibration produced by blasting on opencast coal sites and quarries. When used in tunnels, it is generally found that better fragmentation of the rock is obtained, but it is thrown rather greater distances away from the tunnel face. Usually this is a disadvantage where mechanical loaders require the debris to be piled up at the face.[3]

DETONATOR SHIELDS OR DUMMY PRIMERS.—These are simply dummy

cartridges made from wood, wax, clay, or other harmless substances, and moulded with a central hole to accommodate the detonator. A circumferential and longitudinal groove may be provided for the detonator leads. Further, the dummy primer may be shaped to fit over the end of the first explosive cartridge. It is claimed that the primer (*a*) protects the detonator during charging and stemming operations; (*b*) saves time in charging as there is no necessity to soften and bore the cartridge for insertion of detonator; (*c*) prevents withdrawal of the detonator during tamping; (*d*) prevents moisture from entering cartridges as their wrappers are not disturbed. Detonators should always be handled with care and in accordance with the statutory provisions regarding their issue, carriage and use (see Coal Mines Explosives Order, 1956, No 1767).

STEMMING.—In practice, it has been proved that a moist sand-clay mixture just mouldable in the fingers is best. The addition of a small proportion of calcium chloride to the sand-clay mixture causes it to remain moist in dry situations. Good stemming is essential if maximum explosive efficiency and economy is to be attained. It tends to confine the hot gaseous products until they have been cooled somewhat by pulverisation of both ground and stemming, thus preventing the ignition of firedamp. The practice of preforming short cartridges of clay stemming for use underground has much to commend it. For stone drifting, the Hurricane Stemmer, which injects sand into the shot-holes by compressed air has found favour in some quarters.

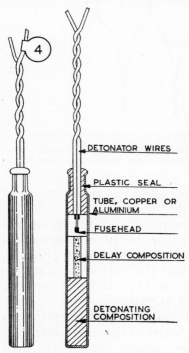

DETONATOR WIRES

PLASTIC SEAL

TUBE, COPPER OR ALUMINIUM

FUSEHEAD

DELAY COMPOSITION

DETONATING COMPOSITION

Fig. 5.—Gasless delay-action detonator.

Exploders.—For use in safety-lamp mines exploders must be of a design approved by the Ministry of Fuel and Power. Such exploders are intrinsically safe and, if maintained in good condition, are most unlikely of themselves to ignite firedamp. Periodic overhauls are required at intervals of not more than three months for single-shot types, and at not more than weekly intervals for multi-shot types.

SINGLE-SHOT EXPLODERS.—These may be divided into three groups, two of which incorporate magnetos. In these latter current is generated at "low tension" by the members of one group, and at "high tension" by members of the other, but in neither group is the amount of current required to pass the ignition test much in excess of that required to fire a detonator and, therefore, unless the efficiency of the exploder is maintained, misfires may occur. This possibility is somewhat greater with the H.T. type. The third type comprises battery exploders.

Fig. 6 illustrates the "Little Demon" magneto type exploder for firing single shots as supplied by Imperial Chemical Industries Ltd. The magneto is enclosed in a small case, $4\frac{3}{4}$ in. $\times$ $2\frac{1}{2}$ in. $\times$ 4 in. It is operated by a half-turn of the detachable firing key.

MULTI-SHOT EXPLODERS.—These may be divided into three groups, the battery, magneto and dynamo-condenser groups. Among these, only the battery type is approved.

The Battery Type.—These may be employed for the firing of not more than six shots in series. A condenser is inserted between the battery and the firing circuit, in such manner that the battery is connected to the condenser to charge it up, but it is then disconnected: the condenser is then connected to the firing circuit to effect its discharge. Direct connection between battery and firing circuit is thus avoided, and the latter can receive only a limited amount of electrical energy. Here again there is very little margin between the energy available and that required for firing purposes, and careful maintenance is essential.

The Magneto Type.—Several unapproved types of this are available, and permission to use them in certain circumstances may be obtained from an Inspector of Mines. Magneto types are available, capable of firing up to 40 or more shots. They are operated by handle or rack bar, and current is passed on to the firing circuit when, and only when,

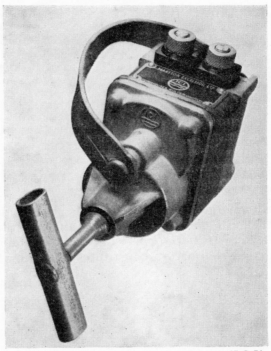

Fig. 6.—"Little Demon" exploder. (*Marston/I.C.I.*)

it has reached a predetermined value. This provides greater security from misfires, but as always, care must be taken to avoid leakages and bad connections.

The Dynamo-Condenser Type.—In this type the turning of a handle operates a dynamo generator, which charges a condenser. When fully charged, a light glows behind a glass panel and the pressing of the firing button permits the condenser to discharge through the firing circuit. Thus well over one hundred shots may be fired with the Beethoven unit illustrated in Fig. 7. A wiring diagram of this is given in Fig. 8.

TESTS FOR EXPLODERS.—

(1) Basic Test.—Single-shot machines depend for "Official Approval" upon their ability to pass a special resistance test.

(2) Ignition Test.—Exploders must pass an official test for intrinsic safety before approval for use in mines.

Use of Unapproved Exploders for Multi-shot Firing.—Permission for the use of such exploders may be given by Her Majesty's Inspectors of Mines, but certain stipulations must be obeyed.

Fig. 7.—Beethoven dynamo-condenser exploder. (*I.C.I.*)

Direct and Reverse Initiation.—It should be remembered that the detonating compound always lies at the closed end of the detonator, i.e., remote from the end at which the conductors enter. A detonator is said to "point" in the direction of a line drawn from its "conductors' end", to its closed or "detonating end".

Direct Initiation.—A sound rule when charging a shot-hole is to place the detonator so that it is pointing in the direction of the charge. In most cases this should mean that it is inserted in the last cartridge to enter the shot-hole and pointing into the shot-hole.

Reverse Initiation.—There are certain exceptions, and the use of delay-action detonators constitutes such an exception. The cartridge containing

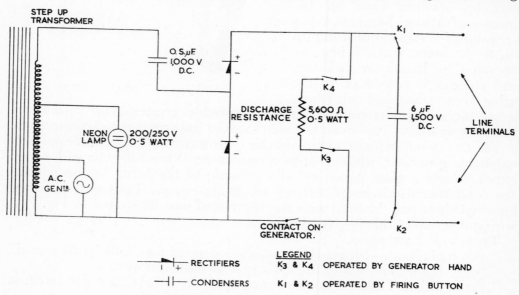

Fig. 8.—Wiring diagram of Beethoven exploder.

such a detonator should enter the shot-hole first, and should point outwards towards the remainder of the charge and towards the mouth of the shot-hole. This must be done to ensure that no unexploded cartridges will remain in any borehole sockets after firing, in fact, the Chief Inspector of Mines insists on the employment of this reverse initiation technique when granting permission for the use of delay-action detonators.

SIMULTANEOUS SHOT-FIRING.—In the firing of single shots, gas may be liberated by an early shot and fired by a later one. Simultaneous firing reduces this risk. Further, there is a saving in time, and the shot-firer may pay more attention to gas testing, roof testing, etc., between the rounds of shots.

Finally, the explosive may be used more efficiently under certain circumstances such as firing in rippings.

Simultaneous firing has been customary in sinkings and stone drifts for many years, but of late there has been an increasing desire to apply it to rippings, and even to the coalface in bord and pillar work. Permission may be sought from the Inspectorate, who may grant it subject to such stipulations as are deemed necessary.

For simultaneous firing, low-tension detonators must be coupled in series and fired electrically. Special attention must be paid to the efficiency of circuit connections, to the insulation thereof from the face and ground and to the avoidance of short circuits between the leads, etc. The use of insulating tape and of neoprene or bitumen joint insulators for insulating and waterproofing joints is commendable practice. Before firing, the circuits should be tested by means of an approved instrument, or by a device incorporated in the exploder.[1]

It should be noted that special care is necessary in testing detonators, for which purpose they are placed in a suitable tube.

CUSHION FIRING.—This is one of the methods adopted to avoid the shattering of the coal into fines. An air space is left within the shot-hole in order to spread the effect of the explosives over a greater area of the hole. A simple way would be to use smaller cartridges in a given sized hole. Another is such a device as the "Voortman" cement plug. When using this plug, the charge, complete with detonator, is pushed to the back of the hole. The plug with its attached cord is pushed by the rammer up to the explosive. Then by pulling the cord and withdrawing the rammer simultaneously a short distance, the requisite space for air cushioning is left. From now on the cord and plug should be held stationary. Stemming should be inserted and pressed up to the plug, but the pressure should be resisted by holding on to the cord and plug until the stemming forms a gas-tight seal. Two more pellets of stemming are added in a similar way, and are followed by the normal stemming procedure. It is claimed that the use of the plug results in larger coal, improved safety and greater economy.

SHOT-FIRING PRACTICE

1. **Shaft Sinking.**—It is customary to arrange and fire the shots in "rounds" or groups in such a manner that the fracture or removal of rock

by the preliminary rounds shall permit the maximum blasting efficiency of the subsequent shots. Details of shot-firing practice in shaft sinking are given in Chapter 5.

2. Stone Drifting.—In drifting as in sinking, the principle governing blasting practice is to place and fire the charges in rounds so as to ensure results that will permit the most efficient work from the rounds which follow. Here again, therefore, the sequence in the firing of rounds of shots is from the centre to the periphery of the drift. Precision blasting within, but not beyond, the maximum dimensions of the tunnel is to be commended: indeed, in contract work degradation of the rock beyond this area may be penalised.

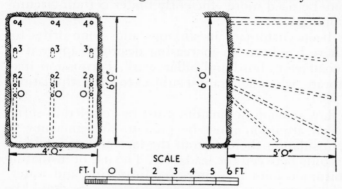

Fig. 9.—Disposition of shot-holes in the drag-cut system of blasting in a small drift driven in sandstone.

Pull of round 4 ft. 6 in. No. of shot-holes, 15
Explosive used—Polar Ammon Gelatine, Dynamite. 1¼-in. diameter cartridges.

						charge		
3 cut holes marked	0.	No.	0	Delay.	1½ lb. each.			
3 cut holes	,,	1	,,	1	,,	1¼	,,	,,
3 easers	,,	2	,,	2	,,	1	,,	,,
3 easers	,,	3	,,	3	,,	1	,,	,,
3 trimmers	,,	4	,,	4	,,	1	,,	,,

Total 17¼ lb.

In homogeneous rock, the shot-holes may readily be arranged to a standard pattern known as a cut to ensure such blasting, and Figs. 9 and 10, taken from the Imperial Chemical Industries' booklet on "Gasless Delay Detonators", illustrate the disposition of shot-holes for the commonly used "drag" and "wedge" cuts, but there are others such as the "double wedge", the "diamond" and the "burn" cut.[1]

A feature of the burn cut is that parallel holes are drilled near the centre, not for the purpose of charging with explosive, but to provide zones of weakness which will permit explosive charges in adjacent holes to "break through" and thus remove a central core of rock.

In Figs. 9 and 10, particulars are given of (*a*) size of heading, (*b*) nature of strata, (*c*) depth of "pull", (*d*) number of holes, (*e*) explosive recommended, (*f*) amount of charge, (*g*) sequence of rounds, according to the delay number of the detonators employed for each round. Fig. 10 shows the method of coupling up the shots in series.

Often, however, the ground varies, beds of different hardness may cross the drift and may, in the interests of economy and safety, demand the exercise of considerable judgment in the placing of shot-holes. The same principles of stemming, coupling up and firing are employed. Cables are laid or installed along the drift to a manhole, located a safe distance away from the face of the heading. Here, a powerful exploder of the magneto or

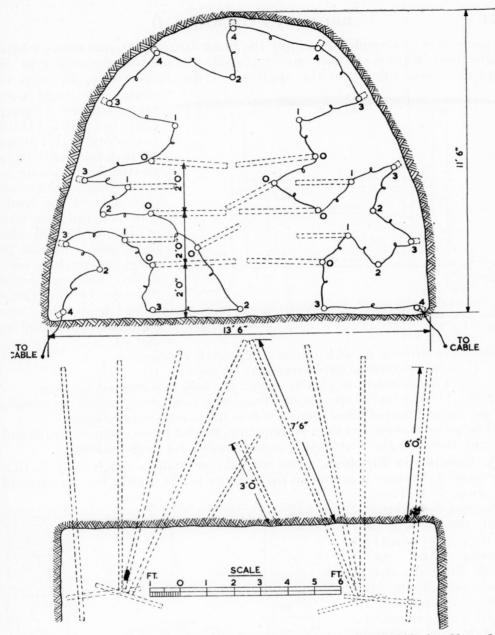

Fig. 10.—Lower figure shows disposition of shot-holes in wedge-cut system of blasting. Upper figure shows method of connecting up in series.

Size of heading	..	13 ft. 6 in. × 11 ft. 6 in.	Pull of round ..	6 ft. 0 in.
Type of strata	..	Hard shale.	No. of shot-holes ..	33.

Explosive—Polar Ajax (Permitted). $1\frac{1}{4}$ in. diameter cartridges.

Charge

2 cut holes marked 0.	No. 0	Delay.	$\frac{3}{4}$ lb. each.		
6 cut holes	,,	0	,, 0	,,	$1\frac{3}{4}$	,,	,,
6 easers	,,	1	,, 1	,,	$1\frac{1}{4}$	,,	,,
6 trimmers	,,	2	,, 2	,,	$1\frac{3}{4}$	,,	,,
8 trimmers	,,	3	,, 3	,,	$1\frac{1}{2}$	,,	,,
5 trimmers	,,	4	,, 4	,,	$1\frac{1}{2}$	,,	,,

Total $52\frac{1}{2}$ lb.

dynamo type is provided to supply the firing current. At coal mines where high-speed drifting methods are employed, a special unapproved type of exploder may, subject to the approval of the Inspectorate, be used to

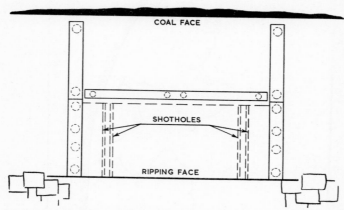

Fig. 11.—Plan showing placement of shot-holes in a ripping lip. Note the packs and breaker bars and props on each side of the roadway, as in Fig. 12.

supply the larger currents required. Greater care must be taken to avoid all forms of leakage, and it is customary to run a single-core cable on each side of the roadway between the face of the drift and the firing point, instead of using a double core cable. The minimum distance of the firing point from the face is usually stipulated as 200 yd.

Speed of drifting in such mines is restricted because:—

(1) Only permitted explosives may be used.

(2) The standard maximum charge per hole is restricted to 28 oz.

Note: H.M. Chief Inspector of Mines may now grant special permission to use a maximum of 48 oz. per shot-hole in special circumstances.

The stone in these headings is frequently loaded by mechanical means and should, therefore, be shattered to a size suitable for such loading.[1, 3]

3. Blasting in Rippings.—For normal conditions a rough guide is that the ratio of depth of shot-hole to the distance to the nearest free face should be about 7:4. There is a tendency to overestimate the burden and hence overcharge ripping shots. As a result, there is a risk of blown-out shots and damage to the roof.

Attention should be paid to the setting of good breaker props and sidebars, as efficient ripping depends on these. They should be

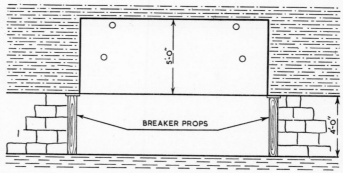

Fig. 12.—Section showing placement of holes in a ripping lip.

set early so that they become thoroughly tightened up by the time blasting is done. This helps to ensure good clean breakage.

Holes should be drilled parallel to the roadway, and the side holes should be 18–24 in. away from the breakers as shown in Figs. 11, 12 and 13.

Simultaneous firing may be employed in ripping with increase in efficiency and speed, and with less risk of gas ignition.[1]

4. Blasting on Machine-Cut Hand-Filled Faces.—Today, most seams are cut by coal-cutting machines to a certain depth all along the face. The object is to provide a second free face of coal and to permit the limited disintegration of the undercut coal and its preparation for loading. The Coal Mines Explosives Order forbids, with certain exceptions, the firing of shots in coal unless the coal has been holed to a greater depth than the shot-holes. Shot-holes are drilled before or after cutting, at specified intervals, to a depth of 6 in. less than the depth of the

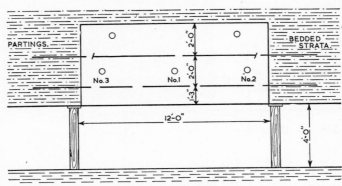

Fig. 13.—Diagrammatic section showing shot-hole placement in ripping lip with bedded strata.

cut. They are charged with a fixed amount of explosive, and fired in succession all along the face. Such routine blasting practice usually results in the drilling of an excessive number of holes and smashing of the coal.

Overcutting tends to give fairly good clearance from gummings (cuttings), but to ensure satisfactory clearance of the cut, mechanical gummers are best, particularly where long jibs are employed. Holes should be drilled, if possible, in a direction normal to the main cleavage of the coal, and here again the distance from the charge to the free face (i.e., the cut) should

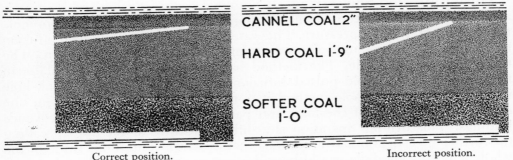

Figs. 14 and 15.—Showing correct and incorrect positions of shot-holes in coal.

be about $\frac{4}{7}$ of the depth of the shot-hole. The aim should be to produce with safety, with economy and without damage to the roof, that size of coal which will command the highest price, and which can most readily be cleared from the face by the system of loading employed.

Blasting at the coalface (Figs. 14 and 15) may be complicated by banded coal, or by the presence of bands of stone or foreign material which requires additional shot-holes (Fig. 16). However, unless great care is taken, the shattering of such bands may produce excessive disintegration of good coal. In narrow work, such as bord and pillar, blasting to produce round coal is a serious problem. Thus, with undercutting, tops may stick to the roof; with overcutting, bottoms may stick to the floor, and thicker seams may require a greater depth of shot-hole. The systematic arrangement of shot-holes may be essential to the successful working of a seam of coal.[1]

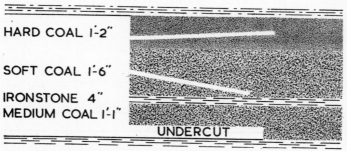

HARD COAL 1-2"

SOFT COAL 1-6"

IRONSTONE 4"
MEDIUM COAL 1-1"

UNDERCUT

Fig. 16.—Illustrating the use of low easer shots over an ironstone or hard layer in a coal seam.

The facility with which shot-holes can be drilled in coal with power drills of the rotary type has led to an increase in the number of shots fired, and the tons of saleable coal produced per pound of explosive in Great Britain has decreased from 8·8 in 1935 to 4·1 in 1954.

Blasting on Power-Loading Faces.—All that has been said concerning machine-cut, hand-filled faces, applies to machine-cut, power-loaded faces, save that, in certain circumstances, power loaders call for more careful preparation of the coal. There may be an optimum size of the coal for maximum efficiency from certain loading machines, especially where the height and width at the face are restricted.

Much can be done by the employment of correct blasting technique to ensure that the coal is blown to a size suitable for the loading machine.

Pulsed Infusion Shot-Firing.—Combined water infusion and blasting is a recent development consisting in firing an explosive charge in a borehole filled with water under pressure. The water is introduced through an infusion tube similar to those used for water infusion for dust suppression. The tube also seals the hole. The method has been applied experimentally in two ways: (a) long-hole pulsed infusion and (b) short-hole or flank-hole infusion. In the long-hole method it is necessary to bore a hole from one end to the other end of the face, and parallel thereto, from short advance leadings. This drilling operation is a difficult feature of the system calling for further investigation. It is obvious that a charge continuous through the whole length of the hole would be excessive, so that individual spaced unit charges are employed. These vary in size and are separated at intervals along the hole, being linked by a special fuse known as cordtex which serves to detonate the charges. The end of the hole remote from the infusion tube is stemmed with sand-clay stemming and, after charging, the water is admitted in such a manner as to ensure that the hole is completely filled with water, and subsequently the pressure of the water is increased to a predetermined value, 100 to 150 lb. per sq. in. After an interval of time to allow of infusion the charge is fired, thereby breaking down the coal along the whole face. A special type of permitted gelatine explosive, known as Hydrobel, and special cordtex fuse have been introduced for use in the system, both of which are capable of detonating correctly after long immersion and while still immersed in water at high hydrostatic pressure.

In the short-hole system, holes bored into the face in the conventional manner, but at an angle of 45 deg. to the line of face, are treated in a similar manner.

The system is primarily designed to break coal for power-loading without forecutting and, since it constitutes blasting of solid coal, special permission is necessary for its application.

It is still in the experimental stage, but it is claimed to simplify blasting in coal as well as increasing safety.

Its application to rippings is also being investigated.

CARDOX AND HYDROX

In gassy mines where the possibilities of gas ignition constitute a real menace, the Cardox or Hydrox methods of blasting may be employed, as either affords a greater measure of safety than does the use of "permitted" explosives.

Fig. 17.—Cardox charging machine for filling Cardox shells.

Cardox System.—In this system, gas at high pressure is produced by the vaporisation of liquid carbon dioxide, and it is made to disrupt the coal or rock around the shot-hole. A machine similar to a refrigerator is required for the rapid filling of the so-called shells or cartridges with the liquid. Fig. 17 illustrates such a machine, and Fig. 18 is a flow diagram for the installation. Fig. 19 illustrates the cartridge which consists of a high-tensile alloy steel tube with the "firing head" screwed on one end, and the "discharge head" on the other. For filling, the discharge is sealed by a soft steel disc which is held in position by screwing home the discharge head. The disc has a definite bursting pressure at which its disruption will release the gases to pass via the vent ports seen in Fig. 20, and to actuate the movable catches or pawls, the function of which is to retain the shell in the hole should there be any tendency for it to be ejected. A heater element, consisting of a non-explosive chemical mixture and a small electric powder fuse primer,

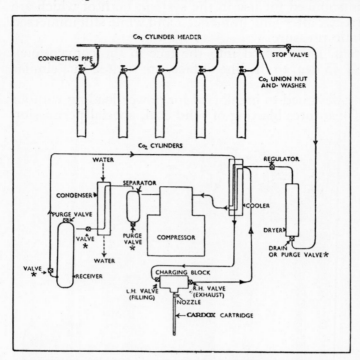

Fig. 18.—Flow diagram for Cardox shell charging plant.

all contained in a paper tube, is placed in the shell near the firing head, shown in detail in Fig. 21. When the firing head has been screwed into position, the charge of liquid CO_2 may be passed into the tube via the end filling valve seen in Fig. 21. Care must be taken to render all joints and valve seatings free from leakage, as this may render a shell inoperative due to failure to build up the pressure required to burst the shearing disc. Shells thus prepared are taken underground in covered and locked trams and stored inbye, preferably in racks until required for use. Shells

are of three standard diameters, $1\frac{3}{4}$ in., 2 in. and $2\frac{1}{2}$ in., and their length varies from 18 to 65 in. Rupturing pressures vary from 8 to $17\frac{1}{2}$ tons per sq. in. Holes are drilled by conventional methods, both in coal and in stone. They must be perfectly straight, and it is important to avoid too much or too little clearance. The boring bit should be $\frac{1}{8}$ in. larger than the drilling rod, which should be of the same diameter as the cartridge.

Fig. 19.—Cardox shell.

Neither stemming nor stone dusting as applied to blasting is compulsory with the Cardox system. Firing is accomplished by the insertion of two tubular connectors into the two transverse holes in the firing head. Current from a low-tension battery is passed via cable and connector to ignite the powder fuse, inflame the so-called "energiser" or heating mixture, and thus volatilise the carbon dioxide. When the pressure of pent-up gases bursts the soft-steel disc, the coal or rock is disrupted by the relatively slow heaving force acting through the existing planes of weakness—rending rather than shattering —thus tending to produce lumps rather than fines. Probably fewer Cardox holes are required on a given length of face than the number of shotholes for normal blasting. Fig. 22 shows lump coal produced by Cardox, being loaded off the face by a Huwood loader at a Northumberland colliery.

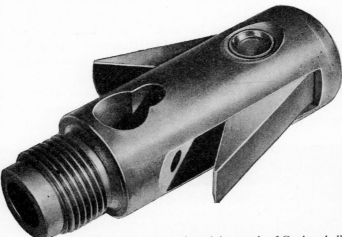

Fig. 20.—Vent ports and retaining pawls of Cardox shell.

Although Cardox finds its greatest application on the coalface, it is also employed in some rippings and dintings. It is probably true that a tender roof suffers less from the effects of Cardox than from normal explosives.

Cardox produces less coal dust and the larger product probably retains more of its inherent strength to withstand rough handling, transport and weathering. While excellent results are sometimes obtained, the method may prove unsatisfactory because of:—

(1) The difficulty of transporting the cartridges to the face, and in manhandling them up and down the face.

(2) The impossibility of readily varying the amount of charge.

(3) The service at the colliery, which cannot be arranged with the simplicity of that for ordinary explosives; it is not nearly so flexible.

(4) The possibility that coal may be brought down in very large blocks necessitating additional labour.

(5) The difficulty of "breaking in".

(6) The possibility that "backs" may not be brought down, thus tending to produce an irregular face line, and overhanging backs in a thick seam constitute a danger in filling operations, etc.

Fig. 21.—Filling valve of Cardox shell.

(7) The fact that such blasting frequently proves unsuitable for use in ripping and for rock drifting.

Hydrox.—There is great similarity between the Hydrox and Cardox systems of breaking ground. A steel tube with firing and discharge heads is used with both, a shear disc functions in a similar way with each; both use an igniter fuse fired by ordinary low-tension battery, but there is no heating element or so-called energiser in the Hydrox shell as in the Cardox and there is no filling valve in the Hydrox firing head. Figs. 23, 24 and 25.

The powder fuse or igniter is fitted into a socket on the inner end of the firing head, which is then screwed on to the end of the tube. A funnel is then

Fig. 22.—Lump coal produced by Cardox.

placed on the other end of the tube, and the charge of white Hydrox powder, a mixture of sodium nitrite and ammonium chloride, is then poured in.

The disc is placed in position, the discharge head is screwed on and the shell is ready for service. Firing results in a chemical reaction producing nitrogen and steam in such volume as to burst the disc. Sodium chloride is also produced, but in the form of a fine powder which is swept along with the gases.[1]

It is obvious that with both Cardox and Hydrox, the force employed may be adjusted within limits, by variation of the number and thickness of the shear discs employed, the size of the shell and the weight of the charge inserted therein.

As with conventional explosives, results depend upon the proper positioning of the shot-holes, a matter which may call for trial blastings and for expert advice.

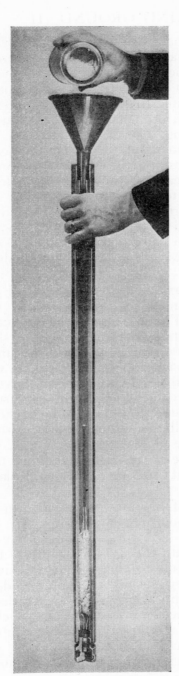

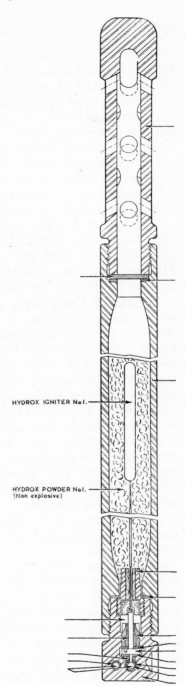

HYDROX IGNITER No1.

HYDROX POWDER No1.
(Non explosive)

Fig. 23.—The Hydrox shell. Firing head at bottom of figure. (*Cardox (Gt. Britain) Ltd.*)

Fig. 24.—Filling a Hydrox shell. (*Cardox (Gt. Britain) Ltd.*)

Fig 25.—Section through Hydrox shell. (*Cardox (Gt. Britain) Ltd.*)

383

Misfires are more frequent than with normal blasting. Transport of shells between the surface and the face is by means of covered cars which are distinctly marked and can be locked.

It must be remembered that the safety of Cardox and Hydrox blasting systems is relative, not absolute. In both systems, electrical circuits and exploders are employed as with ordinary explosives, thus introducing possibilities of danger from sparking. There is also a remote chance that under certain circumstances, the sudden release of inert gases under pressure, common to both systems, may result in the adiabatic compression and ignition of a methane-air mixture in breaks crossing the shot-hole, but the essential conditions for this are unlikely to occur in practice.

The use of Cardox and Hydrox has increased greatly in recent years. At the present time about $2\frac{3}{4}$ million Cardox cartridges and about 100,000 Hydrox cartridges are used per annum compared with 342,600 Cardox and 8,478 Hydrox cartridges in 1938. These are additional to the shots fired in which normal explosives are used.

Breaking Coal with Airdox.—The Airdox method of breaking down coal utilises compressed air under high pressure and was developed in America to replace explosives. The principle of its application resembles in many ways that of Cardox. In its early form the Airdox shell was similar to the Cardox shell except that the discharge disc was ruptured by compressed air instead of carbon dioxide, and no heater element was used. In later applications the Airdox shell was fitted with a special valve to permit release of the air at the back of the borehole at any desired pressure, depending on the nature of the coal and the amount of coal to be broken.

Air at pressures up to 10,000 lb. per sq. in., obtained from a 5- or 6-stage compressor, is conducted to the places of application by steel air-lines and copper tubing. The special valve in the shell is designed to allow of sudden release of the air with consequent breaking down and displacement of the coal without undue fracture.

For efficiency and safety free faces must be provided in the coal, which is usually accomplished by undercutting or shearing, the former being the more general.

Among the safety features with the use of Airdox are the elimination of spark or flame; the dangers of handling and storing explosives on the surface, underground, and in the face regions, are also eliminated, the Airdox tube being inactive until charged with compressed air. A disadvantage is the hazard arising from rupture of the compressed-air line which tends to "thrash about" and may injure persons and raise the mine dust into suspension until the supply of compressed air is cut off.

Trials with Airdox are being carried out in Great Britain.

THE HYDRAULIC BURSTER

THE HYDRAULIC BURSTER.—This consists of a stainless steel bar bored radially at intervals to accommodate telescopic pistons. Suitable channels are drilled to convey water under pressure to the underside of the pistons, and thus force them to extend gradually in a radial direction outwards from the bar. Various sizes of barrel are obtainable to meet different conditions according to the nature and thickness of the seam, depth of undercut, etc.; the minimum diameter being $2\frac{3}{4}$ in., and the length from 27 to 60 in. The Plate facing page 386 shows, above, the single burster equipment for which a small hand pump is normally employed to force the water via a flexible high-pressure rubber hose to the feed port of the burster, and thus to the pistons. With the multiple burster shown on the same Plate, a motor-operated pump is employed.

Each piston is compound; one of smaller diameter is telescoped within one of larger diameter until the larger one has completed its traverse; the smaller one with its mushroom head then emerges and proceeds to its limit. The small pump may be of the hand type or of the power-driven type; the latter is designed so that it can be operated by any portable drilling machine—electric or com-pressed air. The apparatus will withstand working pressures up to 6 tons per sq. in. The total pressure exerted in the hole may be 100 tons or more. For breaking down coal on a longwall face, two conditions are essential, the drilling of holes for the insertion of the burster, and the provision of a free face towards which the

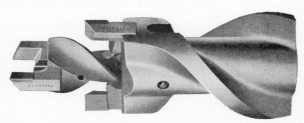

Fig. 26.—Drill head fitted with two Gullick patent "split-shank" bits, one drilling pilot hole $1\frac{11}{16}$ in. diam., the other divided, acting as a reamer. Holes up to $3\frac{1}{4}$ in. diam. can be drilled with these bits.

burster may force the coal. The holes must be drilled perfectly straight and slightly larger than the barrel. Formerly holes were drilled mandrel-fashion by a pilot drill followed by a reamer, but high-speed rotary drilling machines, using special alloy-tipped bits such as the Gullick split-shank drilling bit, have greatly simplified and speeded up the drilling operations (Fig. 26). The free face is obtained by undercutting, middlecutting, overcutting, or by shear-ing the face by machine. The holes may be put in systematically all down the face before or after the machine has passed, the best position being deter-mined by trial, but it is usually found that bursting operations should follow the cutting machine as soon as possible, thus taking advantage of the maxi-mum width of the cut for displacing and breaking the coal bed. It is claimed that the coal can be broken down within two minutes of the insertion of the burster. The Plate facing page 387 shows, above, the burster being inserted and, below, the coal broken and dislodged after bursting.

Among the advantages claimed for the use of the burster are the following:

(1) The elimination of the risk of gas ignition by explosives and by electric sparks from firing circuits.

(2) Roof damage or disturbance such as might result from shot-firing is avoided, and greater safety thus ensured.

(3) Dust is reduced and a stronger, cleaner and more saleable product results.

(4) Stone dusting and shot stemming on the face are eliminated.

(5) Men do not have to withdraw from the face.

(6) There are no fumes.

(7) The actual bursting of the coal is under the observation of the operator.

Some criticisms which have been made of the burster are as follows:—

(1) Where the coal is elastic the burster does not always break the coal.

(2) Where the surrounding strata are soft, the burster may expend its force on these rather than do effective work.

(3) It is sometimes necessary to fire breaking-in shots after the coal has been broken down.

(4) Light shots of explosive may be necessary where "backs" are left on.

OPENCAST AND DEVELOPMENT WORKINGS

Sometimes, but rather rarely, extensive and fairly level deposits of coal are discovered beneath a few feet of overburden, and may readily be won by opencast workings. Where seams approach the surface, they are often steeply inclined, and there is an economic limit to the depths from which outcrop coal can be won by opencast methods. Inclined seams may be opened-up for working by the driving of development headings within the seams, starting from the outcrop and usually in the direction of full dip. Sometimes inclined seams are intercepted by level headings driven across the measures from some point of vantage in a valley at the surface, or in a shaft. In the case of concealed coalfields, shafts are essential. In general, therefore, coal can be won only by extensive "breaking of ground" in opencast workings, sinkings, stone drifts, coal headings and working faces, and these broad headings include most of the "cut and load" operations employed in the direct and indirect winning of coal by various means.

Fig. 27.—The "Euclid" loader excavator, working on opencast site. Capacity 700 tons/hr. (*John Laing & Sons Ltd.*)

Opencast Workings.—It is probable that opencast exploitation of outcrop coal is more successful than the mining of such coal from workings

Single hydraulic burster with manual pump (pistons in "out" position).

Multiple hydraulic burster with motor-driven pump (pistons in "in" position).

(Photographs Gullick Ltd., Wigan)

HYDRAULIC BURSTERS

(*Photographs Gullick Ltd., Wigan*)

THE HYDRAULIC BURSTER IN USE

(*Above*) Inserting the hydraulic burster. The holing nogs will be adjusted before bursting.
(*Below*) Coal dislodged with a single burst. Note the pistons in the "out" position.

which have approached the surface from considerable depths because, in general, opencast affords greater safety, more complete extraction and maybe less subsidence and less surface damage. Sites are now worked where the ratio of overburden to coal is greater than 15 to 1, and depths may exceed 150 ft. Conditions vary widely, and rarely, indeed, are opencast workings ever similiar.

Removal of Overburden.—After the preliminary work of prospecting, drilling, trenching, draining and preparation of any access road, etc., the major task of removing the overburden commences.

Fig. 28.—"Lima" drag-line excavator at work on coal outcrop.

Fig. 27 shows a "Euclid" loader excavator, capable of excavating 700 tons per hour, removing topsoil from a line of outcrop. It employs a plough-type blade which excavates and forces the spoil on to a conveyor belt which delivers into bottom-dump trucks each of 20-ton capacity. The loader is hauled by a D8 tractor of 113 h.p. The spoil is stored separately in readiness for the final restoration of the site when it is replaced and spread by mobile equipment. Top overburden may also be cleared by such excavators or scrapers, but much depends upon the nature of the site or "dig". Bulldozers may be employed to even out gradients and feed material to the scrapers. Wherever possible, it is advisable to arrange for lorries to run on top of the exposed coal.

Where a considerable thickness of overburden must be removed, dragline

Fig. 29.—Walking drag line excavator, with 120-ft. boom. (*John Laing & Sons Ltd.*)

excavators are employed, and Fig. 29 shows such a unit of the walking drag-line type which "frog marches" from one position to another. It is used principally to excavate below its own level, and a skilled operator is able to throw the bucket and dump beyond the end of the jib (boom).

In this country, the average opencast site has a very short life, and the excavator must, therefore, be mobile. In general, the largest dragline which can be transported readily is most desirable. Mammoth machines are manufactured, and jibs are sometimes made extensible for use with a reduced size of bucket. It is probable that the best track machines for opencast work in Britain are those having long, wide tracks for stability, jibs of 90 ft., buckets of $2\frac{1}{2}$ cu. yd. capacity, and capable of being readily stripped down. Fig. 28 shows a "Lima" dragline excavator at work on an outcrop of coal. This method of extraction has been found to be very successful on steep coal measures.

Getting the Coal.— The removal of the coal is usually accomplished by a skimmer scoop if the seam is thin, or by a power shovel. The first differs from the second in that the scoop is hauled backwards and forwards along the jib by ropes, and picks up its load in moving towards the end of the jib.

Fig. 30 shows a power shovel at work;

Fig. 30.—The "rocker" shovel. (*John Laing & Sons Ltd.*)

it has a more positive action than a dragline, is more suitable for digging in hard material, and deals with large lumps more readily. It excavates at a higher rate because of its quick digging cycle, but it has a very small dumping radius, and usually whatever it digs must be transported by other means. It must work at the bottom of an excavation and the maintenance of a suitable and even working level is not always an easy matter.

A recent development of opencast coal technique uses the shovel on a semi-quarrying basis, the overburden being dug by shovel and transported from the cut by 4-wheel-driven vehicles. Sites are being worked to 150 ft. in depth by this method.

Blasting.—For opencast blasting operations, holes may be drilled horizontally or vertically. Horizontal holes, such as that shown in Fig. 31, may be drilled with a horizontal auger, powered by a petrol engine. The holes are usually 5 in. in diameter for a depth of 40–70 ft. They are placed just above the seam, and where necessary, some are placed adjacent to hard beds of rock. They are usually charged with Opencast Gelignite, Ammonal, etc.

Vertical blast-hole drilling rigs are probably the best units for opencast work. They will drill 5 in. holes vertically, as shown in Fig. 32, for 100 ft. or more through the hardest rock. It is usual to drill two lines of holes to a triangular pattern; one near the face of the cut, the other near the new high wall face about to be formed. These vertical holes are deck loaded, i.e., the explosive is not all in one continuous charge, but it is distributed in the hole in separate charges for separate horizons of hard rock to ensure efficient blasting. The explosives employed are similar to those used for horizontal holes and firing is by cordtex and electrical detonator.

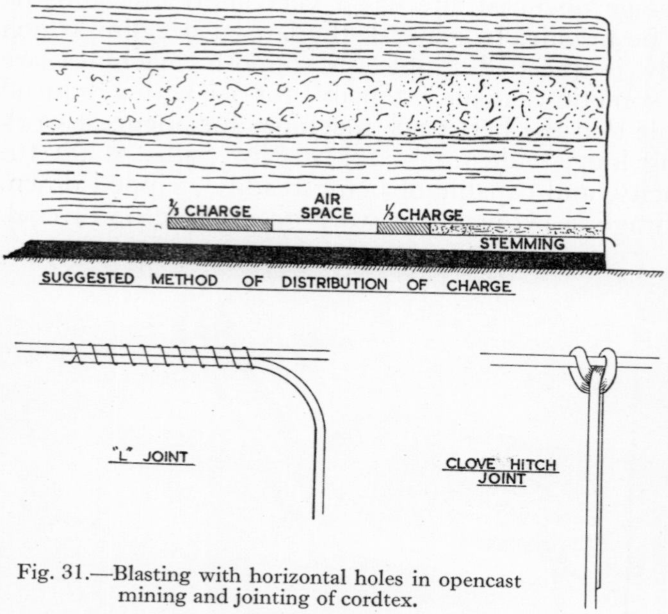

⅓ CHARGE   AIR SPACE   ⅓ CHARGE   STEMMING

SUGGESTED METHOD OF DISTRIBUTION OF CHARGE

"L" JOINT

CLOVE HITCH JOINT

Fig. 31.—Blasting with horizontal holes in opencast mining and jointing of cordtex.

The present output of opencast coal is about 13 million tons per annum, and it is expected that it will increase to 15 millions, but the depletion of suitable deposits will lead to abandonment of opencasting in the not distant future. The cost of excavating, loading, and restoration of site is not the total cost. Costs for prospecting, compensation and marketing must be added.

TUNNELLING, HEADING OR DRIFTING

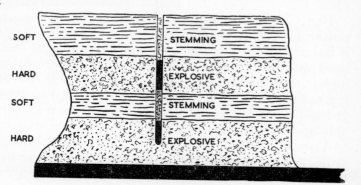

SOFT   STEMMING
HARD   EXPLOSIVE
SOFT   STEMMING
HARD   EXPLOSIVE

Fig. 32.—Blasting with vertical holes in opencast mining.

Driving in Stone.—

Drivings in stone are known as rock tunnels, stone headings, drifts or cruts. They may be driven on a level course or on a slightly rising gradient, which facilitates drainage, into hillsides to intercept inclined seams; these are known as adit levels. They may be driven to the dip, possibly at high gradient, to prove or win seams lying at depth. Sometimes they are driven to prove faults or to connect one part of a mine with another for purposes such as haulage or ventilation, etc. Today, a large number are being driven at high speed from the shaft bottoms, inset levels in shafts or from strategical points in existing roads for the development of horizon mining (Chapter 7). They lie mostly beneath the areas of coal they are intended to win and their gradients are arranged to permit of locomotive haulage.

The size of a tunnel and the method of driving it depend on many factors,

Fig. 33.—Huwood pneumatic pick used in driving drift at Clara Vale Colliery.

such as the purpose for which it is intended, the nature of the ground to be penetrated, freedom of the ground from water, ventilation requirements, nature of supports, costs, etc. The basic tools for rock drifting are very similar to those used in sinking, especially where compressed air or electric power is not available. Where the cross-section of the tunnel is small, and where the rock is relatively soft, hand-drilling machines such as the "Elliott" may still be employed for drilling (Fig. 5 in Chapter 8).

Debris is loaded by shovel into tubs or mine cars, rocks are loosened and shattered and the roof, floor and sides are trimmed by the use of bars, rock wedges, short-bladed picks, etc. Where compressed air is available, and the drift is to pass through shales, rock, binds and strata of a suitable nature, the work may be done by pneumatic pick as illustrated in Fig. 33.

Drilling.—When power is available in small and average-sized drifts, drilling today is usually accomplished by the use of compressed-air hammer drills (Figs. 6 and 10 in Chapter 8), or, if the rock is not extremely hard, by the use of compressed-air or electric rotary drills (Figs. 24 and 28 in Chapter 8), aided by the use of tungsten carbide bits. From what has been said concerning drilling it will be understood that while one-piece bits and detachable bits of steel may be used for percussive drilling in hard stone, rotary drilling in such a medium demands the use of tungsten carbide inserts, or of some form of diamond head. Wet drilling is being adopted on an ever increasing scale to allay dust in rock tunnelling in collieries. Light and medium hand-held drills are preferred where conditions permit, owing to the ease and speed with which holes can be started; careful benching and timely use of the rock-pile permit holes to be drilled at high level without the use of staging.

Fig. 34.—Ingersoll-Rand bogie-mounted drilling unit at work in a small drift.

High-Speed Drifting.—It will be obvious that many factors influence the speed at which tunnels can be driven. Thirty years ago, for a heading of 12 × 6 ft. in ground of medium hardness, and using pneumatic drills, speeds of from 5 to 8 yd. per week were usually quite satisfactory. Today, with the introduction of "horizon mining", speed in drifting has become of great importance, and the more scientific methods of tunnelling that have proved successful on major civil engineering contracts for hydraulic projects and have resulted in speeds of advance up to 60 ft. a day being achieved,[4] are being applied in collieries. Thus, in addition to power-operated drills and picks, drilling frames or jumbos, drill tenders and mechanical loaders, are being commonly employed. It is anticipated that speeds of 30 to 40 yd. per week will soon become a common achievement compared with the earlier average of about half that rate. Where ground is so hard that powerful and heavy drilling machines such as drifters must be employed, it becomes essential to use mechanical supports for the drills. These vary according to the size of the drift.

Rapid rates in stone drifting have been achieved in British mines, even without the use of drilling frames. Thus, using wet-drilling machines such as the Ingersoll J.A.45, and Climax F.2A, by attention to the disposition and length of shot-holes, size of rock pile and by the use of the 8BU and later the 11BU Joy loader, speeds of 40 yd. and more per week were attained in a drift 13 ft. wide by 10 ft. high at Knockshinnock Castle Colliery, New Cumnock. Had drilling frames and larger cars been used, it is probable that these speeds would have been exceeded.[5] At Nantgarw Colliery, South Wales, a

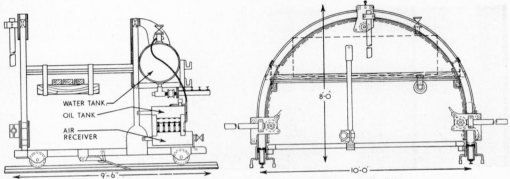

Fig. 35.—Fife drilling rig. (*King's College Mining Bulletin.*)

speed of 38 yd. per week was attained in hard rock, using a rig-mounted drifter for drilling and a Conway shovel for loading.[6]

Column-Mounted Machines.—For small drifts, a steel column, possibly of telescopic structure, provided with a jack screw for tightening between roof and floor, or between the sides of the roads, may be employed to support the cradle which carries the drill. The cradle may be clamped to horizontal or inclined arms extending from the column. Sometimes two or more such columns are employed.

One Ingersoll-Rand unit has vertical columns anchored by pneumatic extension. Drill-carrying arms can be moved up and down the columns or swung round horizontally to any desired position. Fig. 34 shows an Ingersoll-Rand bogie-mounted drilling unit at work in a small drift.

Frame-Mounted Machines.—The Fife drilling frame shown in Fig. 35 is of steel arches 8 ft. high and 10 ft. wide at the base, formed from 5–4½ in. H-section girders, mounted on a 4-wheel carriage running on a very wide track. Tubular arms are fitted to the girder rings, and may be locked in position as required. They may be extended inwards towards the centre and outwards to permit drilling of a 13 × 9 ft. heading. Air and water receivers are so mounted on the carriage as not to obstruct its passage over a tub or loading machine. This machine has proved successful, and in one instance, it helped materially to reduce the drilling period from 5 to 2 hours.[7]

Fig. 36.—Holman balanced drill rig, two-drill type.

Balanced-Boom Drilling Rigs.—A single-machine drilling rig may comprise a central supporting column, with a long arm pivoted on it by a universal joint. This arm carries the cradle and drill, also on a universal joint, at one end, and a counter-balancing weight at the other. This drill can be swung across the heading to operate at any point desired. Fig. 36 shows a balanced drill rig for two drills for larger drifts; a 4-unit balanced boom rig is employed as shown in Fig. 37.

Hydraulic Jib Mounting.—The Hydro drill jib shown in Fig. 38 carries drills on hydraulically-operated jibs. This offers flexibility in operation, and rigidity. The structure may be mounted on a carriage on caterpillar tracks, and the jib may be hydraulically jacked to the roof and further stabilised by hydraulic braking. Hydraulic power can be used for control of the drill feed.[7]

Jumbos.—For the drilling of shot-holes in tunnels of large cross-section, so-called "jumbos", or drilling frames, are frequently

Fig. 37.—Holman balanced-boom drill rig, four-drill type.

employed. These consist of special bogies or trucks which run on rails and which carry a superstructure or framework of metal tubes to afford support for drills or drill cradles at suitable points for drilling at the face of the drift. Such a jumbo should be (*a*) mobile, so that it can be withdrawn from the face of the heading during shot-firing; (*b*) collapsible or hinged, so that it can pass outbye or inbye unobstructed by the presence of a mechanical loader, conveyor, etc. A drill

Fig. 38.—The Hydro drill jib, wheel mounted type.

tender may be attached to carry the drill rods, compressed-air reservoir, hose connections, head-lights, etc., and to provide a platform for the operators working at the upper part of the drift face. Naturally, such jumbos must be withdrawn some distance along the tunnel when shots are to be fired.

Rapid rates of progress have been attained by the use of jumbo drilling frames. In one case in South Africa a maximum advance of upwards of 50 ft. in 24 hours was reported.

Fig. 39 shows an Ingersoll-Rand drilling jumbo in use.

German Methods of Mechanised Stone Drifting.—The British Intelligence Objectives Sub-Committee Final Report No. 1093, Items Nos. 30 and 31, gives an account of a German method of driving of stone drifts by mechanical means. Figs. 40 and 41 illustrate the drilling frame or "Bohrwagen"

Fig. 39.—Ingersoll-Rand drilling jumbo.

employed at some collieries in the Ruhr district of Germany. Fig. 40 shows the frame as erected for drilling. It is screwed to the roof by jacks at AA, and is also clamped to the rails. Hinges at point BB permit folding of the frame as shown in Fig. 41 to allow travel outbye beyond the range of shot-firing, and to afford free passage over mechanical-loading equipment. The frame is constructed of tubular steel, and mountings for drills can be attached wherever desired. The carriage top serves as a platform for drilling upper holes. As many as 6 men have been employed with such a frame to operate

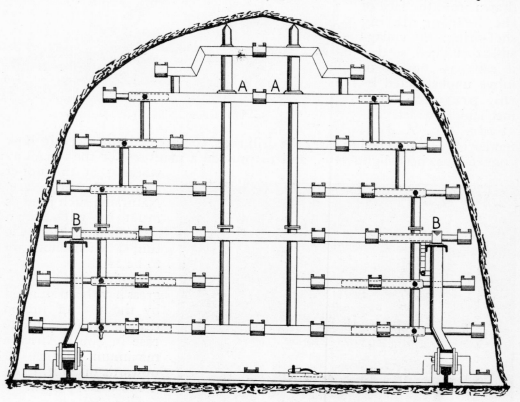

Fig. 40.—German drilling frame or "Bohrwagen" erected for drilling.

10 drills simultaneously with wet drilling. Air and water receivers are either carried on the carriage or are installed on the side of the road. For loading out, the stone mine shovel loader is employed, which is really a large duck-bill loader fitted with a special shovel, Fig. 42.

In Vol. 1 of the Technical Report on the Ruhr Coalfield is a report of the German rotary rock-tunnelling machine shown in Fig. 43. Details of the machine show that the cutting head is fitted with hard metal bits which cut out grooves of rock for an area amounting to about $\frac{1}{3}$ of the total cross-section, the other $\frac{2}{3}$ being broken off by the action of the cutter head. A 200-h.p. electric motor is required to drive this machine. The cuttings and, inci-

RUSSIAN TUNNELLING MACHINE

This machine, type ShBM, is driven by five motors of 140 aggregate h.p. and is used in soft rock and coal. (From *The Coal Industry of the U.S.S.R.*, 1957, by permission of the National Coal Board.)

RUSSIAN TUNNELLING MACHINE

This machine type PK-3 is used in hard rock. (From *The Coal Industry of the U.S.S.R.*, 1957, by permission of the National Coal Board.)

dentally, the heat from the motor are removed by an air suction system. The machine cuts a circular tunnel of 2·4 yd. diameter in a potash mine at the rate of 1·6 yd. per hr., and it is considered that a tunnel of 3·3 yd. dia. could be driven in coal measure sandstone at a rate of 0·88 yd. per hr.

Power Loading in Stone Drifts.—To achieve the best possible results, the mining engineer must match not only the type of machine, but also the model, to the particular job in hand. In the past, the speed of driving has been somewhat of a fetish among tunnellers, but there is little to be gained

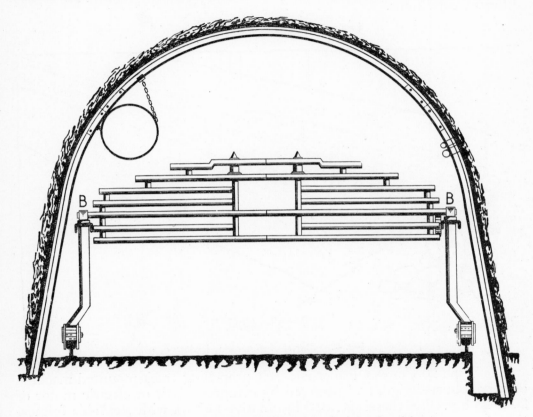

Fig. 41.—"Bohrwagen" folded for withdrawal during shot-firing.

from a machine of excessive capacity if it can be employed only for a short space of time. In normal drifting, loading represents about a quarter of the full cycle, the remainder being taken up by boring, shot-firing, setting, supports, etc. To ensure that such machines shall work nearer to capacity, it is advisable that holes should be drilled to not less than 6 ft. in depth, and so fired as to form a compact heap at which the loader can work effectively.

Various types of power-loading machines are applied to stone drifting in British collieries, and they may be grouped as follows:—

(*a*) Power shovels such as the Conway loader.

    (*b*) Rocker shovels or bucket loaders such as the Eimco-Finlay, New
        Sullivan and the Atlas machines.

    (*c*) Gathering arm and conveyor loaders such as the Joy loader, the
        Mavor and Coulson loader and similar loaders.

    (*d*) Scraper loaders such as the Holman and the Sullivan units.

The British Conway Loader.—This type of loading unit was developed
in the lead mines of America, and has been employed in tunnels ranging in
cross-section from 7 to 20 ft. sq. It is built in several sizes and types to suit
different conditions.

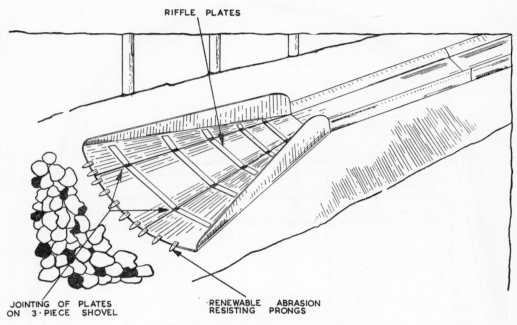

RIFFLE PLATES

JOINTING OF PLATES
ON 3·PIECE SHOVEL

RENEWABLE ABRASION
RESISTING PRONGS

Fig. 42.—Shovel of stone-mine loader.

    The Type 20 Conway loader is a self-propelling track-mounted machine
of very robust design, and powered by compressed-air or electric motor of
20 to 25 h.p. The chassis is fitted locomotive-fashion with steel side frames,
thus forming the body of the machine which houses the propelling and
hoisting units with their gears, shafts, sprockets and chains, etc.

    A glance at Fig. 44 reveals the outstanding features of the unit; the dipper
with its digging teeth on the right, followed by the dipper boom or trough,
which feeds on to the belt conveyor elevator which delivers to the discharge
jib. The hoisting chains which operate the dipper are carried to the requisite
height by the mast which is fitted with chain bollards and rollers for the
purpose. With the dipper lowered, the propelling mechanism forces it forward into the pile until it is full. Haulage on the chains then swings the dipper
until its teeth point vertically upwards. Continued shortening of the chains
raises the dipper and the dipper boom towards the vertical position until the

debris is completely discharged under gravity on to the conveyor belt which delivers it to the tub or car.

At the forward end of the chassis, the steel end members carry a heavy circular platform which permits the dipper boom to swing to right or left across the drift for loading purposes and supports it during loading. The right-hand side of the body framework carries the operator's step and the controls; two foot levers—a forward and a reverse tramming lever —and two hand levers —a left hoist chain control lever and a similar right hoist chain control lever. Thus the machine is controlled in safety from a point of vantage. Important dimensions and other details relative to the Type 20 loader are as follows:—

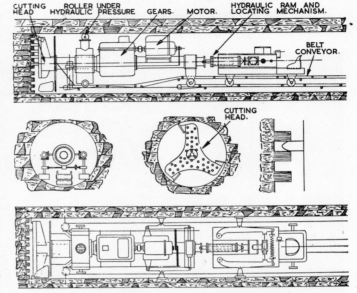

Fig. 43.—Rotary rock-tunnelling machine.

(*a*) Tramming length, 20 ft. 6 in.; tramming height, 5 ft. 9 in.; operating height, 6 ft. 6 in.; clean-up width, 9 ft.; length of boom, 3 ft. 9 in.; width of boom, 30 in.; width of conveyor belt, $21\frac{1}{2}$ in.; loading capacity in cu. yd. per hr., 20 to 25; dipper capacity, $4\frac{1}{2}$ cu. ft.; h.p. to drive, 20; weight of machine, $7\frac{1}{2}$ tons; minimum rail curve, 12 ft.; rail gauge, 24 to 34 in.

The limiting gradients for the machine vary according to fragmentation of the debris and moisture content, from a maximum of about 1 in $12\frac{1}{2}$ to the rise, and from a maximum of about 1 in $16\frac{1}{2}$ to the dip. Figs. 45 and 46 show front and rear views of the machine when in use.

The Type 30 and Type 60 machines are of similar design but of larger capacity. A number of these loaders are in use in British collieries and their application is growing.

Rocker Shovels.—Since the original rocker shovel was invented by Finlay and Royle in 1931, this type of loader (Fig. 47) has been applied extensively to high-speed drifting. A range of models of different capacities is manufactured by the Eimco Co., some of which are operated by compressed air, some by electricity, and some by both. Some are fitted with a conveyor-type delivery jib. The Eimco 12B loader may be taken as a typical unit. It consists of a bogie, driven through gearing and a freewheeling clutch, from a compressed-air motor, surmounted by an upper turntable deck carrying a rocker arm to the end of which is attached the separately driven loader shovel.

The arm moves under power in a vertical plane, but is supported by and rolls upon a rocker path so designed that the shovel describes a curved but not a circular path during its elevation under load from the rock pile at the lower front of the machine, to the top of the tub or car being loaded at the rear. The nature of the curved path is such as to minimise the height required for operation (Fig. 48). The turntable permits loading off centre across the width of the drift, but delivery of the load to the same point over the tub is ensured by a self-centring roller, acting on a profile plate.

Fig. 44.—British Conway loader.

The principal dimensions of this model are as follows:—

Over-all length with bucket extended, 71 to 74 in.; height with bucket lowered, 48 to 51 in.; width, 28 in. The height required for operation varies according to the height of the tub, but is usually from 70 to 83 in. The discharge height of the bucket is 46 to 60 in., and the discharge distance behind the loader is 14 to 22 in. The weight is 4,200 lb.; bucket capacity, $4\frac{1}{2}$ to 6 cu. ft.; average loading capacity, 20 to 35 cu. ft. per min., and the range of the track gauge is 15 to 36 in. The track speed is 3 m.p.h. An operator's platform and controls are located on one side of the machine. Normally, a permanent double track is laid to within 15 yd. or so of the face of the drift, then a 4-yd. crossing to a single line, followed immediately by a second 4-yd. crossing to a double line again. This extends by rails of standard length and final extension rails right up to the face. Holes are usually drilled to give a 6-ft.

Fig. 46.—Rear view of British Conway loader.

Fig. 45.—Front view of British Conway loader.

"pull", and some are located near floor level to facilitate track laying right under the holing, thus permitting the loader bucket to reach right up to the face and to lift all available debris. A side plough may be clipped on to the

Fig. 47.—Eimco rocker shovel, compressed-air type (Model 21).

side of the bucket to deal with side debris; thus hand loading may be reduced to about 5 per cent. The machine works best under dry conditions, but excessive fragmentation of the debris is quite unnecessary. It can load on high gradients (Fig. 49). In Great Britain this loader has loaded 63 tons of debris in 4 hr. 10 min. when serving one contractor, one loader and one haulage hand. Again, in a heading supported by steel arches of 12 ft. × 9 ft., it has handled 35 tons in about $2\frac{3}{4}$ hr. when serving two men. The unit is a robust pit job of great reliability and low cost of maintenance. The latest Eimco Model 521 hydro-electric unit employs one 20-h.p., constant-speed, flame-proof motor, operating two hydraulic pumps, one for traction and one for bucket elevation. There are several makes of rocker shovel which resemble in certain respects the Eimco machine; among these are the Sullivan, the Atlas, and the Gardner-Denver shovel loaders.

The Sullivan Slusher.— Loading by means of the slusher corresponds closely with loading on a longwall face by a box-scraper. The main unit, shown in Fig. 50, consists of a steel ramp with an extended jib carried upon a track-mounted steel base; the power unit is a double-drum

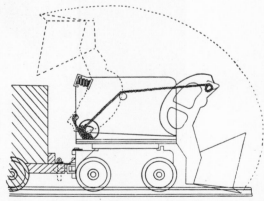

Fig. 48.—Showing curved path of shovel of Eimco loader.

haulage unit driven by a triple chain drive from the motor. The wire haulage ropes pass from the haulage drums, round roller-bearing sheaves situated at the extreme end of the slusher jib; one is secured to the outbye end of the scraper, and the other passes right to the face heading, around a sheave or snatch block anchored beyond the rock pile and back to the inbye end of the scraper. The slusher is located at the end of the rail track over which its loading ramp projects inbye and towards ground level. It terminates in a hinged apron which is lowered to the floor to receive the travelling scraper, but which is raised when flitting. The ramp flattens out at the top to form the landing floor of the long jib which projects outbye, but a hatch is provided therein to permit discharge of the scraper load into a tub located on the tub track underneath the jib on the left in Fig. 50. The ramp is of welded or riveted construction,

Fig. 49.—Eimco shovel loader working on steep gradient (about 1 in 2½).

but is sectionalised to permit dismantling for transport underground. The slusher should be located in the middle of the roadway at a distance of not less than 20 ft. from the rock pile produced by the round of shots. It may

Fig. 50.—The Sullivan slusher or scraper loader (*Joy-Sullivan Ltd.*).

Note the ramp on the right and jib on the left; also the scraper box with its rope passing round the jib pulley and to the haulage drums mounted below the machine. During loading the tub or mine car stands below the dumping hatch in the jib.

Fig. 51.—Sullivan slusher terminal pulley and scraper box in drift.

remain in this position while the face of the heading advances 60 to 70 ft. The rails are then extended towards the face and the slusher is moved up again. It is best to arrange a double track with a back shunt or cross-over to ensure the rapid changing of tubs beneath the jib.

Slushers have worked successfully on gradients as high as 1 in 3. To achieve a high degree of clearance of the debris after firing, a hole should be drilled in the centre of the heading, and then one at 12 to 18 in. from either side, all as near the roof as possible. Sister wedges, to which

Fig. 52.—Sullivan scraper box.

the face snatch block may be attached, are inserted into each hole in turn. The scraper is thus compelled to effect a clearance which may amount to

JOY LOADER

(*Above*) Rear view of a Joy loader in use at an East Midlands colliery. Note scraper-chain conveyor in the right foreground. (*Below*) Front view of a Joy loader.

(*Photographs National Coal Board*)

COAL-CUTTING MACHINES

(*Above*) Coal-cutting machine with two horizontal jibs and two mushroom cutters, or jibs, at Taff Merthyr Colliery, South Wales. Note the prop-free front. (*Below*) Coal-cutting machine with curved top jib, horizontal jib and mushroom jib in use at Windsor Colliery, South Wales. Note the coal-plough pre-loader in the left foreground, and the prop-free front.

(*Photographs National Coal Board*)

95 per cent. of the debris. An advance of 18 to 20 yd. per week in a drift supported by 12 × 8 ft. arches, with an expenditure of 6 to 9 manshifts per day, is typical of slusher achievement. Fig. 51 shows the terminal pulley and the scraper box almost buried in the dirt pile. Fig. 52 shows the scraper box. The Holman scrapeloader is very similar in many ways to the Sullivan slusher, as will be seen from Fig. 53, which shows clearly the ramp, jib and haulage motor

Fig. 53.—The Holman scrapeloader with hauler under slide.

COAL CUTTING IN COAL HEADINGS AND BORD AND PILLAR WORKINGS

Heading in Coal.—By Hand.—Before the advent of the pneumatic drill, coal headings, like stone headings, were driven by means of the basic primary tools, the simplest forms of hand-operated drills, and the use of explosives. In rare situations remote from power supplies, the old methods are of necessity still employed. The manner in which ground is broken depends mainly upon the shape and dimensions of the heading and the nature of the ground to be penetrated. To provide a free face for blasting, hewers may undercut, middlecut or overcut the seam by hand, preferably in some relatively soft layer of fireclay. Sometimes the coal may be hand-sheared down one or both sides of the heading to facilitate blasting. During hand-cutting or holing, the undermined coal or other strata must be supported temporarily by suitable sprags. These are removed immediately prior to blasting, and are replaced by more permanent supports as soon as possible after blasting. The depth of holing varies according to circumstances, and usually ranges from 4 ft. 6 in. to 6 ft. Shot-holes must not extend beyond this depth.

The disposition of shot-holes also varies according to the shape and size of the heading and the nature and direction of cleavages crossing the face of the heading. For blasting in coal, although compressed powder may be used in naked-light mines, the explosive used in a safety-lamp mine must be of the "permitted" class and suited to the hardness of the seam (Chap. 8). In such cases loading is generally by hand-shovelling into tubs.

BY MACHINE.—About fifty years ago, the Stanley heading machine was sometimes employed for the driving of circular headings in coal. A compressed-air engine supplied power to rotate a horizontal shaft on the end of which was fitted a cross head. This carried horizontal arms, one at each end, extending towards the face of the heading. The ends of these arms were fitted with cutting teeth which, moving in a circular path, cut out an annular groove with an outer diameter of from 4 to 7 ft., leaving a central core of coal as the arms advanced into the solid face. The depth of cut was limited by the depth of the arm to about 4 ft. 6 in.; the breaking down of the core and the loading of the coal past the machine by conveyor was difficult. Although good work was done under ideal conditions, the machine was gradually superseded on account of mechanical difficulties.

Auger Mining.—The same principle has been applied in the U.S.A. for partial extraction of coal at opencast sites where the overburden is too thick for removal, and more recently machines for use underground have been developed. Two such machines, the Cardox-Hardsocg auger miner and the Joy AD2 auger drill have been experimented with in Great Britain, the former in the East Midland Coalfield[8] and the latter in Scotland.[9]

The Cardox machine used in these tests drills out a 24-in. diam. hole and comprises a driving unit powered by a 25-h.p. flame-proof motor, an archimedean-screw conveying unit which conveys the coal to the mouth of the hole, and a cutting head of barrel type fitted with cutting bits at its front periphery, and with a pilot cutter comprising an extension of the main driving shaft which also carries the scrolls of the conveying unit. The cutting head is 3 ft. in length and the scrolls, which are added as the hole advances, are 6 ft. in length. The machine has proved capable of drilling holes up to 80 ft. or more in length at the rate of 2·7 ft. per minute. New machines in course of development are designed to drill holes up to 4 ft. in diameter at a speed of 4 ft. per minute, for which it is estimated that a 120- to 150-h.p. motor will be required. The Joy machine works on the same principle but differs in certain respects—particularly in the design of the cutting head and pilot cutter.

For the application of the system the coal to be worked must be split up by an initial working into pillars from which the coal is subsequently extracted by auger mining. The size of the pillars is determined by the length to which the auger holes are to be bored and the distance apart of the holes by the desired percentage extraction.

Auger mining is not adapted for bulk production and its application would appear to be limited to such cases as the following:—(a) the extraction of coal from high quality seams too thin for normal mining methods, (b) the robbing of pillars left for the support of old roadways before their abandonment and (c) the partial extraction of seams where surface damage due to subsidence must be avoided.

Fig. 54.—The Siskol electric coal cutter. (*Siskol Machines Ltd., Sheffield*)

THE SISKOL ELECTRIC COAL CUTTER.—This unit shown in Fig. 54 is designed for narrow development work, and consists of a central column and the machine which it supports. The column is spiralled to permit

Fig. 55.—Cam and roller mechanism giving reciprocatory motion to the cutting tool in the Siskol machine.

adjustment of the height of the machine, and it is tightened between roof and floor by means of a screw jack operated by a ratchet seen at the top of Fig. 54. Two long carrying rods are cross-connected by the carrying arm and sleeves in the middle, by the driving motor and the reduction gearbox at one end, and by a second reduction gearbox and drilling-shaft housing at the other. A transmission rod and feed screw run parallel to the carrying arms.

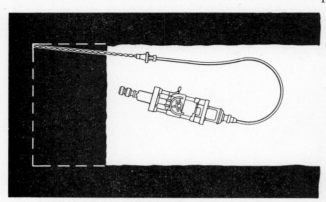

Fig. 56.—Showing arrangement for drilling shot-holes by the Siskol machine.

Rotary motion from the 5-h.p. motor at the rear is transmitted to the forward reduction gear, and converted to reciprocating motion through the cam and roller mechanism shown in Fig. 55. A special chuck on the end of the shaft receives the shank of the cutter rod, Fig. 54. The cutter can be swung through an arc by a large worm gear, and can be fed forward by small pinions; thus a horizontal cut can be made at any level. The motor shaft is slotted at the rear to permit the coupling thereto of a flexible drilling shaft. On the opposite end of this shaft is a drill head containing epicyclic gearing, a chuck and ball-bearings through which rotary motion is imparted to a drilling rod for drilling shot-holes for blasting (Figs. 56 and 57).

THE ARCWALL MACHINE.—Improvements in the design of coal-cutting machines on longwall faces, and particularly mechanical slewing of the jib through 180 degrees or more, made the application of such machines to the driving of headings inevitable. When later they were mounted on self-propelling bogies and caterpillars, like the A.B. Fifteen Arcwaller machine shown in Figs. 58 and 59, and other similar machines, development work in the form of coal headings became in itself an economic proposition in many cases where

Fig. 57.—Drilling shot-holes with the Siskol machine.

previously it had usually been carried out at a loss. The use of larger jibs capable of cutting a heading 15 ft. wide from one position, became possible with machines such as the A.B. Universal heading coal cutter shown in

Fig. 58.—The A.B. longwall-arcwall machine (*Anderson-Boyes Ltd., Motherwell*).

Fig. 59.—The A.B. Fifteen arcwaller on tractors.

Fig. 60.—The A.B. Fifteen Universal heading machine mounted on wheels.

Fig. 61.—The A.B. Universal heading machine mounted on tractors.

Figs. 60, 61, 62, and 63. This machine with others of its type was introduced primarily for the purpose of giving great versatility in regard to the

position of the cut. A later machine made by Messrs. Anderson-Boyes is their A.B. Dreadnought universal arc-shearer shown in Fig. 64. It is designed on similar lines to those of the previous machine, but is of much heavier construction, and is capable of cutting rooms up to 20 ft. wide. Similar machines are supplied by Mavor and Coulson Ltd. and other manufacturers.

Fig. 62.—The A.B. Universal heading machine. Shearing in centre of working place.

Working Shortwall Faces.—THE SHORT-WALL MACHINE.—This machine has become increasingly popular in Great Britain, particularly for the thinner seams; it is usually applied in room-and-pillar workings to the cutting of faces of not more than 20 ft. or so in

width. The jib is fastened rigidly to the body of the machine, and normal mechanical slewing is impossible. In Britain, the h.p. of the driving motor is about 50, and the length of the machine from 4 ft. to 7 ft. 6 in. It is compact, and normally is mounted on a base plate. A small haulage drum having a rope capacity of about 40 ft. is fitted to each side of the machine. By anchoring the ropes to steel props in well-chosen

Fig. 63.—The A.B. Universal heading machine holing (undercutting) near rail level.

positions, and by hauling upon one or other or both of the ropes, the cutter may be manoeuvred to any position. Normally, it is made to haul itself while cutting or sumping-in along the ribside straight into the face, then across

Fig. 64.—The A.B. Universal heading machine mounted on tractors.

Fig. 65.—A.B. shortwall coal cutter.

411

the face and out again at the other end of the short face, keeping the ribside cuts in alignment. Figs. 65 and 66 show the Anderson-Boyes shortwall coal cutter. Shortwall machines are also supplied by other manufacturers.

In the United States of America, shortwall machines such as the Sullivan, shown in Fig. 67, are commonly employed, particularly where cutting is near the bottom of the seam, but the jibs are made up to 9 ft. or 10 ft. long in an attempt to produce more coal per "turn-over" on a given face, to keep the loading unit employed over a longer period, and so to reduce the amount of flitting for a given output. Sometimes shortwall machines are fitted with overcutting jibs, and may also be mounted on jacks to permit adjustment of the height of the cut. Such

Fig. 66.—The A.B. shortwall in action on the face.

a machine is the Sullivan 9B overcutter shown in Fig. 68. The machines are often flitted from one room to another, "pick-a-back" fashion, on mobile tractor-treaded trucks, powered by batteries or by room cables. Owing to mechanical and metallurgical improvements in the production of cutter picks and chains, cutting may be done in bands of dirt, in sequence or simultaneously with double jibs if necessary, in order to produce cleaner coal.

MOUNTED UNIVERSAL MACHINES.—These are really arcwall machines of universal type, track, crawler, or rubber-tyre mounted, which, as the name implies, have complete flexibility for horizontal, shear or inclined cuts. They also have greater manoeuvrability as a result of which their capacity is greater than that of the normal shortwall machines; consequently, they are more favoured for conditions where mobile machines may be kept in action almost continuously.

Loading Machines in Coal Headings and on Shortwall Faces.—Power loaders employed in narrow work in British mines, i.e., in coal headings, breastings and in bord-and-pillar working may be divided into two categories: (*a*) duckbill or shaker loaders, and (*b*) mobile loaders.

THE DUCKBILL LOADER.—Fig. 69 shows that this loader consists of an ordinary shaker-conveyor engine drive with its line of troughs, to the

inbye end of which the following are or may be connected in succession:—
  (a) A swivel trough carried on a ball frame support.
  (b) A feeder trough.
  (c) A shovel trough which telescopes within the feeder trough.
  (d) A shovel head which digs into the broken coal and feeds it continuously to the succession of troughs in tandem behind.

The shaker-conveyor engine furnishes the power, imparting a reciprocating motion to the whole line of troughs. The shovel head and shovel trough are welded into one unit. A so-called "operating carrier", attached to the feeder trough, is used to impart telescopic motion to the shovel trough and shovel. At each side of

Fig. 67.—Joy-Sullivan 5B shortwall coal cutter.

the carrier is a lever which controls two clamps or grip blocks. With the levers in the forward position, the blocks move the shovel forward with every stroke of the pans; with levers in the backward position, they move the shovel back, and with the levers in the upright position, no telescopic movement takes place as the feeder trough and shovel trough are then locked together.

  The swivel trough connects the feeder trough to the main line of conveyors. As the name implies, this trough permits the shovel, shovel trough and feeder trough to swing through a horizontal angle of 30 degrees (in some models 45 degrees) on either side of the centre line, thus permitting clearance of the face over widths of as much as 40 ft. Normally, the shovel is levered through this angle by means of a crowbar. Naturally the swivel trough must be supported as it swings, and a pendulum jack, i.e., a jack prop with a bar attached to the pans at the swivel point —serves as a fulcrum. Sometimes another telescopic trough is inserted in the main line immediately outbye of the

Fig. 68.—Joy-Sullivan 9B, 60-h.p. turret-head overcutter.

swivel trough, and this allows the duckbill to advance several cuts before it becomes necessary to add additional troughs to the main line. Fig. 69 also shows an arrangement of the troughs to allow of loading from a second loading face on the left.

  Duckbill units are manufactured in various sizes to suit different con-

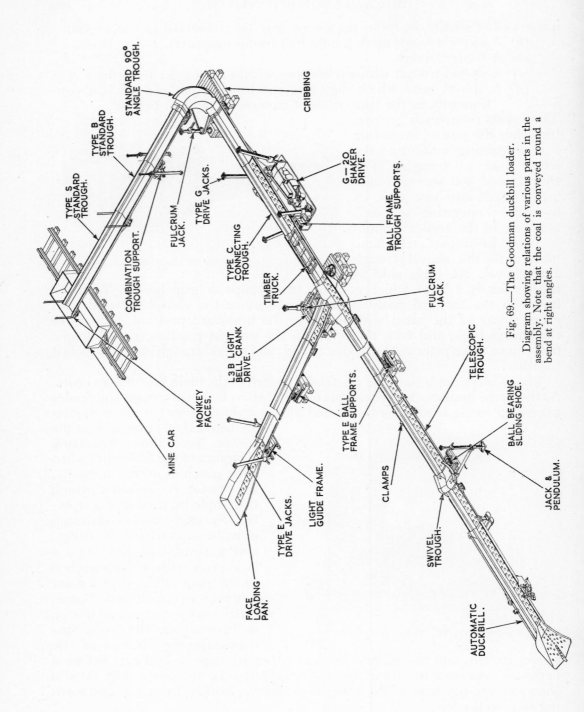

STANDARD 90° ANGLE TROUGH.

TYPE B STANDARD TROUGH.

CRIBBING

TYPE S STANDARD TROUGH.

FULCRUM JACK.

TYPE G DRIVE JACKS.

G—20 SHAKER DRIVE.

BALL FRAME TROUGH SUPPORTS.

COMBINATION TROUGH SUPPORT.

TYPE C CONNECTING TROUGH.

TIMBER TRUCK.

FULCRUM JACK.

MONKEY FACES.

MINE CAR

L 3 B LIGHT BELL CRANK DRIVE.

TELESCOPIC TROUGH.

TYPE E BALL FRAME SUPPORTS.

LIGHT GUIDE FRAME.

CLAMPS

BALL BEARING SLIDING SHOE.

TYPE E DRIVE JACKS.

SWIVEL TROUGH.

JACK & PENDULUM.

FACE LOADING PAN.

AUTOMATIC DUCKBILL.

Fig. 69.—The Goodman duckbill loader.

Diagram showing relations of various parts in the assembly. Note that the coal is conveyed round a bend at right angles.

ditions, and outputs vary accordingly. Gradients, of course, have an important bearing upon the capacity of the machine.

The G.20 with a 20-h.p. drive will deliver 1 ton per min. on the level, and 2 tons per min. when the gradient is 1 in 5 in favour of the load. On the level, a distance of 300 ft. is regarded as about the limit for satisfactory working. This unit can be employed in driving headings and in loading-off very short faces and, therefore, it finds its greatest application in opening up bord-and-pillar work and in the extraction of the pillars. Each room may be worked by one team consisting of (*a*) the shortwall cutting machine operator; (*b*) the duckbill operator; (*c*) the driller, who also assists (*a*) and (*b*); (*d*) the conveyor attendant who is responsible for the loading of coal from the shaker conveyor on to the gathering belt or into the tubs. Fig. 70 shows the A.B. Fifteen shaker conveyor driving gear for duckbill loading, and Figs. 71 and 72 show the duckbill in operation.

Fig. 70.—A.B. shaker conveyor drive for duckbill.

THE JOY LOADER.—This is a mobile loading machine which was first applied to narrow work in the U.S.A. in the early twenties and was introduced into British coal mines for similar work about 1931. It has three main parts: the chassis, the gathering head and the delivery conveyor.

(A) The chassis is fitted with caterpillar tractors which operate singly or together, thus affording forward and backward movement at variable speeds, and the ability to steer by braking on or applying power to one caterpillar or the other as required.

(B) The gathering head is formed by a sloping apron which is forced into the coal pile, bringing the coal within the radius of action of two gathering arms, which make alternate sweeps serving to gather the coal and push it on to a central chain conveyor. The apron may be raised for flitting.

(C) The central conveyor raises the coal up the forward ramp and carries it over the top of the chassis, and along the delivery jib to the tub or conveyor. The jib can be raised or lowered, and it can be swung through 45 degrees on either side of centre by means of ropes operated by hydraulic rams. The conveyor chain is fitted with swivel links to permit this.

The loader may be operated by compressed air or by electricity; the

Fig. 71.—The duckbill in operation with fulcrum jack in foreground.

Fig. 72.—Another view of duckbill in operation, showing operator manipulating the loading handle or lever.

latter type incorporates two motors for the caterpillar, two for the gathering head and one for the pump which operates the hydraulic rams. Controls are centrally located to permit complete operation of the unit by one person.

There are seven different sizes of Joy loaders, and care must be taken in selecting the most suitable model for any set of conditions. Rated capacities vary from $\frac{3}{4}$ of a ton to 4 tons per min., heights from 2 ft. 2 in. to 4 ft., widths from 4 ft. 8 in. to 7 ft. 1 in. and lengths from 22 ft. 2 in. to 25 ft. Total h.p. required ranges from $27\frac{1}{2}$ to $32\frac{1}{2}$. It is claimed that the Junior model will work in a 30-in. seam and the largest model, the 11BU, is suitable for work in a 60-in. seam.

The Joy loader is a somewhat versatile machine. Obviously it can be used for headings, driftings or certain face work, if inclinations are not too severe,

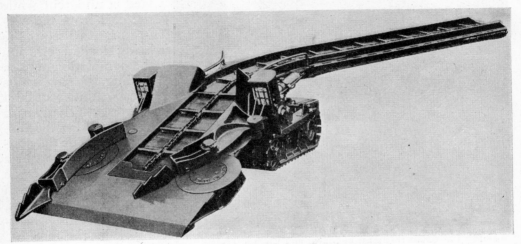

Fig. 73.—Mavor and Coulson loader, type 8 BU4.

and if conveyors can be kept up to and in tandem with the machine or arranged alongside the machine where provision is made to deal with prop obstruction. Probably the Joy loader has its greatest application in bord-and-pillar work where it operates so frequently in conjunction with shuttle cars (Vol. 2, Chap. 7), particularly in U.S.A.

Figs. 73 and 74 illustrate the Mavor and Coulson loader, type 8 BU4, but it should be noted that there are several other American loading machines[10] which are similar to the Joy loader, both in principles of operation and in appearance. Their loading heads are fitted with gathering arms, the coal is conveyed by chain conveyors up elevating ramps and along delivering jibs, which may be moved vertically or horizontally to any desired position. Such are the Goodman, the Jeffrey and the Myers Whaley Automat. They differ from the Joy machine in that they are usually track-mounted machines and incorporate different gathering or loading arrangements. The maximum rated capacity of such machines is about 6 tons per min., and the average loading rate about 2 tons per min. An American loader of somewhat different type is the Jeffrey shortwall loader. It is really a cutter-loader and differs from the others, because the gathering head is replaced by 3-cutter chain jibs. The lowest of these is about twice as long as those surmounting it.

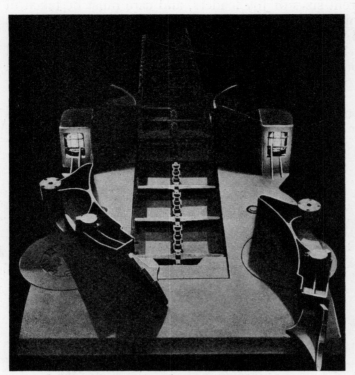

The long jib sumps into the coal well in advance, while the other two deliver the coal, remaining from the previous cutting operation, on to the chain conveyor as usual. Thus the short face is undercut while the coal from the previous undercut is being loaded off. On the completion of each loading, the face stands already undercut and awaits drilling and blasting. Also the discharge end of the conveyor is anchored by a small 4-wheel bogie centring truck, which rides on the conveyor, thus facilitating loading while the machine traverses the face.

Fig. 74.—Gathering arms of Mavor and Coulson loader.

COAL CUTTING OR HOLING ON LONGWALL FACES

By Hand.—Breaking ground as applied to the winning of coal by hand, either in bord-and-pillar work, or on longwall faces, is usually a matter of hand holing, spragging, blasting and loading. Hewers may be allotted a certain "stint", i.e., a certain length of face to undercut by hand to a certain depth. Alternatively, the face may be divided into stalls, each in charge of a stallman, or long lengths of face may be worked under the supervision of a contractor. The cut or kerf usually tapers towards the back for convenience and, as it is made, the coal is supported by sprags, holing nogs or wedges until it is required to be brought down for loading. The great variety of conditions encountered render it futile to describe any one system of coal-getting by hand. The holing may take place in a dirt band below, within or above the seam but is little practised nowadays as less than 6 per cent. of the coal is now handgot. The shot-firing practice varies accordingly.

By Machine.—Over 85 per cent. of British coal is won by machine

Fig. 75.—The Samson 15-in. machine, general view.

Fig. 76.—Samson 19-in. machine at work, showing haulage end and controls. Note holing nog in centre foreground.

cutting, and of the machines employed the most important is the longwall coal cutter.

Longwall Coal-Cutting Machines.—STANDARD MACHINE.—A cursory glance at the illustration of the Samson 15-in. machine made by Mavor and

Fig. 77.—The A.B. Fifteen longwall coal cutter with gummer.

Coulson (Fig. 75) shows that such a unit may be divided into two main parts: the main body of the machine, and the long jib which carries the chain and its cutting teeth. Closer inspection shows that the main body may be divided into three sections. The middle section contains the driving motor of 35 to 50 h.p., the end next to the jib contains the gears for driving the cutter chain, etc., and the other end contains the haulage mechanism. This rotates a haulage drum, which can be seen under the machines in Fig. 75, and which

will hold 120 ft. or so of rope by means of which it can haul itself along at different speeds, say from 9 to 54 in. per min. for cutting, and 40 ft. per min. for flitting from one cut to another. Jibs vary in length, the shortest giving an undercut of about 3 ft. 10 in. and the longest about 9 ft. 3 in. The cutting chain consists of cutter-pick boxes linked together; each box carries a cut-ting-pick, of which there may be from 20

Fig. 78.—A.B. Fifteen longwall coal cutter at work on the face, showing convenience of controls.

to 39 per chain. The thickness of the cut or kerf varies in practice from about $3\frac{3}{4}$ in. to 7 in., but is usually about 5 in. During cutting, a jib lies at an angle of slightly less than a right-angle with the body of the machine. It may cut on a level with, below or above the centre line of the machine; if above the machine, it may swing back over the body during flitting; otherwise it is flitted in tandem with the body. Slewing into the cut from the flitting position is accomplished while the chain is in motion, and usually by means of the haulage mechanism and the rope. A spiral gummer is usually suspended from the gearhead to lie alongside the chain, and its function is to remove the cuttings brought out by the chain and prevent their re-entry into the cut. The foregoing gives a broad outline of the main features of a standard longwall coal cutter, shown at work in Fig. 76. There are many variations in type, size, power and purpose. Occasionally they are mounted on tracks or on caterpillars, but mostly on skid plates: some machines are fitted with two jibs, one above the other, usually for the removal of dirt bands in the seam to produce cleaner coal.

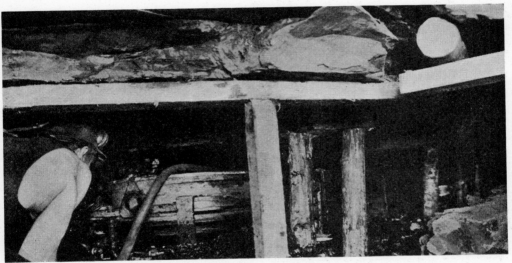

Fig. 79.—A.B. Fifteen coal cutter leaving roadhead.

Fig. 77 shows the Anderson-Boyes Fifteen longwall chain coal cutter complete with gummer. Figs. 78 and 79 are photographs of the machine at work on the face. Such machines may be driven by compressed-air turbines, by a.c. or by d.c. electric motors with horse-power up to 60 or more, depending upon local requirements. Thus a variety of machines is available to meet a variety of conditions. Again, the jibs of some overcutting machines are carried upon turrets which may be telescopic to permit adjustment of the cutting height (Figs. 80 and 81).

As the machine progresses along the face during cutting, timber or steel nogs or wedges are placed in the cut to support the coal undercut, until shots are about to be fired, where necessary, or the coal loaded out.

Such machines are usually employed on single-unit faces of about 100 yd. in length, or upon double-unit faces of about twice this length, the faces being kept as straight as possible; all face operations being highly organised, and run in sequence to schedule. Working on a 24-hour cycle, the most common practice is to do the cutting, timbering and shot-hole drilling on the night shift; firing, loading off and timbering on the day shift; and flitting or moving over of the conveyor, ripping and packing on the afternoon shift. Where two-shift working is practised the operation on the various shifts may be varied, but the sequence is maintained. Cutting time varies with conditions, but the length of face allotted to be cut, power of machine, and other factors, should be such as to afford ample margin in time, to allow for unexpected delays.

PICKS FOR CUTTER CHAINS.—Each cutter chain is "laced" with picks carried in pick boxes and arranged in a certain sequence which has been determined carefully to afford the easiest, quickest and most effective cutting.

Fig. 80.—The A.B. Fifteen coal cutter with hydraulically-operated turret for overcutting.

The picks are set at various angles to give several (up to nine) cutting lines. It is probable that the wedge or "flying V" formation is most frequently employed. It is the cutting pick which does the work, and its nature, shape and condition determine its cutting characteristics and the power consumed. A good cutter pick has the following properties:—

(1) Toughness to resist stress. (2) Hardness to resist abrasion. (3) Correct shape to cut efficiently at low power consumption. (4) High productive capacity measured in sq. ft. of cut per sharpening. (5) Low cost performance as reflected in over-all cutting expenses. (6) It should produce coarse cuttings.

Various shapes of cutter pick are employed, viz., the chisel-edged, the needle-pointed, the duckbill, the reversible throwaway, the duplex, and the specially tipped bits. Makers usually produce bits from 0·85 carbon steel with a rake angle of 25 to 30 degrees, and a front clearance of 23 to 30 degrees. In resharpening, every endeavour should be made to reproduce the original angles. Sharpening may be by hand forging, but machine sharpening is best, and indeed, is almost essential if the bits are made from alloy steels. Pick-sharpening machines are supplied by various manufacturers.

Only practical tests will determine the most suitable bits for each cutting project. Hard alloy bits may show no superiority over ordinary bits where cutting is easy, but they may be essential in cutting in very hard stratum. In the latter case, not only may the direct saving in cost of bits be considerable, but the indirect saving may be much greater due to (*a*) increased cutting capacity, (*b*) reduced power consumption, (*c*) reduced transportation and resharpening costs, and (*d*) reduced over-all costs of cutting.

Fig. 81.—Mavor & Coulson 15-in. Samson machine with hydraulic turret for cutting at varying height.

In the illustration it is cutting 3 ft. 2 in. above the floor. At the end of the shift the turret is lowered out of contact with the roof.

Almost any form of pick may be tipped with fused tungsten carbide, which is more resistant to wear than austenitic steels or true alloys but bits fitted with sintered tungsten carbide inserts give the best service. It is recorded that in certain holing, standard steel picks failed after 30 yd. of cutting, picks tipped with fused tungsten carbide failed after 100 yd., but picks tipped with sintered tungsten carbide inserts served to cut 9,000 yd.

COAL CUTTERS WITH CURVED JIBS.—The standard type of coal-cutting machine is now being employed for simultaneous cutting and shearing with a single jib. Obviously the jib must be curved from the horizontal to the vertical and a special flexible chain is required to negotiate the curvature (Fig. 82). The horizontal portion of the jib is usually about 4 ft. 6 in. in length and the vertical about 2 ft. 2 in. The jib may be arranged so that the shearing portion extends from the floor upwards or from the roof downwards. In a thick seam with middle cutting either the upper section or the lower section may be sheared as desired. The disadvantages of the curved jib are:—(*a*) more care is required when jibbing in and out, (*b*) the speed of cutting is reduced, (*c*) power consumption is increased, (*d*) gas may accumulate in the cut, (*e*) a mechanical gummer is almost essential. Advantages which may derive from its use are (*a*) the coal may be worked more readily, with a reduction in face-workers and a corresponding increase in O.M.S., (*b*) shot-firing may be reduced, (*c*) the size of the product may be improved.

Fig. 82.—A.B. Fifteen coal cutter with curved jib in operation at the coalface.

The Pneumatic Pick.—This was first

employed in British mines about 1928. Fig. 83 shows that it is very similar in appearance and in action to the hand-held pneumatic drill described in Chapter 8. It differs therefrom in that it does not contain mechanism for rotating the drill. The pick is solid, only 12 to 18 in. in length, and usually pointed. The machine contains the usual air-control valve mechanism, and a piston which imparts hammer blows at high speed to the end of the pick shank inserted into its chuck. Figs. 84 (*a*), (*b*) and (*c*) illustrate the action of the pick. The object is to drive the pick into the coal, the pick point

Fig. 83.—Huwood pneumatic pick in use.

acting as a wedge, tending to open the cleavage planes or "breaks" into which it is driven, thus facilitating deeper penetration. When a sufficient depth has

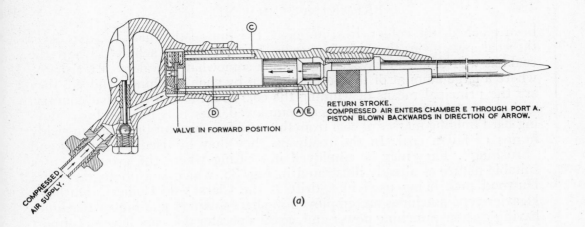

RETURN STROKE.
COMPRESSED AIR ENTERS CHAMBER E THROUGH PORT A.
PISTON BLOWN BACKWARDS IN DIRECTION OF ARROW.

VALVE IN FORWARD POSITION

COMPRESSED AIR SUPPLY.

(a)

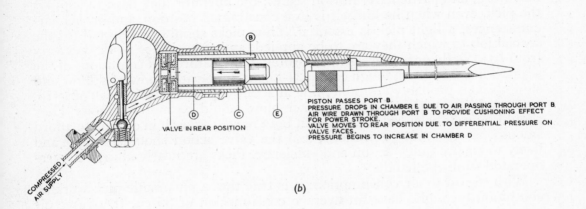

PISTON PASSES PORT B.
PRESSURE DROPS IN CHAMBER E DUE TO AIR PASSING THROUGH PORT B.
AIR WIRE DRAWN THROUGH PORT B TO PROVIDE CUSHIONING EFFECT
FOR POWER STROKE.
VALVE MOVES TO REAR POSITION DUE TO DIFFERENTIAL PRESSURE ON
VALVE FACES.
PRESSURE BEGINS TO INCREASE IN CHAMBER D

VALVE IN REAR POSITION

COMPRESSED AIR SUPPLY

(b)

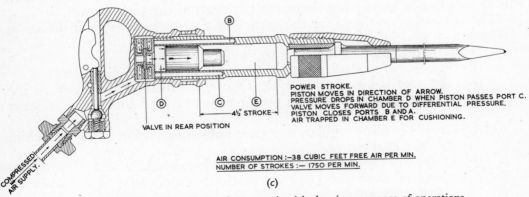

POWER STROKE.
PISTON MOVES IN DIRECTION OF ARROW.
PRESSURE DROPS IN CHAMBER D WHEN PISTON PASSES PORT C.
VALVE MOVES FORWARD DUE TO DIFFERENTIAL PRESSURE.
PISTON CLOSES PORTS B AND A.
AIR TRAPPED IN CHAMBER E FOR CUSHIONING.

4½" STROKE

VALVE IN REAR POSITION

COMPRESSED AIR SUPPLY.

AIR CONSUMPTION :—38 CUBIC FEET FREE AIR PER MIN.
NUMBER OF STROKES :— 1750 PER MIN.

(c)

Fig. 84 (a), (b) and (c).—Huwood pneumatic pick showing sequence of operations.

been reached, the collier, by a judicious twisting of the machine, may lever the coal away from the face. Naturally, best results are achieved where the coal has well-defined cleavage, a condition somewhat prevalent in Germany, where a large amount of the output is won by such machines. Indeed, they are the principal means of winning the coal in some seams in that country, and even where longwall cutters are employed, they may be used for removing hard bulging masses of coal from the solid face, and for breaking unwieldy lumps of fallen coal. In the roadways they may be used for dinting and "brushing". They may be employed in drifting where the ground is of a suitable nature as already illustrated in Fig. 33, which is a photograph of a Huwood pick being used in a drift at the Clara Vale Colliery, Durham. Heavier-type machines are employed in shaft sinkings, the bigger machines having greater punching power and, as the operator does not have to support them, the more powerful machines can be used to great advantage. On coalface work, and particularly in thin seams, the operator may have to support the pick, even when he himself is in a constrained position, and in such circumstances, a light pick is essential. Thus picks should be selected for the special job to which they are to be applied, and for coalface work they vary from 16 to 24 lb. or so in weight, according to the nature and conditions of the seam. Thus in a hard, tough coal, a 24-lb. machine with a powerful blow and slow speed is probably desirable, but in a soft or brittle coal, a pick of 18 lb. or even 16 lb. with a lighter, quicker blow would be more suitable. They should be well balanced for use with both hands, smooth in outline to afford smooth passage over projections, and the valve action should be light and lively to ensure quick action and efficiency. Picks are nearly always trigger-operated from the handle.

With regard to air consumption: it is true that a pneumatic pick working continuously might have an average consumption of 35 cu. ft. of free air per min., but in practice all the machines on a face are rarely in action together. It is probable that the provision of 15 to 20 cu. ft. at 75 to 80 lb. per sq. in. per pick is usually adequate. About 22,000 pneumatic picks are used in British mines, producing about 9·5 per cent. of the total output.

The advantages claimed for the getting of coal by pneumatic picks are as follows:—

    (1) Supports may be set close to the face.
    (2) The use of explosive may be partially or entirely eliminated.
    (3) The roof is less shattered; thus faces and roads are safer.
    (4) Cleaner coal is produced owing to better roof conditions, absence of gummings, etc.
    (5) Output is more regular, as it does not depend upon a single machine —the coal cutter.
    (6) Output per manshift of coal may be increased.
    (7) Costs of explosives, power, machine supervision and transit are generally lower.

They have the disadvantage of limited application and excessive dust production.

POWER LOADING IN LONGWALL WORKINGS

Until comparatively recently all coal mined was loaded by hand shovel, formerly into tubs but latterly largely on to conveyors installed along the coalface. Filling coal in this way is an arduous task and for many years mining engineers envisaged its performance by machines with consequent increase in production and reduction of cost. Many types of machines have from time to time been tried for this purpose and their use is gradually increasing, but that much remains to be done in this connection is evidenced by the fact that only about 11 per cent. of the total coal produced is power loaded. (N.C.B. Report for 1955, Vol. 1, p. 23).

The Huwood Power Loader.—When coal is to be loaded off a machine-cut face by means of the Huwood power loader, it is essential that a haulage rope shall be laid along the back of the undercut as cutting proceeds and before the coal is blown. This is normally done by means of a threader bar attached to the coal-cutting machine. This rope is thus buried beneath the coal, and serves as one of two anchor ropes by which the loader subsequently hauls itself along the face. A second, and parallel rope on the conveyor side of the machine is anchored by steel prop in the same way as for a coal cutter. Fig. 85

Fig. 85.—The Huwood loader. Front view, showing loading flights and haulage ropes.

illustrates the loader and shows the two haulage ropes clearly. The box-like metal cover serves to protect the motor and gearing shown diagrammatically in Figs. 86 and 87. In action the machine pulls itself along on the two ropes pressing forward slowly but continuously into the fallen coal, sweeping it sideways from the face towards and on to the conveyor. This lateral transfer of the coal is achieved by the six flights which are seen resting upon the base or skid plate in the retracted position. When loading, the flights travel a circular path, and during the forward half of this movement, they dig into the coal and sweep it towards the conveyor. During the other half, they retract towards the machine, leaving the coal in its new position. Constant repetition of this movement produces a flow of coal on to the conveyor, and as the machine advances, the face is gradually cleared.

Fig. 86 shows the manner in which the flights are operated. They are hinged to a common bar which is coupled by a driving pin to the underside

Fig. 86.—Huwood loader, flight operating mechanism.

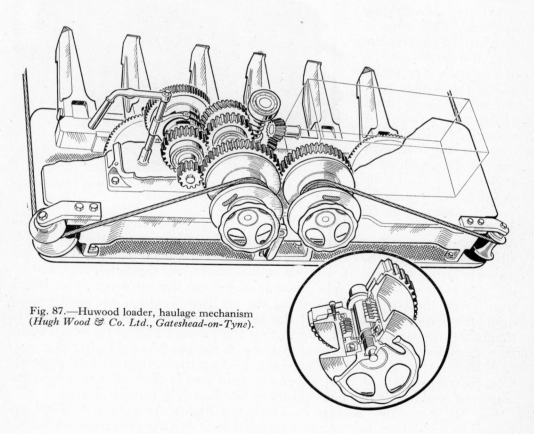

Fig. 87.—Huwood loader, haulage mechanism
(*Hugh Wood & Co. Ltd., Gateshead-on-Tyne*).

of a driving disc beneath each of the two larger toothed driving wheels. The figure shows quite clearly how these are themselves driven through pinions, dog-clutch and bevel gearing from the motor, the position of which is shown in outline.

The haulage mechanism is shown in Fig. 87. The same bevel gearing transmits motion via the worm gearing, dog-clutch and train of gears to the haulage drums which enclose clutch-plate mechanisms. These are readily operated by two control wheels on the driver's side of the machine, which permit of immediate correction of the alignment of the machine.

It is claimed that where good coal and face preparation has been achieved, the Huwood loader can load at the rate of 70 to 90 tons per hour, and fourteen were in use in 1956.

Box-Scraper Loading.—This system of loading was first employed in a British colliery in 1929. It is an adaptation of the main-and-tail haulage

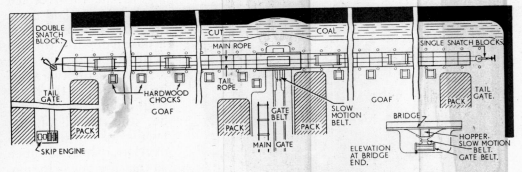

Fig. 88.—Diagram showing layout of longwall face equipped for scraper skips in tandem.

system, and in its simplest form consists of a double-drum hauler which pulls a bottomless scraper box, scoop or a skip backwards and forwards along the face by means of main-and-tail ropes. Jack props and snatch blocks are located at points which must be chosen carefully to confine the ropes and the skips to the correct paths. Sometimes several skips are employed on one face. Fig. 88 illustrates this system of loading, showing how several skips may be employed simultaneously on a coalface. A useful form of skip engine is the double-drum scraper haulage made by the Joy-Sullivan Co. (Fig. 89). It is powered by electric or air-turbo motor of 25 to 35 h.p., which drives either of the two ropes as required through a system of epicyclic gears and two hand-operated strap friction clutches. The direction of haulage can instantly be reversed without stopping the motor, simply by releasing one friction strap and operating the other. This is an essential feature for rapid loading. Rope speeds are usually about 300 ft. per min. although the speed of the return run may be made to exceed that of the loading run. Skips may be supplied in any size to suit the particular conditions on a given face: if height and width are limited, the length may possibly be increased to accommodate the load required. A skip consists of two vertical steel side plates braced by cross pieces at the top at each end with a hinged flap door attached at the back. This door is so arranged that it lifts and rides over the coal when travelling away from the loading gates, but falls and is held in the vertical position to catch the coal when travelling in the reverse direction and to drag it to the loading point.

Loading arrangements differ, but in thin seams the loading gate may be dinted right up to the face and may be spanned at floor level of the seam by a bridge consisting of a flat steel sheet, with a hole in the middle, through which the coal drops out of each bottomless skip as it is hauled over and is fed on to a belt, Fig. 88, or into a tub. Guide rails are usually arranged to lead skips across the bridge. The coal may fall direct into tubs or into a hopper feeding on to a belt conveyor.

Fig. 89.—Joy-Sullivan double-drum scraper haulage.

Sometimes false flooring in the form of flat steel sheets is laid upon the floor before the coal is blown down or thrown across on to it.

When using two skips on each side of the loading point, as in Fig. 88, the travel of the two skips is made to overlap a short distance so that the one skip may pick up the load left by the other at the midway point.

When the coal has been cleared off, it is relatively easy to move the false floor forward, to disconnect the rope lengtheners between the skips, to move them and the skips forward, and finally to wind the two ropes on their drums and then run them out again along the new track. Signalling is usually by means of a pull wire along the face which operates electrical signals at the bridge and at the engines.

Results averaged over long periods have proved that such installations can be very reliable and economical. In one instance, as much as 19 tons per "filler" per shift was achieved over a period of 6 months.

Scraper loading may solve many difficult problems, especially in thin seams where small faults occur.

Box-Scraper Cutter Loading.—A development in Holland and West Germany is the employment of box-scraper loaders, the face-side edges of which are fitted with cutting blades to plane off coal from the face in a manner similar to that of the Coal Plough. The coal is picked up by each of the boxes running in tandem and finally delivered at the end of the face. In a Dutch State mine with a seam of soft coking coal 60 to 90 cm. thick, eleven scraper buckets in series are hauled at high speed backwards and forwards along a face of 200 metres in length by powerful winches located in the gate roads. The face-side blades are set at 50 deg. and are held into the coal by a guide rail pushed forward from the goaf-side by compressed air rams which cushion the pressure against the rail. Twenty-six face-men are employed each of whom is responsible for drawing off and caving about 8 metres. As much as 1,224 tons have been loaded off in $1\frac{1}{2}$ shifts. The O.M.S. for the face-men alone is said to be 13 tons.

Cutter Loaders.—THE MECO-MOORE CUTTER LOADER.—The prototype of this machine was installed in 1934 at Chisnall Hall Colliery of the Wigan Coal Corporation. It consisted essentially, as it does today, of a coal cutter with an undercutting jib and a mechanically operated loader. Procedure was to cut the coalface in one direction, trailing the loader unit in tandem behind, and having completed the cutting, drilling and blasting, to swing the loader section through a right-angle into the mass of blown coal, which it loaded out during the return trip. Thus in traversing the face, it could cut or it could load, but it could not do both at the same time. A shearing jib was added later to make a vertical cut along the back of the web of the coal in the hope that it would permit the coal to fall away in such a manner as to facilitate loading. For various reasons the machine was unsatisfactory.

In 1941, as a result of reduced manpower at their collieries, the Bolsover Co., in a joint enterprise with the Mining Engineering Co. Ltd., started tests on a similar machine rearranged to cut and load simultaneously. It was hoped that it would eliminate blasting. At an early stage, Anderson-Boyes and Co. Ltd., became associated with this work and, as a result of practical tests at Rufford Colliery, improvements in jibs and chains were effected. Another jib, to cut at an intermediate level in the seam, was also introduced by mounting a second coal cutter on top of the first. The chain of the upper jib travelled in the opposite direction to the first, thereby helping to stabilise the machine and to break up the coal as desired. While this experimental machine was quite unsuitable for productive work, it established that simultaneous cutting and loading was possible and desirable.

In the light of practical experience gained, another machine was designed, the cutter unit, gummers and shear jib in particular being completely new. In 1943 this machine was put to work at Rufford Colliery and proved fairly successful. Many valuable lessons were learned concerning the preparation of machine stables, the effect of the direction of the line of cleavage, etc., before the unit was transferred to Clipstone Colliery.

In 1944, at Clipstone Colliery, the important discovery was made that under certain conditions the employment of a bottom jib of greater length than the upper jib may so alter the distance ahead of the face of the induced break as to afford better natural breakage of the coal, a better product for loading and also give better control of the roof. The machine gave very satisfactory service over a period of $7\frac{1}{2}$ months' continuous working without loss of a single cut, and by 1945, the initial testing period over, the machine was of proven utility. This machine, shown in Fig. 90, was known as the High Type. In order to extend the application of the cutter loader to thin seams, a new machine known as the Low Type was introduced in 1947, and after a period of testing was adopted as standard for all conditions.

Fig. 90.—High type Meco-Moore cutter loader.

THE A.B. MECO-MOORE—LOW TYPE CUTTER LOADER.—Reference to Fig. 91 shows that the unit may be divided into (1) a cutting and haulage section, and (2) a shearing and loading section. Two a.c. driving motors, each of 60 h.p., have been incorporated in one motor frame: one motor drives the two horizontal cutting jibs and the haulage gear, while the other drives the loader and the shearer jib.

Fig. 91.—Low type A.B. Meco-Moore cutter loader.

The motors are interchangeable; each is cooled by a fan and each may be started independently by remote-control switches.

The gearhead contains two separate trains of gears—one for the horizontal jibs and the other for the loader and the shearer jib, which is driven through a special coupling shaft. Both cutting chains are controlled independently from the haulage end of the machine (Fig. 92). The height of the upper jib may be adjusted by the use of different heights of jib bracket. A modified design of gearhead incorporates a hydraulic turret support for the upper jib, giving a range of adjustment of 7 in. or so in height. The haulage unit provides a fast flitting speed and an adjustable cutting speed up to a maximum of about 30 in. per min. The haulage drum accommodates 45 yd. of $\frac{5}{8}$-in. rope. Gummers of a special type are employed: they are really large-diameter

Fig. 92.—Low type A.B. Meco-Moore cutter and loader working on coalface.

transverse screws operating at floor level and demanding the use of a bottom-belt face conveyor or some structure not exceeding 7 in. in height. These gummers are fitted with clutches which cut out when overloaded above a predetermined amount.

Power is transmitted through a detachable driving shaft and spring dog couplings to the shearer and loader section of the combination. The loading member is a projecting frame which carries an endless rubber belt fitted with steel slats, each of which is attached by lugs to chains which are driven by sprockets on the driving shaft. Situated immediately in front of and parallel to the loader, is the rifled bar, which is fitted with picks set in a double helical form. These rotate in slots in the leading edge of the loader jib, thus lifting the bottom coal and transferring it to the loader belt. The arrangement is duplicated on the other side of the loader frame in order to permit loading when traversing the face in either direction. Spring-loaded friction clutches are employed in the drives to both gummers and belt, to avoid breakage due to excessive obstruction. An outstanding feature is the roughly triangular-shaped shearing jib which is mounted on the end of the loading frame. It is fitted with a gearbox at its apex and is driven by a detachable shaft. A rigid angle plate is bolted to the end of the loader frame and to this is attached a swivel joint upon which the shearing jib is mounted. It is possible to adjust the vertical height of the jib over a range of about 5 in. Provision is made for the reversal of the shearing jib when travelling in the opposite direction along the face. By virtue of its spring dogs, the driving shaft is simply and rapidly detached, four bolts are then removed and the jib is turned round completely on the swivel joint. The driving shaft and bolts are replaced, and the picks are reversed. When the unit "cuts out" into a stable at either end of the face, it must be "turned round" for the return journey and, to facilitate the operation, the cutter portion is separated from the loader portion. When the two portions of the machine have been manoeuvred into their correct relative positions for the return journey, and corresponding members have been matched, attachment is effected by a special device which also provides articulation for any local variations and irregularities in the floor.

The following is a brief specification of the machine:—

    Weight, 10 tons. Height with top jib, 2 ft. 7 in. Length, 16 ft. 9 in. Width, 3 ft. 1 in.

    Power units—Two motors, each of 60 h.p.

    Undercutting jib and chain—depth, 6 ft. 6 in., with a $5\frac{1}{2}$-in. kerf.

    Middle cutting jib and chain—depth, 5 ft. 6 in., with a $4\frac{1}{2}$-in. kerf.

    Shearing—height, 4 ft., with a $4\frac{3}{4}$-in. kerf.

    Haulage—speed variable up to 27 in. per min.

    Rope, $\frac{5}{8}$ in. diam., 45 yd. long.

It will be realised that the lengths of the horizontal jibs and the size of the shear jib vary with conditions. The size of the shear jib is governed more or less by the height of the seam. The lengths of the horizontal jibs are based primarily on the web to be taken. Consideration has also to be given to the extent of the pre-cut in either of the jibs, if conditions merit such a pre-cut.

The following is a summary of the most important factors concerning the operation of the low type machine. It has been applied to the working of seams of 3 ft. upwards in height, and usually to faces of about 130 yd. in length. Stables of about 16 ft. to 29 ft. in length, and of a depth of at least twice the depth of the cut are usually required at each end of the face. The faces of these stables are cut by an ordinary coal-cutting machine and are filled off by hand; their roof areas are supported by long steel bars which are best mounted on steel props fitted with Sylvester P.T. heads which can be tightened up effectively after setting and yet can be withdrawn readily when manoeuvring the cutter loader. Such props are desirable on the main length of the face, and particularly on the goaf side. Rows should be 4 ft. 2 in. apart. Corrugated steel straps about 7 ft. in length are usually employed at about 4 ft. 6 in. intervals, and a web of coal of about 5 ft. 6 in. is taken. Sometimes, for purposes of better roof control and of better coal preparation, the bottom cut exceeds the middle cut in depth and the passage of the unit still leaves 1 ft. of undercut coal to be supported by nogs. The bottom loading type of belt conveyor has been proved to be most satisfactory for service with this unit.[11]

The Joy-Sullivan Gloster Getter.—This cutter-loader machine has been employed in experiments in continuous longwall mining at Bolsover Colliery. The machine is illustrated in Fig. 93. The main body is 12 ft. long, 2 ft. high and 1 ft. 3 in. wide and houses the standard motor, gears and rope-haulage mechanism. Controls are provided at both ends of the machine.

Fig. 93.—Joy-Sullivan Gloster Getter cutter loader.

About midway along its length, two horizontal jibs project in parallel, one being slightly above the other, and special hinged picks in the upper chain serve to cut out the thin fillet of coal between the jibs. The upper jib is longer than the lower and affords a pre-cut of 4 in. In the early design a vertical jib follows the horizontal jib and shears at a distance of 2 ft. 6 in. from the machine. In later models two vertical shearing jibs and an overcutting jib are provided, as shown in Fig. 93, making in all five cutting jibs. This is claimed to improve the performance of the machine when working in hard coal. It appears that continuous slabbing sometimes enables the face to be kept in front of normal "weighting" of the roof and even friable seams may then "toughen".

Maximum speed for cutting and loading is 5 ft. per min. A light guide-rail may be fitted where necessary to bear against the last row of props. The machine trails a simple tray and a curved chute via which the coal is passed on to the face conveyor. The driving motor is of 75 h.p.

The machine starts from a stable at one end of the face and proceeds at an average speed of 3 ft. per min. to the second stable at the opposite end. On cutting through it is pushed forward in the stable without turning round, to commence the return run. The jibs and chains are prepared for the return trip and the curved chute is transferred to the other end of the machine, the change-over being completed in 30 min.

The face conveyor is advanced by simply pushing both the gearhead and the tail unit forward 2 ft. 6 in.

The men needed per shift for a 100-yd. face on the Bolsover system is 1 deputy, 2 Gloster Getter operators, 2 timberers, 4 packers, 4 stable-hole men, 4 main-gate dinters, 2 airway-gate rippers and 2 gearhead attendants, a total of 21. The output per 24 hours is 525 tons and the O.M.S. 8·33 tons.

The wide recognition of the need for a satisfactory machine which would cut and load in a single operation led to trials with numerous designs of machine. Amongst these may be mentioned the Logan slab cutter, of which a prototype was experimented with at Lumphinnans Colliery in Scotland, and the Bolton cutter-loader developed in Durham, but subsequently abandoned.

Two other machines, the Uskside mechanical coal miner and the Soest-Ferrum miner (Germany), employ a single cutting chain running in a channelled jib of roughly triangular or rectangular section. This enables undercutting, shearing and overcutting to be performed simultaneously by the single chain in its travel round the jib, thereby eliminating the need for separate jibs and chains for cutting in different planes.

The Coal Plough.—The coal plough was originally introduced in Germany in 1942 since when the technique of coal ploughing has been considerably developed and improved. The framework of the original unit known as the standard plough (Fig. 94) is of fabricated steel with articulated sections to facilitate its use on uneven floors and to enable it to negotiate small faults. It comprises the cutter loaders carrying the shearing blades, the track-clearing device and the pulling bars. The machine shears and loads in both directions as it travels along the face, the above-mentioned units being duplicated at each end. When working parallel to the cleat of the coal both shear blades are identical, but for other directions of advance it may be advantageous for the blades to be set at different angles. The blades are made of $\frac{7}{8}$-in. steel plate with cutting edges of hard alloy electrically welded thereon. The design of the blade is important and has been the subject of much investigation both in Germany and in Great Britain, in order to ascertain the appropriate angles between the vertical and the cutting edge and the best wedge angle. Normally the cutting edge slopes back at an angle of 25 deg. to the vertical and the wedge angle is 38 deg. with a clearance of 7 deg. between the blade and the coalface. The blades are detachable to allow of regrinding, which becomes necessary after a cutting travel of 12,000 to 15,000 yards. The standard plough used at Morrison Busty Colliery in a seam 3 ft. 0 in. thick is 20 ft. long, 2 ft. high, 2 ft. 4 in. wide and weighs 2·5 tons.

The cutter holder is plough-shaped in profile to deflect the coal on to the conveyor. The plough unit is pulled to and fro along the coalface by rope haulages, installed in the gate roads at each end of the face, which are capable of exerting a pull of 10 to 12 tons with a single rope or double these values with double purchase. The normal pull required varies from 3 to 8 tons but may go up to 20 tons in hard coal. The ropes used have a breaking strain of about 35 tons.

The trials with this, the only standard plough installed in Great Britain, demonstrated the possibility of the successful application of the machine under British conditions and led to the introduction of modified ploughs in a number of collieries, and many more installations are planned.

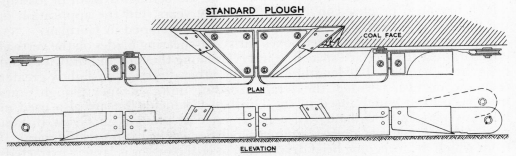

Fig. 94.—The standard coal plough.

Amongst the improved types of plough mention may be made of the following:

The Cutter Plough or Schramhobel which was developed in the Ruhr for coals which were too hard for the standard plough. In this type the single shearing head is replaced by two blades, the leading one arranged to plough out the upper sections of the seam and the lower one to take out the bottom coal. On the leading end of the structure are four horizontal stepped blades which pre-cut the coal to the normal depth of shear of 8 to 12 inches. As used in Britain the units work only in one direction owing to the great length of the double-end type which requires a much longer "stable" at each end of the face. The cutting speed is 16 ft. per min. and the flitting speed 34 ft. per min. Cutter ploughs have been installed in a number of collieries in Wales, Lancashire, Scotland and Durham.

The Rapid Plough or Westfalia–Lünen Löbbe Hobel is a short plough unit only 4 ft. long and with its haulage chain forms part of the armoured conveyor with which it is used.

The shear blades comprise two series of renewable cutter types which take a shear of only 2 to 3 in. The plough works in both directions and travels at 75 ft. per min., being driven by an endless chain driven by the conveyor motors, which chain returns in steel tubing forming part of the conveyor structure. Rapid ploughs are in use in the South Western, the East Midland, the Scottish and the Durham Divisions of the National Coal Board.

The Multi-plough was developed in Holland and consists of small plough units about 3 ft. in length and spaced at intervals of 15 to 20 yards along the face. The units are connected by steel wire ropes, the free ends of which, at each end of the face, are attached to small-diameter drums driven from the conveyor motors, and the units are hauled to and fro along the face. The length of travel is slightly greater than the distance between the plough units. A narrow armoured conveyor is used which reduces the length of the prop-free area and allows of improved roof support. A new British multi-plough has been designed in which the ploughs are pulled backwards and forwards, by round-link chains operated by hydraulic cylinders sited in one of the face roadways.

The Scraper Plough is a development of the scraper system of loading which has been practised in Britain for many years, but the application of the ploughing principle to scraper loading was developed in Germany.

Strongly constructed scraper boxes with coal-shearing blades on the vertical edges nearest the face are spaced at intervals along the face and drawn to and fro by rope haulage. The length of travel in either direction is slightly greater than the interval between the scraper loading units. Scraper plough units have been most widely used in the Durham Coalfield, but are also used in South Wales and Scotland. In a paper on coal ploughs in Great Britain read at the Centenary Congress of the French Société de l'Industrie Minerale,[11] from which the foregoing brief description of coal ploughs is largely extracted, H. E. Collins concludes: "There appears to be a wide field for the further application of the coal plough system of coal mining and loading."

The British Samson stripper and Huwood slicer described later both make use of the principle of the coal plough.

CONTINUOUS MINING

For many years the use of conventional types of coal-cutting and conveying machinery has enforced a three-shift cycle of operations at the working face. Thus coal cutting would be done on one shift, drawing off and setting of supports and advancement of the conveyor on a second shift, followed by stripping or coal loading on the third shift, although the actual sequence is sometimes modified to meet conditions.

Satisfactory working depends upon rigid adherence to the correct sequence throughout the 24-hour cycle. Failure to complete any operation in the shift causes dislocation of routine, loss of output and increased cost. It is obvious that a system of continuous coal production in which all operations proceed simultaneously, and in which men commencing any shift can take over from the men on the previous shift, possesses advantages. It ensures the more even flow of coal from the face and allows the machinery to be used to greater advantage. Such is the aim of continuous mining, an essential requirement for which is a machine which cuts, breaks down and loads the coal at one operation without the necessity for blasting, with its attendant dangers and delays.

A number of continuous-mining machines or so-called "continuous miners" have been developed in the U.S.A. for use in narrow (bord and pillar) workings and some have been used in Great Britain. The following descriptions of two such machines illustrate the general principles of design and operation. British machines designed with the same object in view for use in longwall workings are described later.

Continuous-Mining Machines for Narrow Work.—THE JOY-SULLIVAN CONTINUOUS MINER.—This machine is a logical development from the Joy loader, and is designed for continuous operation in trackless room-and-pillar mining. It is 25 ft. 6 in. long and 7 ft. 6 in. wide. There are two models, the over-all height of the low model is 34 in. and of the high model 48 in. It weighs about 16 tons. Fig. 95 shows that the machine is caterpillar mounted

Fig. 95.—The Joy-Sullivan continuous miner.

and consists of three main sections, the cutting and loading head, the intermediate conveyor and the discharge conveyor.

The cutting and loading head has a width of 30 in., a vertical movement of 64 in., and a horizontal swing of 16 ft. It also has a forward movement of 18 in. independent of the movement of the chassis. The head is carried on a large turntable and advances through slides incorporated in the turntable casting. Two hydraulic jacks swing the turntable, two advance the ripper and two elevate it. Thus the head is operated hydraulically except for the cutting chains which are driven through reduction gearing by two electric motors. The "ripper-bar" head is equipped with six chains each driven by a separate sprocket on a main driving shaft. The operating speed of the chains is 500 f.p.m. Each chain is fitted with 20 replaceable bits, and its travel is from the underside of the ripper-bar head, forward and upward through the coal and back over the head towards the rear.

An intermediate conveyor which swings and advances with the ripper-bar is located at the delivery end of the chains and carries the coal to a hopper.

A rear conveyor constructed from a single chain with cantilever flights receives the coal from the hopper, carries it at 200 f.p.m. along the delivery jib and dumps it into a shuttle car (see Vol. 2, Chap. 7) on the outbye end of the unit at the rate of about 1 ton per min. This discharge jib may be swung horizontally through 45 deg. on each side of the centre line to afford manoeuvrability. The flitting speed is 35 f.p.m. The machine often trails a shuttle car in tandem at the end of the delivery jib to act as a surge bin and to feed the other shuttle cars.

Operation of the machine proceeds in the following manner. The whole unit is advanced towards the centre of the working place until the cutter teeth almost touch the coal. The ripper-bar is then swung to the extreme right of the section about to be cut and is then lowered to the floor. It is then "sumped" forward hydraulically for 18 in. into the coal, raised to tear the coal away to the top of the seam, retracted, lowered and swung 30 in. to the left about the turntable ready for the next forward sumping stroke. When the standard width of cut is completed, the ripper-bar is swung to its central position and the whole unit is advanced 18 in. on its caterpillars to repeat the cycle.

Power-operated jacks supplied with the machine may be used if required for temporary roof support.

For the machine of American manufacture electric power is required at 500 volts d.c. to supply seven motors, viz., two for the ripper-bar at 65 h.p. each, two for the caterpillar tracks at 7·5 h.p. each, one of 10 h.p. for the hydraulic pump and two of 5 h.p. for the rear conveyor. The total demand is therefore 165 h.p., but provision should be made for short sustained current peaks of 300 amps.

This machine produces a high proportion of small coal and dust, but to mitigate this two dust-collecting scrolls are located along each side of the cutting chains and spray nozzles are carefully positioned to prevent dust-cloud formation.

The personnel required in connection with the continuous miner will vary considerably with the circumstances in which it is employed, but the following may be taken as a guide for good conditions: 1 operator, 1 conveyor attendant, 2 timberers, 2 shuttle-car drivers, 1 deputy, 1 fitter electrician and 2 supply men.

At Donnisthorpe Colliery over a specific period this machine drove headings 16 ft. wide by 5 ft. 8 in. high yielding an average of 186·1 tons per shift worked, equivalent to 56 feet of heading. The best daily tonnage was 600 tons (two-shift working) and the highest weekly tonnage 2,440 for $10\frac{1}{2}$ machine shifts. The average O.M.S. was 20 tons which included overtime shifts and all manpower on to the main trunk-conveyor system.

THE JEFFREY "COLMOL" CONTINUOUS MINER.—Another continous miner, the Jeffrey "Colmol" (Fig. 96), has an arrangement of rotary drill-heads, each having widely spaced and progressively receding teeth that chip the coal in overlapping concentric curves. Also, the rotary heads are designed and arranged to sweep the coal from the floor of the mine-working to a conveyor leading to the rear. The rotary chipping heads are mounted in two horizontal rows with eight in the top row and five in the bottom, so that there are thirteen heads in all.

The normal dimensions of a cut are $9\frac{1}{2}$ ft. wide and 4 ft. high, the latter being variable by raising or lowering the cutting-head assembly as the thickness of the seam may require. The adjustments of the cutting head are hydraulically operated; the cutting edge may be tilted upward or downward, and the distance between the two horizontal rows of cutting heads varied. Each of these motions is operated by its own manual control, and the rotating heads are powered by two 30-h.p. motors. The assembly is mounted on two

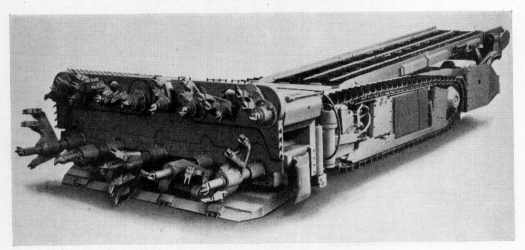

Fig. 96.—The Jeffrey "Colmol" continuous miner.

continuous tractor treads, each powered by a $7\frac{1}{2}$-h.p. motor. The travel speed of the tractor varies from 20 to 35 ft. per min., the low-speed range for the actual mining operation being from 0 to 60 in. per min. All the drives are hydraulic.

The over-all dimensions of the "Colmol" are:

Height	38 in.
Width	8 ft. 6 in.
Length	24 ft. 9 in.
Weight	26 tons.

A production rate of from three to five tons per minute is said to be attainable with the "Colmol" cutter loader in the U.S.A. Other types of continuous miners of American manufacture are the "Koal-Master", the "Konnerth", the "McKinlay Entry Driver" and the "B.C.R." machines.

Continuous-Mining Machines for use in Longwall Work.—As in the case of narrow work, in longwall workings advantages accrue from continuity of face operations, and a number of machines have been introduced with this end in view.

THE SAMSON STRIPPER.—In 1948, Messrs. Mavor and Coulson introduced a machine known as the "Samson stripper" (Fig. 97) to work in the Parkgate seam of a South Yorkshire Colliery. This proved very successful in the continuous mining of coal under the prevailing conditions. It is self-propelled and in traversing the face it removes a 2-ft. web of coal and loads it on to a face conveyor alongside the machine, both the stripper and the conveyor operating between the face and the front line of props. A stable must be provided at each end of the face and on stripping through into a stable, the machine is moved forward 2 ft. and then commences stripping the face in the opposite direction as soon as the conveyor has been moved bodily forward

Fig. 97.—The Samson stripper.

and a new line of supports has been set. As the machine is double-headed it does not require turning round at each end of the face.

The machine consists of three main sections, two of which, the wedge-heads, are identical and located at opposite ends of the unit. The third or middle section consists of a hydraulic propulsion unit mounted alongside a very substantial vertical hydraulic jack. Two strong horizontal rods pass through the central section and are joined at their extremities by the end plates upon which the wedgeheads are mounted.

When the jack is fixed firmly between roof and floor, these rods, mounted in bearings in the central unit, carry the wedgeheads in their lateral movements, to left or right, parallel to the face. Also when the jack is retracted and the wedgeheads rest upon the floor, the jack and the propulsion unit as a whole may move along the rods in either direction as far as the wedgeheads, to take up a new position from which the next thrust is to be made.

Thus the jack and the central propulsion unit carry the rods and the wedgeheads during thrusting; the wedgeheads and the rods carry the jack and propulsion unit as these move forward to the next position.

Power is supplied by a 30-h.p. motor which drives a two-stage hydraulic pump. A horizontal cylinder with a double-acting piston and a piston rod coupled to each wedgehead gives a maximum thrust of 42 tons, for a distance of 2 ft. 7 in. into the coal. The hydraulic supply to the jack is by three flexible pipes, two to the cylinder to raise the jack and one to the annulus to lower it. When retracted, the jack is clear of both roof and floor. A remote control unit is mounted directly above the motor, and the hydraulic pump and valve gear are contained in a tank on top of the machine. The operator on the waste side of the machine has only one handle to operate and this he may turn full circle through four positions at 90 deg. apart to obtain the following responses:

1. Expansion of the jack to grip between roof and floor. 2. Forward or stripping stroke of the piston, piston rods and wedgeheads. 3. Retraction of the jack from roof and floor. 4. Traverse of the propulsion unit and jack along the rods to the next position.

Clockwise rotation of the control handle ensures these movements in correct sequence when stripping from left to right. Anticlockwise rotation gives correct sequence when stripping from right to left. The machine may be stopped at any time by pushing the handle inwards.

The jack is offset slightly from the lengthwise centre-line of the machine and this helps to keep the wedgeheads into the coal and prevent the machine wandering towards the conveyor and the waste.

The wedgeheads consist of multiple blades or ploughs, of which the uppermost is adjustable and is specially arranged to strip the roof cleanly. Below this are four vertical blades which shear the coal behind the buttock, and any one of them may be set in advance of the others to give a bursting effect. The bottom vertical blade is combined with a loading ramp up which the coal is pushed on to the conveyor. A horizontal floor blade which also forms part of the loading ramp ensures the cutting of an even floor. All the blades are made of armour plate and each is detachable for resharpening. The following is a brief specification of the machine: Length, 18 ft. 7 in. Width, 2 ft. 7 in. Height, 3 ft. 7 in. to 6 ft. 0 in. Forward stroke, 2 ft. 7 in. Jacking range, 1 ft. 9 in. Motor 30 h.p., one-hour rated, 1,500 r.p.m. Maximum forward thrust at low pressure, 21 tons. Maximum forward thrust at high pressure, 42 tons. Maximum thrust on vertical jack, 139 tons. Weight 10 tons. Speeds at high pressure average up to $4\frac{1}{2}$ f.p.m. Speeds at low pressure range up to 6 f.p.m.

The performance of the stripper and the men required depend upon many factors such as the thickness of the seam, its inclination, the direction of cleavage relative to the line of face, the nature of the roof and roof support, the suitability of the face conveyor and the skill of the operators. Six of these machines were in use in the Scottish, East Midlands and West Midlands Divisions in 1954, producing a face output of 6 to 7 tons per man-shift, but mechanical difficulties have since led to their withdrawal.

THE DOSCO CONTINUOUS MINER FOR LONGWALL OPERATION.—The Joy-Sullivan continuous miner already described can be employed with great success for the rapid driving of headings in coal, and the rapid development of bord and pillar workings, but the original design was not suited for long-wall work. A modification of the machine which employs a similar cutting head but substitutes a tail-end side chute for the long rear jib is, however, proving successful in Nova Scotia. It is known as the Dosco continuous miner for longwall operation. As it travels along the face it delivers the coal through its tail-chute on to a face conveyor.

The machine is 40 in. high and takes a buttock 4 ft. 6 in. wide for the full height of the seam and fills off a 500-ft. length of face in a shift, leaving adequate time for turning round, etc., in preparation for the next working shift. All operations which form the cycle must proceed simultaneously; thus while coal is being cut and loaded out, the operations of conveyor-

Fig. 98.—Huwood slicer loader on coalface, with P80 Python conveyor, at a North of England colliery.

moving and drawing-off the goafs must also be carried on. To facilitate this the conveyors, cables and water pipes are laid in duplicate lines along the face, one line of each being in use while the other is "dead" and in the process of reassembly behind the machine in the path just created. Steel props and metal straps are withdrawn from the goaf, passed across the operating conveyor line and speedily re-erected behind the Dosco machine. Production is 500 tons per working shift giving an O.M.S. of 10·6 tons per man. Three Dosco miners were in use in Great Britain in March 1956.

THE HUWOOD SLICER.—This machine applies the activated principle to a coal plough. It is mounted on an armoured conveyor and embodies a double plough-shaped assembly fitted on the face side at each end of the unit with vertical oscillating plough plates carrying a series of renewable cutter sides. A 2-in. eccentric motion imparts a rotary motion at 340 r.p.m. to the plates which causes the cutter picks to strike the coal in an action similar to that of hand picks. The pick blades cut a groove or vertical shear about 1¾ in. wide at the back of the slice of coal removed which has a maximum thickness of about 14 in.

Each plate has its separate electric drive and the machine is hauled in both directions along the face by means of an endless-chain haulage at a speed of about 15 f.p.m. The machine at present constructed is about 9 ft. 6 in. long,

Fig. 99.—The B.J.D. Anderton shearer loader. (*British Jeffrey-Diamond, Ltd.*)

is powered by a 60-h.p. motor and its speed of travel varies from 12 ft. 9 in. to 21 ft. 3 in. per minute. It is suitable for seams 4 ft. or more in thickness and experience indicates that they will get and load relatively hard coal.

Fig. 98 shows the slicer loader on a face with its P80 Python chain conveyor at a northern colliery and the plate facing page 446 shows the same machine with Schwarz props and Schlom bars supporting the roof, together with pneumatic rams for advancing the conveyor and a water infusion tube in position on the face.

THE ANDERTON SHEARER LOADER.—The basic design of the Anderton shearer loader resembles that of a coal cutter from which the normal jib and jib bracket have been removed and a small gear-box substituted for the latter. This gear-box drives a horizontal shaft which protrudes from the face side of the machine and upon which is mounted a drum (Fig. 99) or a series of discs, usually six in number (Fig. 100). This drum or the discs which carry pick holders vary in diameter; originally they gave a diameter of 40 in. over the pick points and thus limited the application of the machine to seams not less than 44 in. in thickness; but the introduction of a shallower gearhead enables it to be used in seams down to 34 in. in thickness. The disc-carrying shaft is set to lag about 8 deg. behind the line normal to the machine, although machines with no lag on the disc shaft have proved satisfactory. During shearing, which takes place in one direction only, the six lines of cutter picks take a cut or slice of about 15 to 20 in. from the face. The normal direction of rotation is such that the cut coal is thrown over the discs on to a deflection plate. Each disc is designed to carry 12 pick boxes, but it is the practice in some areas to fit only six picks, leaving blank alternate boxes which are so disposed as to give cutting lines suited to the conditions.

The standard speed of rotation of the discs is 66·5 r.p.m., but this may be varied to suit conditions. The machine is hauled to and fro by an endless rope system of haulage which allows of varia-

Fig. 100.—The A.B. Anderton shearer loader with A.B. hydraulic turret overcutter mounted pick-a-back. (*Anderson-Boyes, Ltd.*)

tions of speed. During shearing this may be up to 10 f.p.m. and during the return journey may be up to 80 f.p.m. according to the capacity of the chain conveyor, upon the framework of which the machine travels and which serves to transport the coal along the face. On arriving at the end of its shearing journey the discs are disengaged and the direction of travel reversed for the ploughing journey when the coal is ploughed on to the conveyor.

Fig. 99 shows the standard machine as manufactured by British Jeffrey-Diamond, Ltd., while Fig. 100 shows the shearer loader with a hydraulic turret overcutter and curved jib mounted pick-a-back, for use in thick seams. Each of these firms manufacture both types. Although only introduced in 1952 the machine proved so successful that by the end of 1955 there were

(*Hugh Wood & Co., Ltd.*)

THE HUWOOD SLICER-LOADER

The slicer-loader is seen with a P. 80 Python conveyor, Schwarz probes and Schlom bars at a Northern colliery. Note the prop-free front,
hydraulic rams (on left) for advancing the conveyor and the water infusion tube in the face.

FAST COAL PLOUGH (LOEBBEHOBEL) IN USE ON COAL FACE

83 such machines in use which produced 3,360,000 tons of coal in that year. Four British firms are now manufacturing Anderton shearers and it was planned to install a further 200 machines in 1956.

CONCLUSION

During the last half-century there has been a gradual change from the winning of coal by hand and by crude coal-cutting machines on ill-organised faces, to more scientific working by very efficient machines on carefully planned faces worked by conventional methods on a rigid three-shift cycle. Approximately 80 per cent. of the output in Great Britain is obtained by that system.

Between the wars, the use of arc-walling and similar machines reduced the cost and expedited the driving of coal headings and other development work. Attempts were made to apply American methods and machines to British conditions for which they were unsuitable. At present, efforts are being made to prove that coal may be worked continuously with the cutting-loading machine and the conveyor in the same track between the coalface and the last row of supports (the so-called "prop-free-front") so that getting and loading proceed without hindrance and the conveyor can be advanced after or during each strip without being dismantled. However, although cutter loaders, coal ploughs and other types of continuous miners show the modern trend of face mechanisation, it must be realised that they

DEEP-MINED COAL PRODUCTION, 1954.
METHODS OF WORKING AND GETTING COAL AT MINES
OPERATED BY THE NATIONAL COAL BOARD
(Thousands of tons raised and weighed)

Method of working	Mechanical picks alone	Mechanical picks with coal cutters	Coal cutters alone	Cutter loaders	Coal ploughs and strippers	Hand got	Total	Percentage of total
Longwall	14,783	16,640	159,766	8,543	5,575	7,711	213,018	90·4
Room and pillar	7,098	24	7,946	—	250	5,100	20,418	8·6
Other methods	177	73	1,290	—	2	745	2,287	1·0
Total	22,058	16,737	169,002	8,543	5,827	13,556	235,723*	—
Percentage of total	9·4	7·1	71·7	3·6	2·5	5·7	—	100·0

* This value is 99 per cent. of the total output of coal. (Ministry of Fuel and Power Statistical Digest 1955.)

do not as yet account for more than some 11 per cent. of the output. The true relative importance of the various methods of working and of the types of machines employed is revealed by the following figures for 1954.

It is, however, worthy of note that the percentage of coal got by hand is decreasing as shown by the fact that in 1946, the last year of private enterprise, about 18½ per cent. was so gotten, whereas in 1955 the percentage was only 5·7.

The Reid Report published in 1945 revealed the need for drastic changes in the methods of work, road construction and haulage as practised in Great Britain, and the preceding pages show clearly that great endeavours are being made to solve the vital problems of the economic production of coal, especially in the direction of increased mechanisation at the coalface.

REFERENCES

[1] Imperial Chemical Industries Ltd., Booklets on Explosives, Blasting Practice, etc., and R. A. McCormick and J. Hancock, *Colliery Guardian*, Vol. 188, 22nd April, 1954, p. 475.

[2] Shot-firing and explosives in coal mines. J. Taylor and J. Hancock. *Trans. Inst. Min. Eng.* 1947, Vol. 106, p. 678.

[3] Imperial Chemical Industries Ltd., Explosives Dept., Service Section Staff.

[4] Construction of new collieries in Scotland. H. R. King, *Trans. Inst. Min. Eng.* 1956, Vol. 115, p. 597.

[5] Fast headings in stone. J. G. George, *Colliery Guardian*, 27th April, 1945.

[6] Storage and transport of explosives at collieries. Riley and Westwater, *Trans. Inst. Min. Eng.* 1952, Vol. 112, p. 41.

[7] University of Durham, King's College Mining Bulletin, No. 3 Series: Mech. No. 8. Drifting.

[8] M. H. Young. *Sheffield University Magazine*, 1955, p. 16.

[9] H. W. Wilson. *Trans. Inst. Min. Eng.* 1953–4, Vol. 113, p. 524.

[10] Simultaneous cutter and loader for longwall mining. T. E. B. Young and W. H. Sansom, *Trans. Inst. Min. Eng.* Vol. 104, p. 192.

[11] Coal ploughs in the Durham coalfield. H. E. Collins. *Trans. Inst. Min. Eng.* 1952, Vol. 112, p. 137. Coal ploughs in Great Britain. H. E. Collins. Read at Centenary Congress of the *Societé de l'Industrie Minérale*, Dec. 1954.

[12] Power loading in longwall workings. I. C. F. Statham, *Sheffield Univ. Min. Mag.* 1943; Power loading in narrow workings. I. C. F. Statham, *ibid.*, 1944.